Hope with Anxiety

To Kevin, Charlotte and Samantha
and
To all my friends and family – thank you for loving me!

Hope with Anxiety

a self-help guide for those affected and their families, friends and carers

Lynn Crilly

With a foreword by Jeff Brazier

Hammersmith Health Books
London, UK

First published in 2020 by Hammersmith Health Books – an imprint of
Hammersmith Books Limited
4/4A Bloomsbury Square, London WC1A 2RP, UK
www.hammersmithbooks.co.uk

The information contained in this book is for educational purposes only. It is
the result of the study and the experience of the author. Whilst the information
and advice offered are believed to be true and accurate at the time of going to
press, neither the author nor the publisher can accept any legal responsibility or
liability for any errors or omissions that may have been made or for any adverse
effects which may occur as a result of following the recommendations given
herein. Always consult a qualified medical practitioner if you have any concerns
regarding your health.

British Library Cataloguing in Publication Data: A CIP record of this book is
available from the British Library.

Print ISBN 978-1-78161-180-7
Ebook ISBN 978-1-78161-181-4

Commissioning editor: Georgina Bentliff
Designed and typeset by: Julie Bennett, Bespoke Publishing Ltd
Cover design by: Julie Bennett, Bespoke Publishing Ltd
Index: Dr Laurence Errington
Production: Helen Whitehorn, Path Projects
Printed and bound by: TJ Books Limited, Cornwall, UK

Contents

About the Author

Lynn Crilly is an award-winning counsellor and mother of twin girls. When one of her twin daughters, Samantha, struggled with OCD and anorexia nervosa, having followed the conventional therapy routes to no avail, Lynn took the decision to follow her gut instincts and rehabilitate Samantha herself. She subsequently developed her unique form of counselling to support sufferers and their families going through similar experiences. Lynn continues to work with families every day, battling mental health issues at her clinic in Surrey, UK. She uses the knowledge and experience she has gained to write self-help books covering an array of mental health issues, with the aim to help combat stigma and destructive myths whilst also providing a positive and constructive way forward for families and carers affected. She is admired for her passion and understanding – something she attributes to the strength and loyalty of her family and friends, with whom she spends as much time as possible.

Other books by Lynn Crilly are:

Hope with Eating Disorders, 2nd edition

Hope with OCD

Hope with Depression

Fundamentals: A guide for parents, teachers and carers on mental health and self-esteem, with Natasha Devon

www.lynncrilly.com

Acknowledgements

First and foremost, I would like to say a BIG thank you to my wonderful husband, Kevin, who has always given me his unconditional love and support. His unquestioning belief in me has given me the strength to achieve all I have so far … I love you more with every new day.

To our beautiful twin daughters, Charlotte and Samantha; I am so proud of the gorgeous young ladies you have become and love you both very much!

A big thank you to Callum and Jay for loving our girls unconditionally and making my family complete … love you both loads.

Much love to my mum and dad, who have always been there for me with the kettle on and ready to listen, with their constant love and support.

My brother Steve and sister-in-law Sue, thank you for being there.

A special thank you to Kate, Wendy, Gill, Gerry, Leanne, Hannah, Dionne, Kyra, Michelle, Shauna, Melissa, Mitch, Neil, John, Bobby and all my friends who continue to love me unconditionally, your friendship is a rare valued gift.

A warm thank you to our wonderful GPs, past and present, John Dalzell and Sarah Benney, who over the years have given us as a family and me as a professional their unreserved support.

Thank you to all my clients, both past and present, who have put their trust and belief in me and my work, which has enabled me to help and support them to make the positive changes needed in their lives and, in doing so, changing mine.

A huge thank you to Mel Hunter, who has been my writing hand to help create *Hope with Anxiety*.

A special thank you to my life coach and loyal friend, Jeff Brazier, who, when I was lost, helped me find myself again; for that I will always be grateful. As a father, husband and coach yourself, I could not have anyone more qualified to write the foreword for *Hope with Anxiety*. Thank You!

I have been incredibly privileged to have been supported by so many wonderful people from all walks of life, who have all trusted and believed in me enough to make a contribution to this book; for that, I thank you all.

Lastly and by no means least, thank you to my lovely publisher Georgina Bentliff (Hammersmith Health Books) for being so supportive, open-minded and a total pleasure to work with.

Once again, a big thank you to all those mentioned above and the many others who have championed, helped and supported me over the years; without each and every one of you, I know I would not be who and where I am today, both personally and professionally; for this, I will always be grateful.

Foreword

Anxiety comes in many guises. It can be obvious or hidden, logical or baffling. Its symptoms can be clear, or they can require some detective work. Often anxiety feels like an unstoppable force, out of our control, and watching someone we care about in the grip of it can be both frightening and frustrating.

Few of us are immune to the impact of anxiety. Even if it does not have a scene-stealing role in our own lives, almost all have watched from the wings as someone we care about struggles with its destructive effects. It is all around us, and yet still quite misunderstood.

In my life-coaching practice, I hear about anxiety on a daily basis, and through the experiences of my clients I have come to recognise it in the many different ways it takes hold in people's lives. This became particularly evident during the most anxious times we've ever experienced as a society, through the Covid-19 pandemic.

This book is therefore more relevant than ever. Lynn ploughed her energies into finishing it during the difficult months at the height of the epidemic, to give hope to the increasing number of people who find themselves in the grip of an anxiety disorder. Through these pages, she gives them both a supportive hand to hold and an invaluable roadmap through their experience of anxiety, whether that is their own illness or that of someone they care for.

Her knowledge of the subject, backed by scientific evidence, is deep, coming from a place of compassion and care rather than simply from science. The stories from her contributors further bring this accessible and comprehensive book to life. Theirs – the lived experiences of those affected by anxiety in its many and varied forms – show the depths that this illness can take people to. Their stories also demonstrate the light at the end of a long, dark tunnel that they never lose sight of.

As the title of the book suggests, hope with anxiety is a truly powerful force that can change lives. With hope, change is possible. With hope, brighter and better times are ahead. With hope, the tremendous effort required to break free from anxiety is worth it. With hope, families can work together rather than be pulled apart.

I have no doubt that this book will become a much-thumbed resource to a huge number of people. Lynn has worked tirelessly to add this to her portfolio of books helping break the stigma around mental illness. Just like *Hope with Depression*, *Hope with Eating Disorders* and *Hope with OCD*, I fully expect *Hope with Anxiety* to change the way people understand these kinds of condition and to give families real help – and hope – to move forward.

Jeff Brazier
Father/Husband
Life Coach and NLP Practitioner
Television presenter
October 2020

To cut a long story short...

Anyone looking at us 16 years ago would have assumed from the outside that we were a perfectly 'normal' family: my husband Kevin and I and our beautiful twin daughters, Charlotte and Samantha, seemed to have everything anyone could possibly wish for and more. We were in a really good place in our lives, glued together by the strong foundations of our marriage and two happy, healthy girls. Of course, we had our ups and downs like most couples and life threw challenges our way, but we always worked together to overcome them and move forward, trying carefully to balance our scaffolding business and family life, just like any other working parents. We were doing okay... or so we thought.

Our picture-perfect little world fell apart when Samantha was diagnosed with the early stages of anorexia nervosa at the start of her teenage years. Her battle with this particular mental illness tested our family to its limits and just when we thought we had come through the worst, she was diagnosed with obsessive compulsive disorder (OCD). We had no knowledge at all of eating disorders or OCD when the girls were young, and tackling these two illnesses, one following the other, was akin to climbing a mountain without a map, a guide or any of the right equipment.

The main thing as a mother I was armed with was love, and empathy as a fellow sufferer of mental illness. I had faced my own struggle in the years before Samantha's issues became apparent. For me, the diagnosis was depression and for three years I tried to shift the black cloud that permanently overshadowed my life. With the unconditional love of my family and close friends, and a supportive GP who prescribed antidepressants, I was finally able to pull myself free, but I can now see that I too am pre-disposed to mental ill health and I have since had to be alert to and act on the tell-tale signs that those dark and threatening clouds could once again be gathering. I now realise it is something I will probably have to be aware of for the rest of my life.

Along with that personal experience of depression, it was also the battle we faced with Samantha that ultimately led me to where I am now, writing this book ... *Hope with Anxiety*.

Like any parent, I wanted to do the best I could to help my daughter to recover. We tried everything we could to get her the help she so desperately needed, from our local (very supportive) GP to both NHS and private clinics, but sadly nothing appeared to be working for Samantha. I read many books and scoured the internet for as much information and guidance as I could get my hands on, but I could not find anything that I or my family could truly relate to or which gave me any real hope that there was a light at the end of the tunnel for Samantha and for us as a family.

Every website, book or support group I found seemed to focus mainly on the actual person experiencing the illness and not the family, friends or carers whom I felt needed help and support just as much as the sufferer. I desperately needed answers and was keen to reach out to others, anybody with a genuine understanding of what was happening to us, to help us stop Samantha's condition in its tracks, but there was nothing.

In a moment of desperation, with my family falling apart, I let my intuition guide me and took the decision to rehabilitate her myself. Thankfully, with the full support of our GP, the girls' school and our family and friends, I was able to dedicate myself completely to Samantha, injecting positive thinking, love and hope, whilst trying to show her a life outside of the eating disorder and later the OCD, never giving up on my belief that she could and would get better, no matter how difficult the situation became.

I slowly encouraged her to start communicating with me. She began sharing her distorted and, at times, highly irrational, views of her world and her innermost thoughts, her head engaged in a constant battle with itself. Patience, love and open-mindedness were paramount, not just with Samantha but for the family as a unit. It was the steepest learning curve I could have ever imagined but, step by step, Samantha slowly found her way back to us.

Despite Samantha's illnesses and my own experience of depression, Kevin my husband has never really understood mental illness, and has never pretended to. At the height of Samantha's illness the pressure and enormity of it all took its toll on us briefly, to the point that I once asked him to leave … Thankfully he ignored my request and stayed, continuing to provide his powerful and unconditional love and support, without which we could never have survived. He used to think Samantha was intentionally behaving as she did for attention, but now he readily accepts things for what they are, supporting Samantha unconditionally even though, sometimes, he struggles to get his head around her quirky ways of thinking.

Samantha's twin sister, Charlotte, has also been pivotal in her recovery and now works alongside me at my practice, with an empathy that can only come from first-hand experience. She has forfeited pieces of her own life so that Samantha could be given the full-on care that she needed and the bond between my two girls is now unbelievably strong. Their mutual respect for one another, as a result of the journey they have shared, is testament to that.

I have learnt through all of this, the importance of constant communication, patience, non-judgement, unconditional love and, most of all, HOPE, and that in fact there is no such thing as the 'perfect' family. Trying to be perfect is not only unrealistic; it can be dangerous.

Some time into Samantha's recovery, I was contacted by the mother of a 17-year-old girl who was suffering from an eating disorder. She asked me if I could help them as they were finding, as we had, that none of the conventional routes were making any difference. Encouraged by my husband, I approached their situation just as I had Samantha's, looking beyond her illness to the person within and giving her the unconditional and non-judgemental support that I realised from our experience had been so beneficial. Having been able to help her and her family successfully, I made the decision to build my own counselling practice based on everything I had read, learnt and experienced from our own journey with Samantha. I then went on to do some studying of my own, including training as a Master of NLP (Neuro-linguistic Programming – see page 105) and as a PsyTaP practitioner (see page 115). I was keen to work with other sufferers and their families, giving them the unreserved support and complete lack of judgement that my own experience had taught me was both vital and necessary. I tentatively opened my doors to people from all walks of life, struggling to deal with mental illness, be it the sufferer or a supportive loved one. My little successes were never shouted from the rooftops but from then on people seemed to find me through recommendation and word of mouth. I am now contacted on a daily basis by frantic and frightened parents, carers and siblings from all over the world, all of whom have concerns about loved ones, some as young as eight years old, most just wanting to talk to me, desperate for a glimmer of hope. I now help people suffering from anxiety, OCD, eating disorders, depression, self-harm and low self-esteem. The way I interact with my clients may seem a little unorthodox to some; however, I feel it is important to get to know the person as a whole rather than just seeing them through the lens of their illness, and working alongside the family rather than just the sufferer helps to build a united front against the illness.

No two people who enter my office are ever the same and they all experience the issues in a way that is unique to them; hence, the way I approach their treatment is similarly unique to each client. I am learning about each individual case as it naturally unfolds so I can give as much time and attention as we need, both in and outside our sessions, to build a mutual trust within our relationship which enables me to be one step ahead of the illness, in turn facilitating a quicker and more effective recovery for all concerned; we may do puzzles together while we chat, make jewellery or do other arts and craft projects. The atmosphere tends to be much less intense than the traditional image of the patient-therapist relationship and can at times even be fun! I have certainly learnt a lot from working with people in this way and I focus on maintaining a positive environment, so from the minute they walk in they feel comfortable and at ease and from the very start they know they can get better and that they are in control of their own recovery. I also respond on an emotional level rather than a clinical one to the things they tell me.

I do not always get it right and I do not pretend to; on the odd occasion there may be the need for additional assistance and input from other avenues. However, my practical and down-to-earth approach has earned me the endearing handle of 'Fairy Godmother'!

So here I am, many years later. If you had told me over 10 years ago that I would be doing what I am doing today I would not have believed you. Nor could I have foreseen that our future as a family would be so much healthier and happier, our dynamics have changed in a way I did not think possible. During these rewarding years I have had the privilege of working with some wonderful people and their families, each and every one of them unique. Whilst I have been able to support and guide them through their journeys, I too have learnt from them. My clients have said that they find my practical and down-to-earth approach really refreshing and have even compared me to the therapist in the film *The King's Speech* on more than one occasion! His methods were unconventional and unorthodox – but they got results. I never expected my practice to expand to the scale it has, but through this I have been able to share my ever-growing knowledge of all kinds of mental illness and help clients to find the best route towards recovery, not just for the sufferer but for those close to them as well.

My ever-increasing client list highlighted just how little emotional support or real empathy there was available for the carers, friends and families of those suffering from mental illness and, having had first-hand experience of the destruction it can cause within the family unit, I felt compelled to write my first book (*Hope with Eating Disorders*, published in 2012). I was keen to share what I had learnt from our journey with Samantha in the hope that it would bring some guidance, comfort, strength and hope to others. Outwardly it was impossible to identify families who were going through similar experiences, yet when I spoke openly about what we had experienced within our family, I learnt that most people I knew were struggling with something behind closed doors. They had been too afraid to talk about it for fear of the stigma or judgement, which sadly still surround mental health issues, even in today's society when a staggering one in four of us will experience or suffer from some form of mental illness at any one time. It was then I realised how widespread issues like self-harm, anxiety, depression, OCD and eating disorders were and how confusing the wealth of information available on these subjects can be to the reader. Despite many high-profile initiatives by the Government and various celebrities, making mental health awareness a target, there are still countless people of all ages suffering in silence, in need of help and support, and many loved ones, friends and carers confused and unsure of how to help them. These resources have become even harder to access during the Covid-19 pandemic and I fear waiting times for mental health services will have lengthened significantly.

Looking back, although Samantha had left most of her issues behind, she never truly felt comfortable in her own skin until recently, when she reignited her love for drama and the arts and completed a BA Hons in Drama and performing arts. Consequently, we have watched her grow into a beautiful, confident and vibrant young lady, pursuing a passion that allows her to express herself. Her passion and desire for life have been strengthened by the encouragement of her supportive and loving fiancé, Jay. Charlotte also has a wonderful, understanding husband, Callum, who has been on this journey with us since the beginning, so I am hugely relieved – being happy and healthy is all I have ever wanted for both of my girls.

As for me…

Which brings us to *Hope with Anxiety*…

Having experienced first-hand some of what you are probably going through, my main aim in writing this book is to help you understand anxiety disorders and identify the symptoms of this destructive mental illness as early as you possibly can, allowing you to intervene swiftly and with more insight into the different treatments available, which are paramount for a quicker and more effective long-term recovery.

After the first edition of *Hope with Eating Disorders* was published in 2012 and was, I am very proud to say, very well received by sufferers, carers and those who work in the eating disorder world, I went on to write more books: in 2015 John Blake Books published *Fundamentals, A Guide For Parents, Teachers and Carers on Mental Health and Self-Esteem*, with co-author Natasha Devon; in 2018 *Hope with OCD*, was published by Hammersmith Health Books; then I wrote the second edition of *Hope with Eating Disorders*, followed by *Hope with Depression*, both again published by Hammersmith Health Books, in 2019 and 2020 respectively.

In the eight years since the first edition of *Hope with Eating Disorders* was published, many things have moved on and changed in the way mental illness is portrayed and understood. The wider public's understanding of these complex conditions has in many ways grown, but at the same time the pressures that society faces are evolving at such a pace that it can be difficult to keep up. The media landscape has altered, with the internet and social media exerting a stronger influence than ever before – and this is something we do our best to influence positively with our *Hope with Mental Health* YouTube channel.

Furthermore, my own understanding and experience have also grown, thanks to my clients who continue to teach me so much. No two people who walk through my door are the same, and every single one of their experiences has allowed me to grow and expand my knowledge of mental illnesses and how these affect individuals and the people caring for them.

In the chapters that follow, I will try to answer some of the questions that I am asked frequently and my objective is to give you, the reader, the hope and belief that you have the strength and courage not only to support and guide your child/friend/ loved-one through these turbulent waters, but also to be able to see them safely to the other side, where they and indeed everyone closely involved with them will be able to move forward with their lives. I would like this book to act as a road map not only for those who simply do not know where to turn for help, but also for those who would like to have a clearer understanding of anxiety disorder in general.

I hope to relieve you of some of the burden, confusion and pain you may be feeling, as you enter the unknown and to arm you with as much knowledge, guidance and strength as I can, to enable you to continue your journey with courage, trusting in your own personal skills and instinct, just as I did. Remember always that communication is the key, along with unconditional love, perseverance, non-judgement, patience and hope.

This book emphasises that there is no 'right' or 'wrong' path to recovery. My own experience demonstrates that each family or support network must take whatever action is right for them; if one option proves ineffective, try another – never buy into the myth that people with an anxiety disorder cannot recover. Never give up hope and never give up trying.

With hope, perseverance, love and a lot of effort from us all, my family has reached a very positive place. Samantha graduated in 2018 with a 2:1 in performing arts, and has written her own book *Hope Through Poetry* (some poems from which are in this book) to be published by Hammersmith Health Books in October 2020. She has become engaged to Jay, who I know will continue to love and support her through any difficult times that may lie ahead. Above all, she is happy and healthy – bubbly, funny and waking with a smile on her face. Her sister, Charlotte, is forging her own path with her loving husband, Callum, and has a bright future ahead; my husband and I can look forward to the next phase in our lives, finally content that our girls are happy and surrounded by love. Our experiences of mental illness have brought us to where we are now: wiser, more appreciative of each other, and with more understanding of others. I never stopped hoping we would one day reach this point, and now I am able to hand that hope on to you. Anything is possible... my family is living proof of that.

Please note

Over the pages that follow you will share the experiences of other carers and sufferers and realise that some of the emotions you may be experiencing are natural and normal. You will be given an insight into how your loved one is thinking and feeling, with the aim of providing you with a genuine understanding of their condition. I have also included an unbiased guide to some different types of treatment available, both mainstream and alternative. All the contributing individuals and therapists are real people, but some have changed their names to protect their identity.

Monster on my back

by Samantha Crilly

It sat on my back quite comfortably most days,
Merrily playing along, singing my praise.
The taste of misery always kept it near
As it wined and dined lavishly on fear.
I fed it for years, very generously so
It never had any motive to get up and go.
Only when I gradually stopped feeding it
Did it then grow weaker and weaker, the less I needed it.
Soon, having nothing to stay for
That's when it began to walk out of my door.
The stronger I grew, the weaker it became
As it starved profusely on the lack of my pain.
Light as a feather it soon blew away …
It can fly by my window from day to day
But I will always tell it to be on its way.

Chapter 1

What is anxiety?

'Anxiety' is a familiar word, one which can seem hard to escape from in today's busy world. We may hear that anxiety is 'on the rise', that we are raising a generation of 'anxious' children or that our constantly 'switched on' way of life is leading to a more anxious state of mind. But what does that really mean? What does anxiety actually feel like, and what effect is it having on the way we live our lives? Is it a by-product of modern life that some people are inevitably saddled with or is it a severe mental health condition which can be overcome?

So, what is anxiety?

Anxiety, in its clinical sense, is defined as a feeling of unease, worry or nervousness. However, in reality it is much more than that. It is a deep-rooted, debilitating and destructive mental illness that affects both the sufferer and their carers alike. Once well established, the severity of this dreadful illness and the tormented misery it rains down on the sufferer can destroy relationships and ruin the lives of not only the person suffering but also everyone around them.

The word 'anxious' is actually derived from the Latin word *'angere'*, meaning to strangle or to choke. This feeling of physical distress is a common symptom felt by those suffering

1

from anxiety. Some may describe anxiety as 'being trapped in quicksand; the more you struggle to free yourself of the thoughts, the worse they get', others as 'an inner scream they want to let out, but feel as though they are paralysed', or even as 'a swarm of bees constantly buzzing around in your head, leaving you unable to think clearly and rationally'.

Anxiety can change a person's way of thinking, their feelings and/or their behaviour. This can cause the person high levels of distress and difficulty in being able to function mentally, and sometimes physically too. Individuals who have an anxiety disorder may not always look as though they are ill, particularly if their symptoms are mild. However, some sufferers may show more obvious and explicit physical signs (see page 32).

Together, anxiety and depression are two of the most common mental illnesses and are thought to affect around one in five of the British population at some point in their lifetime.[1] Like all mental illnesses, an anxiety disorder does not discriminate and can affect anyone, regardless of age, gender, sexuality, ethnicity and/or social background.

An anxiety disorder is a serious mental illness deserving of the same attention and respect as any physical illness, yet sadly, it is often still woefully misunderstood, feared and even trivialised. If we were to break an arm or leg, not only would a doctor know how to fix it, but we would probably receive a lot of sympathy and support from the people around us. This is not the case with an anxiety disorder.

Dave Davies, manager of Frank Bruno, who himself has suffered from anxiety and many of whose family members and clients have suffered from depression, talks about how anxiety and most mental illnesses have been misunderstood for many years:

> My mother worried about everything. I thought at first she was just a concerned parent but anxiety along with depression was ultimately what it was. In the 1960s, if someone was not 'right' it was either ignored or explained that the person was having 'a bad day'.

With anxiety, there is no such obvious cure, and people around the sufferer tend to fear what they cannot see, so they can be inclined to draw away and/or worry that they will say or do the wrong thing. This can be frustrating for someone experiencing anxiety, as they may feel that their condition has not yet been acknowledged or taken seriously, or that the people close to them do not care.

Everyone's experience of and journey with anxiety are unique to them; anxiety can present itself in many different guises and can be an illness of extremes. For some it may produce an overwhelming force of adrenaline, causing insomnia and lack of sleep, while others may find themselves struggling to stay awake and keep their eyes open due to the constant worry and angst exhausting their body.

For someone suffering in silence it can take an act of great courage and strength to admit to a loved one or a medical professional that there could potentially be something wrong. Once it is all out in the open, it can be such a relief for that person to know they are not going mad and that what they are experiencing is, in fact, a very common mental health issue suffered by millions of people across the globe. The duration for which someone can suffer from an anxiety disorder differs from person to person: in some cases, it can take root and manifest itself for months or even years at a time; in other cases it can pass through like a succession of rainstorms.

An anxiety disorder is rarely a response to a real threat. Rather it is the expectation of a danger which may or may not actually occur. Sometimes that feeling is appropriate to the situation, but

it becomes problematic when it happens so frequently or disproportionately that it begins to impinge on someone's life and
limits their experiences as a result.

Amy, who went through a period of regular panic attacks and
severe anxiety, says:

> I would feel worried about absolutely everything, and always
> something that would seem totally irrational (something I have
> worried about would be that the earth would fall from beneath
> my feet).

Anxiety is not simply a 21st-century malady. It has not been
born out of stressful commuting, juggling childcare or being
constantly switched-on to social media, although all these things
can exacerbate it. In fact, its roots go back to our caveman days.
Back then, when humans sensed danger, their body would be
flooded by a surge of adrenaline that would boost their heart
rate sending oxygen shooting to their limbs so they were better
equipped to fight their foe or flee from danger – the well-known
'fight or flight' response.

What, however, is different today is that the churning stomach
or tingling fingers we may feel, or the head-rush of inappropriate
panic, is often a disproportionate reaction to a situation which
should not hold any extreme danger.

When, in some people, it happens over and over again, the
stress acts like a tap dripping into a cup of water. Drip by drip
the pressure and worry build up until one day the cup overflows.
That is when someone's anxiety may reach tipping point, their
mind and body overloaded by these constant surges of adrenaline, and what started as a few worrying niggles can become a
full-blown anxiety disorder.

Garry shares his thoughts on how his anxiety developed:

Chapter 1

> I think it's been a drip, drip rather than a specific incident or set of circumstances.

At its most destructive, anxiety invades the tightest corners of a person's mind, invisibly and insidiously feeding on their every thought, transforming all the potential joy in life into possible disaster, leaving them unable to achieve peace of mind, and having a huge effect on those around them, from parents to partners, employers to friends.

You may turn to the internet hoping it may help you to understand a bit more, or you may scour articles in the press on the condition; this could find you ending up even more confused and frustrated. As there is so much varied information available through various channels, it is difficult to know what applies to you and your own situation.

Throughout the course of this book, you will discover that as a parent, carer, friend, teacher or work colleague you are not alone. I hope you will learn that some of the mixed thoughts and feelings you and your family may be experiencing, inevitably including concern, worry, sadness, frustration, even resentment and anger at times, are normal and natural; most importantly, I hope that you will arm yourself with a real understanding of your loved one's illness and discover some of the most effective ways to help them and the rest of the family towards recovery.

From my own experience, one of the most important things I have learnt and would like to share with you at this point in the book, is that, you cannot apply logic to something illogical the same way you cannot apply reason to something unreasonable, and you cannot make sense out of something nonsensical. In other words, 'you have to accept what is, to enable you to understand'.

My mum, Samantha's grandma, echoes the above with her feelings throughout our journey:

In the beginning, I was frightened and useless – after all, it's a mental illness, an illness that cannot be seen. As a little understanding came about, I felt unsure as to the best way to help. As time went by, with more understanding and acceptance through talking with Sam, ease and more self-assurance and confidence crept in. We have become closer during this long journey, the reason being we can talk as equals and listen and accept. She tells me her thoughts; I tell her mine. We laugh when we say or hear something funny and we hug when it is sad.

Within this book I aim to provide you with the information that I think really matters, with no agenda other than helping you, the reader, to understand some of the different types of anxiety disorder, the signs to look for, and some of the treatment and support options that are available to both sufferers and their carers.

What does anxiety feel like?

Anxiety may be recognised as a state of mind, but its effects can be physical as well as emotional. Think of the word 'anxiety' as something of an umbrella term made up of a whole host of symptoms, from which each individual will have a set of feelings that characterise their own anxiety.

For some people 'anxiety' means a constantly whirring and worried mind, for others it may mean not being able to leave the house. Some will make others very aware of how they are feeling, while others will keep their difficult feelings to themselves. A number of people may not even realise that anxiety is the under-lying cause of their physical symptoms, such as stomach upsets or insomnia.

As the following examples show, anxiety affects people in myriad of ways.

Eve describes how her anxiety makes her feel:

Anxiety makes me feel like I'm trapped constantly trying to fight off a monster chasing me.

Jo tells us how anxiety makes her feel:

It feels like a sudden overwhelming heat in my body. My chest starts to tighten and then it's like my body goes cold. I feel ill and like everything is taking over and is out of my control.

Pete says of his anxiety:

It feels as though I am in extreme fight or flight mode at all times, even when there is no reason at all to feel this way. It's terrifying and deeply upsetting.

Everyday stress versus an anxiety disorder

One of the most common misconceptions surrounding anxiety is that it is the same as being stressed. In today's demanding world, it is virtually impossible to find someone who would not describe themselves as stressed, at least some of the time. As a result, many people may sometimes, or even quite often, feel anxious. That is not to say though that everyone has a problematic anxiety disorder. Some stress or anxiety throughout life is natural. It can even be helpful, keeping us on our toes and helping us face and overcome some of the daily challenges that life brings. However, too much anxiety – and the unpleasant symptoms it can cause – can have the opposite effect, paralysing us and stopping us from living our lives and moving forward.

As Lottie explains how her anxiety makes her feel:

I find it hard to think rationally and can get extreme thoughts with it. Anxiety makes me feel annoyed as I can't do simple things and can make you feel like a failure. I would find it hard to breathe and focus so I could never do the things I wanted.

In today's society, particularly on social media, there does seem to be a tendency by some people to use the word 'anxiety' glibly, almost as a badge of honour, without any in-depth understanding of what it really means, and doing so can do a disservice to the legions of people who are truly suffering with an anxiety disorder.

It is vital for all of us to understand the distinction between feeling stressed and actual anxiety. The examples in Table 1 successfully highlight the difference. Again, it is worth noting that someone with debilitating anxiety will have individual symptoms that are unique to them and may not identify with all these examples.

Table 1: The differences between stress/everyday anxiety and anxiety disorder

Everyday anxiety	Anxiety disorder
Feeling self-conscious, embarrassment and awkwardness in social situations.	Avoidance of social situations and of being around other people for fear of being judged or humiliated.
Realistic fear of a dangerous object, place or situation.	Irrational fear causing avoidance of a place, object or situation that does not pose a significant threat.
Being nervous when preparing for an exam, job interview, performance or other big event.	Constant, agonising worry about everyday events, possibly accompanied by unexpected panic attacks.
Worrying about paying the bills, getting a new job, relationships and other major life events.	Constant and distressing worry that causes significant misery and interferes with daily life.

Feeling sad or anxious and not being able to sleep after a traumatic incident.	Suffering from repetitive nightmares and flashbacks of the event. Extreme insomnia.
Feeling nervous about flying or travelling to a new or unknown place.	Feeling physically unable to travel, even if it is for work and could put their job in jeopardy.

How common is an anxiety disorder and who does it affect?

An anxiety disorder is very common, yet it can be quite hard to accurately measure how many people are affected. We all feel anxious from time to time, but it is the frequency and depth of the feelings that accompany it that determine how problematic the anxiety actually is. If the anxiety is impacting on someone's life, affecting them in the long term, or stopping them doing things they once enjoyed, then it may fall into one of the recognised anxiety disorders. Furthermore, anxiety can accompany or be a by-product of another mental health issue, making it even harder to identify.

Paige shares her experience of suffering from multiple mental illnesses:

Since I was suffering with anorexia and bulimia, I only became aware of the anxiety after I started having counselling and I started to realise that when I was in situations where I was around food, that my thoughts would race and I would start to get panicked.

Despite these difficulties in pin-pointing and ring-fencing anxiety, the statistics paint a stark and concerning picture: According to the Mental Health Foundation's *Fundamental Facts About Mental Health 2016*, there were 8.2 million cases of anxiety in the UK in that year.[2] When it comes to generalised anxiety disorder (see page 34), it is thought that around one in 20 of the population are affected.[3]

Anxiety disorders cut across age, gender, race and social class – many of the most successful people battle with its effects – yet evidence also shows that certain groups in society are more vulnerable.

Both men and women can suffer from anxiety; however, being a woman can put you at a higher risk of developing this illness. In adulthood women are thought to be twice as likely to have an anxiety disorder as men,[4] with this acceleration between the sexes happening in the mid-teens. It is fair to interpret the Mental Health Foundation's 2014 statistic that 22% of women feel anxious 'a lot' or 'all of' the time (compared with 15% of men) as strong evidence that up to a fifth of women may be suffering from, or be at risk of, some kind of anxiety disorder.[5]

This statistic may be slightly skewed by men's continuing reticence to recognise and talk about their mental health, but nevertheless the statistic does suggest that women may be more susceptible to the effects of anxiety. The reasons for this are complex, and may relate to their hormonal cycles, the stressful caring roles women can be more likely to take on, the pressure of 'having it all', along with the feeling of judgement by society if they get it 'wrong'.

Margo says of how making her life simple has helped her in recovery from anxiety and overload:

Looking back, for many years I was constantly trying to be the perfect wife, mother and daughter, all while holding down a high-pressured job, probably not doing any of it very well! It wasn't until I hit the menopause that I fell apart, everything caught up with me and I was forced to take the time to re-evaluate myself and my life. Thankfully life is less complicated now, I left my job and spend more time at home doing simple things while spending 'quality' time with the family. I feel like a different person.

Causes of anxiety

It is clear that anxiety disorders can have a range of complex factors at their root, including biological and psychological causes, as well as factors linked to society and the knocks and challenges that life can throw at us. Although there are various theories surrounding its development, it is thought to be a combination of biological, genetic, cognitive and environmental factors acting together or individually as a trigger.

The common factors that can play a part in the onset of an anxiety disorder include:

- Imbalance of chemicals
- Genetics and family history
- Historical experiences
- Stressful life events
- The impact of stressful world events
- Long-term physical and psychological health conditions
- Hormonal imbalances
- History of drug or alcohol misuse
- Side-effects of medication
- Diet
- Personality type
- Caring for someone else.

Imbalance of chemicals

One of the possible causes underlying an anxiety disorder may be an imbalance of the brain chemicals ('neurotransmitters'), particularly serotonin and noradrenaline, that are involved in the control and regulation of mood. This is a simple explanation of a very complex process, involving the way that nerves connect and communicate with each other. If they are out of balance, it could contribute to someone developing anxiety, depression and/or another mental illness. It is a complex area, which is still not fully understood and requires more research, but it is widely accepted that these neurotransmitters do have a part to play in making someone susceptible to anxiety, although other factors from the list below are also likely to have a role.

Genetics and family history

While anxiety is often linked to someone's experiences in life, it is also now known that genetics can play a part and if you have a close family member with anxiety, you are more likely to develop it yourself.[6] While there may be a genetic link – research is ongoing – it is also worth bearing in mind that the link may also be due to the fact that we learn behaviour from those closest to us as we are growing up.

Myrtle, who has suffered from generalised anxiety disorder since she was a young child, shares her thoughts below:

> Both of my parents are very anxious and do not acknowledge that or talk about it. Growing up, my parents worried a lot and would make the world feel stressful and they continue to do so.

It is also important to note that having a parent or close relative who has experienced an anxiety disorder, or another mental illness, does not necessarily mean that someone will develop it themselves.

Tom shares his thoughts on his family and anxiety:

> My mum is a worrier and it's far too simplistic to blame her as my brother is fine and we had the same upbringing, though I do think her worry gave me the idea there was something to be worried about.

Historical experiences

It is now thought that going through difficult experiences when you are a child, or early in your adult life, may leave you more susceptible to an anxiety disorder later on. Abuse, neglect, an unstable family life and/or another traumatic event can have an impact that can last a lifetime.

Anabelle shares her experience with post-traumatic stress disorder (PTSD) from past traumatic events:

> The trauma built up over a number of years, possibly up to 10 years before it got to the point where I just couldn't ignore it any more. It was a gradual increase – slowly – relying on alcohol more and more, slowly developing phobias, then panic attacks settling in a number of years later. So by the time I realised I was in trouble, I hadn't even immediately linked it to something that had started to happen when I was 7 or 8 years old.

Battling through painful emotions and situations as a child can lead to low self-esteem, leaving that person less able to cope with life's knocks, and this could impact someone's chances of developing a more anxious mind-set.

Stressful life events

Often a stressful event or long-term stress can be the precursor to an anxiety disorder developing. This may be because self-esteem, which when strong can be an important defence against mental illness, is compromised. It is understandable that difficult experiences can leave people feeling uncertain or apprehensive, with trust issues towards others or a shaken belief in their own ability to handle challenging situations. Without support to help someone cope with the emotional fallout caused by stressful chapters in their lives, it is all too easy for an anxiety disorder to develop. People who have experienced a relationship breaking down, redundancy, bereavement or even a stressful 'positive' event, such as moving to a new house, having a baby or getting married, may also experience anxiety.

Rachel tells us of her stressful life event:

After losing my beloved daddy I was so fearful of my mum and brother leaving me. I was so young I didn't understand death and just thought my dad didn't want me but as I got older and watched my mum become ill I started to understand and the fear grew and grew around health and death and when she did die when I was in my teens my anxiety was that bad I was terrified to leave my house, talk to people etc in the fear they would die too. Due to my anxiety and other mental health issues I started to believe I was cursed as everyone I got close to died or left.

The impact of stressful world events

In recent years, the rolling 24-hour news agenda, book-ended by the constant interruption of social media posts, has made it hard to escape the impact of world events. The reams of headlines, reports, analyses and campaigns can feel overwhelming and induce feelings of anxiety in even those who have never suffered from mental illness before.

There are some obvious global issues that have particularly impacted people's mental health; the destruction of the planet and the impact of climate change are an ever-present worry, so much so that this has been dubbed 'eco-anxiety'. The associated changing weather patterns, causing droughts, floods or freak meteorological events, only add to the pressure.

Wendy gives us her thoughts on 'eco-anxiety', since her young daughter has started excessively worrying about the planet and climate change:

Since climate change has come to the forefront of people's minds and the news, my daughter, who is only 8, has been worrying herself to the point of not sleeping; she is scared that the world is going to end imminently. It is a concern, as she is young, and I would like her to enjoy being young and without anxieties.

The coronavirus pandemic of 2020 has sent stress levels soaring to possibly unprecedented levels (the mental cost will still be counted for many years to come), exacerbated by the need for many to self-isolate, robbing them of the opportunity to share the mental burden with others.

Matty says of how the pandemic has affected his drug and alcohol misuse and mental health issues:

> As for the coronavirus, I know that I will probably survive the illness. I'm not scared of the illness taking my life but myself taking my life through extreme loneliness being isolated alone.
>
> Isolation is fine for someone who lives with their whole family and has support around them. My being alone has taken a huge toll on my mental health.

Garry shares his wise words during the coronavirus epidemic despite suffering from multiple mental illnesses:

> I keep telling myself not to worry over things I can't control and, somewhat surprisingly, it helps with the virus anxiety.

For decades now, the ongoing threat of terrorism has been buzzing constantly around, punctuated by acts of violence that create spikes of real fear for millions of people. Alongside all those huge issues, there will be smaller news events that nevertheless have a massive impact on individuals, taking an often-unseen toll on their mental health until a dangerous or distressing tipping point is reached.

Whatever the news agenda at the time, the effect is the same, creating a climate of fear that leaves people struggling to cope, perhaps trapped in a cycle of rumination or wakefulness that can turn the dripping tap I have talked about into a gushing torrent. Panic attacks, obsessive compulsive behaviours, eating disorders or substance abuse may be among the multitude of unwelcome knock-on effects. This anxiety can all too easily spiral into depression, sending sufferers plummeting into the depths of despair.

While it is important to be well informed, and often to act on the advice or information we are given, it is also vital not to become so caught up in global events that we do not leave time and space to rationalise and recover, giving our minds a rest from the 'doom and gloom' that can so easily become overwhelming. With the news now available 24 hours a day on TV, radio and social media, it is all too easy to become almost addicted to the constant adrenaline-fuelled 'fight or flight' response, not leaving our minds any time or space to clear, enabling us to see things in a different light.

Long-term physical and psychological health conditions

Having a long-term illness, whether it be physical or mental, can raise a person's risk of experiencing anxiety. This may be a symptom of the illness itself – for example, the signs of an overactive thyroid may mirror those of anxiety or the anxiety may be a by-product of coping with another condition reflecting the restrictions, fears and worries that the primary illness brings.

Suzie, whose daughter suffers from social anxiety disorder, shares their experience:

It became apparent through talking to the psychiatrist that, as a young child, she would never make friends easily; if we were out as a family, she would rely on her younger sister to join small groups of children and make friends and then would join in once the friendship was secure. From a very young age, she suffered with perennial rhinitis but, despite my early efforts, this was not diagnosed until she was about 6. As a result of this chronic condition, she was bullied at primary school from a very early age through to junior school, which in part led her to suffer with anxiety in her adult life.

It is very common for an anxiety disorder to overlap and co-exist with other psychological illnesses. The link between depression and anxiety, for example, is very well documented, while others – such as eating disorders or self-harm – may also have a strong crossover.

Jo shares her thoughts on how her anxiety and borderline personality disorder are interlinked:

> Having borderline personality disorder means anxiety becomes an extreme emotion. Anxiety can start to come on with no apparent cause and escalate quickly towards panic attacks. But just as quickly it can dissipate too.

People who live with conditions such as ADHD (attention-deficit hyperactivity disorder) or dyslexia are more prone to anxiety, not least because of the low self-esteem that so often affects those with one of these diagnoses. When you struggle with reading, writing, concentrating, paying attention or sticking to the 'rules' it can be difficult to feel good about yourself and this can in turn lead to many worries about different areas of your life. People with ADHD and/or dyslexia may be upset at how others perceive them, and worry about the future. Their anxiety may be particularly tied to their ADHD or dyslexia, or it may be about a broader range of issues.

Phil, whose son suffers from ADHD and anxiety, shares their experience:

> My son was diagnosed with ADHD at the age of 6. He found it difficult to concentrate and sit still, with his mind and anxiety all over the place. School was a challenge for him, being seen as unruly and troublesome. Eventually we managed to get him seen and he was prescribed drugs to help him control the ADHD and the anxiety that seemed to co-exist alongside it; this helped immensely. Now aged 14 he still takes the medicine, but has managed to control the ADHD; he does have some

lapses at school, but fortunately his school has a special unit to help, advise and guide him through everyday situations. He finds it hard to make and maintain friends of his own age, as his interests tend to be more of someone younger, which can upset him and cause him to be anxious. He does seem to thrive best with a structured environment where he knows what is required from him but we do need to keep him on track every now and then. He is a lovely boy, well liked with a unique personality.

Anxiety is almost always embedded in autism, a condition where people may struggle to understand the unwritten social rules that are part and parcel of everyday life and where senses can be heightened, making the world a bewildering, noisy, confusing place. Understanding and relating to other people can be a real challenge, and people with autism can take things very literally, struggling to understand things like jokes or sarcasm. This can make them very anxious about doing or saying the right thing. Worrying about the world and their place in it can lead to autistic people questioning why they are 'different', which can also give rise to a huge amount of anxiety, which they and their loved ones have to find ways to manage throughout their lifetime.

For people with autism, routine and familiarity are absolutely key and so the arrival of the coronavirus pandemic was for many a massive extra challenge. It took away all certainty, upended routines, kept loved ones away, messed up weekly schedules, and took away the normality of school, college or work. All these things that are essential for keeping an autistic person's stress and anxiety in check were suddenly taken away, without warning, and the impact for those on the autistic spectrum was huge.

Hormonal imbalances

Every day, as we live our lives, the hormones (chemical messengers) inside our body are hard at work. The levels of these hormones can fluctuate depending on all sorts of things, including our body's make-up, the experiences we are going through, the challenges we face, the time of the month, the food and drink we consume and whether another health issue is at play.

Progesterone, for example, increases in a woman's body in the days after ovulation or during menopause, which can prompt a more downbeat and anxious mood. This may be because progesterone is believed to stimulate the part of your brain responsible for fight or flight responses, which can make people feel 'on edge'.

Eve shares her experience with us:

> I suffered with bad mood swings when my periods started and then stopped at 15; since then the mood swings have stopped and I've been diagnosed with PCOS [polycystic ovary syndrome]; my consultant did wonder if there was maybe a link there as I was always in a bad anxious state which spiralled me into outbursts.

Anxiety can also be the result of stress hormones, including adrenaline and cortisol. In today's society, where we are on the go almost 24/7, our bodies can be almost permanently 'on alert'. Instead of helping us deal with stressful situations as they are designed to, the flood of these hormones may end up causing anxiety instead.

Also consider the hormones that drive different parts of our bodies. If out of kilter, the thyroid hormones, for example, can lead to unpleasant edginess and are linked to panic attacks.

Freida talks of how the menopause has brought on anxiety that she had not experienced before:

> Since I have been going through the menopause, I have found that my levels of anxiety have risen. I seem to constantly worry about things that I would have previously taken in my stride. This is starting to affect my everyday living, in a negative way.

History of drug or alcohol misuse

Substance abuse frequently co-occurs with anxiety. As something of a chicken-and-egg situation, the substance may be used in a bid to deal with the unpleasant anxious feelings that someone is experiencing; however, it can also work the other way, with alcohol or drugs also recognised as potentially making someone's anxiety worse, particularly as the numbing effects of the substance wear off.

Furthermore, the chemical changes that drugs and alcohol bring about in our bodies and brains can have a significant effect, with the plummeting lows that come once their effect wears off often contributing to feelings of anxiety. In someone who regularly drinks alcohol or misuses other substances, the constant rollercoaster of highs and lows can have a profound effect on mental well-being.

Matty gives us his thoughts on what potentially could trigger his anxiety and other mental health issues:

> Past drug use and alcohol caused me issues and the fear of falling back in with the crowds of drug using and dealing with the people associated with that side of my past triggers my anxiety massively.

Side-effects of medication

Some medication may, as a side-effect, trigger anxiety or mimic the symptoms of it. The list of which drugs can do this is long and varied, so those at risk of anxiety, or who are looking for the causes of their anxious thought patterns, should consider the medication they are taking and talk to their GP if they have concerns. Among those that may cause problems in some people are drugs containing caffeine, as well as some of those used to treat conditions such as asthma. Those who are taking medication for a thyroid disorder may find they experience side-effects, including anxiety, if the balance of the drugs does not correctly meet the needs of their illness.

Jo shares her experience with some medications:

> I've found that certain a medication makes my anxiety worse. When I was on a specific anti-psychotic, my anxiety increased to the point I was waking up, physically sick with anxiety.

The best advice is to read the information leaflet that accompanies any medication and, should problems arise, contact a GP or medical professional as soon as possible.

Diet

A poor diet may not directly cause anxiety but, in some cases, it can make the symptoms worse. Drinking high levels of caffeine, for example, which is found in tea, coffee, cola and energy drinks, can simulate familiar feelings of anxiety, such as the heart beating faster and/or the breathing rate increasing. Caffeine can also contribute to sleep difficulties which in turn can exacerbate mental health issues.

Other negative eating patterns can also worsen the symptoms of anxiety. Skipping meals or eating a diet high in sugar can make someone's blood sugar levels suddenly dip, mimicking some of the symptoms of anxiety. Eating regular meals packed with complex carbohydrates, protein and high in fruit and vegetables, and hydrating regularly with water, is the best recipe for calming an anxious mind.

Personality type

There is evidence that people of certain personality types are more susceptible to anxiety than others. Those who have perfectionist tendencies or poor self-esteem are among those who may be vulnerable. People who have a glass-half-empty outlook, frequently worrying and seeing the world through a negative lens, could be at a greater risk of developing an anxiety disorder, while those who appear to thrive on drama may also find anxiety accompanies the adrenaline surges that frequently punctuate their lives.

Juliet, who suffers from generalised anxiety disorder, shares her thoughts on this with us:

I feel as though the anxiety is underpinned by perfectionistic and controlling tendencies in my personality. The anxiety seems to have always been there and gradually got worse as I have got older.

Caring for someone else

While having another physical or mental illness may trigger anxiety, so can caring for someone who is unwell or who needs extra support. Being on hand for them around the clock, often putting their needs first, while also shouldering countless worries about their health and well-being, and the financial or social concerns that go with this, can really take its toll. According to Carers UK, almost eight in 10 carers say they feel more anxious as a result of their caring role.[7]

Looking after someone can of course be immensely rewarding but, all too often, carers push their own needs to the bottom of the pile, limiting the time they have to themselves to do the things they enjoy or that are beneficial to their own health. In addition, their role may lead to isolation and a degree of loneliness. When this is combined with the tsunami of worries that can almost inevitably accompany looking after someone you love, it is no wonder that this is such a stark risk factor for some kind of anxiety disorder.

Support is available for carers but this can sometimes be

patchy and difficult to access. With so many other demands on their time, it is little surprise that many carers ignore their own mental well-being until they reach crisis point.

Jess, who developed anxiety whilst caring for her partner who suffered from borderline personality disorder, explains how her anxiety grew:

> My girlfriend was highly paranoid of my every move, and scrutinised my motivation for things like exercise and socialising. I was also forbidden from discussing anything pertaining to our relationship issues as they highlighted her own mental health issues and were thus 'her problem and no one else's'. This shut me off from friends and family support. I felt trapped, too afraid to end the relationship because of anticipated consequences such as her attempting suicide.

The power of 'What if... ?'

There is a Swedish proverb which translated means 'Worry gives a small thing a big shadow'. This is particularly relevant to the 'What if… ?' question that plagues most of those with anxiety.

One of the key aspects of worry is that it muddles our thought processes, making us focus on the possible scary impact of doing something rather than the more likely, harmless outcome. As such, by dwelling on these negative thoughts, anxiety can stop people doing what they want to do or need to do, limiting their life experiences.

That said, some form of 'What if... ?' questioning is actually essential. Someone pondering whether to go out partying on a Monday night is right to ask themselves 'What if I am too tired to work in the morning?' Similarly, if they are pondering whether to take a taxi home or risk a walk through the park, it is absolutely correct to ask that 'What if... ?' question. Applying this kind of logic keeps people safe and avoids them upsetting or hurting themselves or others.

Flip to the other end of the anxiety spectrum, however, and excessive worry can make us over-apply 'What if... ?' leading to things like social occasions, working life and even journeys on public transport, appearing fraught with possible danger, embarrassment or fear. This can also be applied to health worries, with anxious people elevating a mere headache to the potential catastrophe of a brain tumour or indigestion being perceived as a possible heart attack.

Caitlin says:

> I dread so many things in life and the current virus (Covid-19) is not helping this! I worry what if my partner dies, what if I die, what if our wedding can't go ahead, what if I lose my job, what if my mum's breast cancer comes back... What if everything. It's always worst-case fears with me, although not on purpose!

These negative thought patterns can be wearing and demoralising and can undermine much of the good work that a person puts into other areas of their life. At their worst, reaching these illogical conclusions can stop people leaving their homes or cause serious issues in their school and working life.

The good news is that 'What if…?' can be tackled, although doing so can take a huge reserve of courage and willpower. To silence that negative voice, the person needs to dig deep and replace the 'worst case scenario' thinking with a positive, rational thought, and apply that optimism to whatever it is the anxiety is stopping them from doing. I know that it is far easier said than done, but with the right help and support and the sufferer's own determination, it really is possible.

Myths and truths

One of the barriers to fully understanding an anxiety disorder and the ways it can affect people's lives is that so much misinformation abounds in relation to it. It seems that many people either belittle its impact, dismissing anxiety as something everyone experiences to a greater or lesser extent. Or, at the other end of the spectrum, they believe that anxiety only really affects an unfortunate few, whose 'nervy disposition' or inability to cope with life's challenges marks them out as susceptible to its effects.

In fact, anxiety is much more complex than this and myths such as these can be unhelpful and prevent people from getting to grips with, and really being able to understand, this all-consuming illness.

Among the many misconceptions that exist, the following are often quoted in relation to anxiety:

- Anxiety is not a real mental illness
- Someone with anxiety should avoid stressful situations
- Medication should be avoided by those with anxiety
- People with anxiety have a 'nervy' disposition.

Myths and truths

Myth: Anxiety is not a real mental illness.

Truth: While experiencing some level of anxiety is both normal and important, helping us deal with the challenges life throws at us, when it takes on the form of a disorder negatively affecting the decisions someone makes and their ability to fully live their life, often to a disabling degree, then it is indeed a mental illness that needs addressing.

Some people with anxiety will experience physical symptoms, but for many the effects are more to do with the constant worry or panic they experience rather than a stomach ache or headache they can describe to a doctor. These feelings may be hard to measure or even describe, but they are very real and need to be diagnosed and treated as much as a broken leg or debilitating back pain.

Those with anxiety cannot simply 'snap out of it' or 'get over it'. In fact, dismissing their fears may well have the effect of making them worse. Instead, it is important to acknowledge those feelings and support the person experiencing them, just as people would for anyone with a physical illness.

Myth: Someone with anxiety should avoid stressful situations.

Truth: Avoiding the stresses and strains of life simply is not possible, and neither is it actually desirable. Even for those who suffer from anxiety, exposure to challenges and difficult situations is absolutely crucial. Learning to deal with the things that terrify or stress them, in a way that is healthy and productive, may in fact be one of the ways of treating their worries or panic. Regardless of the difficult feelings such challenges may give rise to, those with anxiety should be able to do the things that are important to them. Avoiding the things they fear completely may have the converse effect of magnifying those concerns. Paying the anxiety that attention may give it the fuel to grow.

Myth: Medication should be avoided by those with anxiety.

Truth: People often assume that anxiety is not 'severe enough' to need medication, and that taking it is a sign of weakness. They may also see medication as something to be feared (and often avoided), because of the concerns about its side-effects and whether it could lead to an addiction. Those concerns should certainly not be ignored, but neither should they put people off seeking medical help for anxiety.

Sometimes medication can be important for breaking the cycle of negative thinking, a kind of buffer, allowing people to step back and understand more clearly how to handle difficult or upsetting situations. Taken under strict medical supervision, as part of a wider treatment plan, medication may have a positive part to play.

The best person to advise a patient about whether medication might be suitable, and what the effects of taking that medication might be, is your GP. However, that is not to say that all responsibility should be handed to a medical practitioner. The patient themselves, along with their loved ones and carers, should ask about side-effects and remain alert to any potential problems they might cause.

Medication is also only one line of treatment; therapy or counselling can also be very effective, while other alternative therapies may also be helpful (see Chapters 4 and 5 for more information).

Myth: People with anxiety have a 'nervy' disposition.

Truth: Anyone – even those who seem the most confident and outgoing – can experience anxiety. While the symptoms in some people may be noticeable, others can experience them without anyone else realising for years. They may be able to mask their symptoms, or their friends and loved ones may dismiss the signs – such as stomach problems or substance misuse – as something else. For many, anxiety will grow from that constant 'drip, drip' of stress and worry that I have already talked about and to which anyone, from any walk of life, can be susceptible. The thing to remember is that if the behaviour of someone you care for has changed, look beneath the surface and talk to them to try and find out what is going on.

Hope with anxiety

An anxiety disorder is recognised by the professional medical community and can be treated successfully with time, perseverance, determination, the right kind of therapy and, in some cases, medication. No two cases are ever the same, which is why treatment techniques and recovery journeys can be so varied. Sadly, there is no magic pill, and whilst acceptance, understanding, support and patience are paramount to the sufferer's recovery, the only person that can really make the change is the sufferer. It is not an easy journey, but it is definitely one worth taking, to free them from their life-limiting spiral of seemingly constant worry ... remembering always that recovery is possible.

Chapter 2

Types of anxiety

Suffering from an anxiety disorder can be compared to being lost at sea, anchored down, struggling for air, and with an overwhelming sense of impending doom whilst everyone else around you is swimming freely, seemingly okay. As a wave of anxiety floods through their mind and body, the sufferer can have an overpowering sense of drowning, leaving them feeling helpless and trapped within their own body and mind as the anxiety continues to build a powerful mountain of mental torment and chaos inside their head.

Sadly, there is no escape without the sufferer's own determination and willpower, alongside the right kind of help and support, be it professional and or from a loved one(s). For the sufferer, they are fighting an internal war with themselves, with no clear resolution. This can be utterly exhausting, and the more tired the person who has the anxiety becomes, the more space the head creates for it to occupy. Being at war with any part of yourself can never bring peace, whether it be for the sufferer or their loved ones.

If you are the sufferer, I have the greatest compassion for you; I have felt and seen myself how tormenting it can be both for you and the people who love and support you. You will no doubt, at some point, feel that you are losing your mind, particularly if the people around you are fearful or dismissive about your experience. Or, on the other hand, you may be too frightened or embarrassed to tell anyone, leaving you feeling utterly trapped and unsafe within your own head. Please remember, you are not alone, you are not mad no matter what the content of your thoughts is; you will not be judged by people who truly accept and understand or those who try to. These are symptoms of a treatable mental illness, not a reflection on you as a person, and best of all, by reading material like this, you are well on the way to taking steps in a much more positive direction and expanding your own understanding and knowledge.

If you are a loved one, or the carer, not only can it be frustrating and confusing, but also very upsetting, and at times push your patience to the limit and beyond. The sufferer can sometimes seem evasive and rude, but usually they are not meaning to be or to appear in that way, it is often all part of the illness – their head is full of so much chaos and mess that it is a major undertaking keeping things together, let alone being able to hold a half decent conversation with anyone.

Lucy says of her mother, who has anxiety, depression and alcohol misuse:

When my mum is feeling well, we get on so well and share wonderful times together; as soon as she is feeling low and riddled with anxiety, she becomes a different person; she can be rude and quite aggressive. I used to take this to heart and it upset me so much. After many years and reading a lot about the illnesses, I now realise this is the illness and her frustration with it and nothing to do with me. It's hard but you have to try and move on from it rather than holding a grudge.

Pippa shares her own frustrations with her boyfriend's anxiety:

I know when he is struggling as I can see the worry on his face and in his behaviour, but, when I ask what I can do to help, he often does not know. This makes me feel really helpless as I want to take away the negative thoughts he has and make him feel better, but I know that I can't help him. I haven't been able to overcome this hurdle, but I have started to do anything I can to help, which often is simply sitting with him while he works to get himself out of the negative thoughts he has.

Opportunities to communicate with someone suffering from an anxiety disorder about how they feel should be encouraged; the information you receive from them will prove vital in the recovery process. Do not always apply logic; accept that their mind is a confused place and that, in talking, they are providing you with an important glimpse into its inner workings.

There is so much information available now, we can often end up utterly baffled and vaguely hysterical, and therein lies the problem. The term 'anxiety' actually covers a multitude of different guises, hence affecting people in a multitude of different ways. With the aim of trying to understand this multi-faceted illness, it can be useful to be aware of the many different types of anxiety disorder. At this point, it is also important to stress that these 'labels' can often have blurred boundaries. Your loved one may show signs of more than one of them, or may exhibit different behaviours altogether. So, while labels can be helpful, it is important to keep in mind that everyone displays their signs and symptoms differently.

The common signs and symptoms of anxiety

While this chapter will continue to explore the 'labels' that help to identify some of the different types of anxiety disorder, there are some symptoms that may commonly occur across many of these different types.

It can be helpful to divide these signs and symptoms into two distinct groups: psychological and physical. It is important to remember that there will be a constant interplay between the two, with the balance between them changing. Some people will live with just a few of these symptoms, while others will experience a greater range. Individuals may also find that their anxiety manifests itself in different ways that are not covered below. Anxiety is complex, its effects are wide-ranging, and it can also highlight the myriad of ways, big and small, that our state of mind can affect the way our brains and bodies function.

Psychological symptoms

- Ruminating, over-analysing and over-thinking
- A sense of dread
- Feelings of irritation
- Difficulty concentrating
- Feelings of panic
- Nervousness about the future
- Feeling you might die
- Fearing you are going mad
- Worrying you may be seriously ill
- Wanting to run away or escape
- Avoiding situations you think may be risky or uncomfortable.

Physical symptoms

- Tightness in the chest or a pounding heart
- Having tense or aching muscles
- Pins and needles
- Stomach-aches
- Bowel problems
- Feeling hot and flustered
- Experiencing dizziness
- Feeling sick
- Having a panic attack

- Sweating more
- Feeling breathless or having a choking feeling
- Hyperventilating.

It may also be helpful to recognise the thought patterns that can accompany an anxiety disorder. While those with anxiety may not look different from others, it is highly likely that they do think and feel differently.

You may recognise the following in your loved one:

- They are desperate for approval from others and worry excessively about what people think of them.
- They assume the worst possible outcome and think negatively about what lies ahead. Another word for this kind of thought process is 'catastrophising'.
- They may be a perfectionist, desperately striving for the highest goal and fearing that any mistake means failure.
- They may focus on negative events, amplifying them out of reasonable proportion.
- With so many worries crowding their mind, they may struggle to concentrate or remember things.
- They may experience an almost continuous stream of racing thoughts and worries that seem to bombard their mind uncontrollably.

Jayne, whose daughter has suffered from chronic anxiety since the age of 14, shares the first signs she noticed:

She started to avoid meeting up with friends, something that she had always enjoyed and valued. She wasn't sleeping very well and her eating habits had changed – she would no longer finish a meal. She was also spending more time in her room and seemed quieter and more distant than normal. She wanted to be off school more and more.

Different 'types' of anxiety

Perhaps you have heard a number of terms used to describe anxiety? In this section I will endeavour to explain what some of these mean. It is important to remember that this is not an exhaustive list; there will be types of anxiety disorder that express themselves differently and may not have been included here.

Generalised anxiety disorder (GAD)

Some people refer to generalised anxiety disorder as the common cold of anxiety disorders. Also known as 'GAD', it afflicts more people throughout the world than any other anxiety disorder. It is thought to affect around five in every 100 people. Slightly more women are affected than men, and the condition is more likely to affect people between the age of 35 and 59.[8]

Everyone has feelings of worry or anxiety at some point in their life – for example, they may feel worried about going to the dentist, having a job interview, receiving medical results, sitting an exam or taking their driving test. During times like these, the feelings of anxiety and worry are perfectly normal.

However, for some, these feelings of worry can be longer lasting, leaving them in an almost constant state of tension and unease. The sense of constantly being on high alert can have an effect on their working and personal life, and, with little respite, it can feel exhausting and unending.

Natalie says of her experience with generalised anxiety disorder:

Anxiety affects everything. How you see things, your relationships, your work, home life, etc. It makes you worry about everything and it feeds on that and just grows. You overreact sometimes to what someone says. You have emotional outbursts when overwhelmed with anxiety and what's going on around you. My anxiety flares up very much when

> there is too much going on around me at once. You can't shut it
> off. Your mind goes non-stop and it's exhausting.

GAD can sometimes be hard to diagnose as it can be difficult to isolate and to pinpoint a particular cause. A doctor may be more likely to ask someone how long they have felt this way and if they have felt anxious most days for at least six months; they may also ask if it has had an impact on the person's everyday life. If so, they may then give a diagnosis of GAD.

Generalised anxiety disorder shares many of the common symptoms of anxiety, as listed earlier in this chapter; however, those suffering may also feel restless, have trouble concentrating or sleeping, and experience dizziness or heart palpitations.[9]

For most people suffering from GAD, it can often be successfully treated with a combination of therapy, medication, and/or lifestyle changes.

Social anxiety disorder (social phobia)

Social anxiety disorder is the fear of a social situation that includes interaction and contact with other people. Those suffering have a fear of being negatively judged and evaluated by others, and believe that they are inadequate in some way; consequently, they assume that they will make a social 'faux pas', such as spilling their drink, saying the wrong thing or generally making a fool of themselves.

Adam, who suffers from social anxiety, shares how it makes him feel:

> It makes me feel worthless, stupid, inadequate. I feel like I'm
> boring, I don't have anything to say of any interest to anyone.
> It makes me feel like nobody likes me even though I know they
> do, but sometimes I can't understand why.

Those with social anxiety disorder can be seen as being shy, withdrawn, unfriendly and/or uninterested in social situations, often avoiding eye contact and looking ill at ease; on the contrary, most sufferers actually want to make friends and be part of, and engage with, social groups. It is the fear of 'what if?' that holds them back.

Social anxiety disorder can also extend far beyond the usual social gatherings and have an impact on areas such as work and school life, affecting situations like meetings, lessons and general everyday peer and colleague interactions. Sufferers can worry excessively that they are being watched or judged, and fear that they are going to do something which could show their incompetence. The intense fear and dread associated with these events may render them panicky and upset, leading them to sweat, blush and have a shaky voice or a racing or pounding heart, and they may even experience debilitating panic attacks. This may lead them to completely avoid events or occasions, which can end up with them limiting the way they live their life.

Tom gives us an insight into what it is like to live with anxiety:

It's like listening to all the bad news on TV/Radio in the background but the news is about you and it's about how you can't do x, y or z. It'll be telling you you'll fail; you'll cry or you'll be sick in front of everyone and they'll hate you. Feeding me the worst case scenario and my brain believes that as fact. It also causes physical reactions, such as retching/vomiting, racing thoughts and things like that. It's very powerful propaganda that you believe without question because it's your own brain saying it.

Social anxiety disorder can often take hold during the teenage years (although may affect younger children or older adults) and can lead people to worry for weeks or even months before an approaching social event.

Holly tells us how her social anxiety affects her on a day-to-day basis:

My anxiety also causes me to run things through in my head a lot, such as before going out, I had to go through every possible social outcome I could before going to a party or going to the shops as if to prepare myself for the worst possible outcome. Another consequence of this thought process is feeling like I always had to look my best in any situation outside of my house, which started to become an issue at the age of 13. This would cause me to be late for a lot of things, as I would get changed into multiple outfits until I was comfortable.

The Covid-19 pandemic and social anxiety

The coronavirus pandemic in 2020 had a tremendous impact on those prone to social anxiety. Everyone got out of practice with meeting others, leaving those who particularly struggle with social occasions even more adrift than they had felt before. Without seeing others, who they might be able to talk and rationalise their feelings with, many of their fears became disproportionately magnified.

For people in society already living a more isolated life, the effects were heightened. The Office of National Statistics reported in the summer of 2020 that those who often felt lonely were almost five times more likely to report high anxiety than those who 'never' feel lonely.[10]

At the height of the pandemic, mixing online – whether for work or socialising – became the norm, but these unfamiliar meeting groups also came with an increased level of demand for those who struggle with social stress. Then, as lockdown eased, the process of meeting others became increasingly fraught with anxiety. For people who already felt worried about how others would perceive them , the fear of unwittingly passing on or contracting coronavirus, coupled with the long list of new social 'rules', put yet more obstacles in the way of those who find face-to-face encounters challenging. These factors have had a long-term impact on people who suffer from social anxiety.

The good news is that social anxiety disorder can be treated effectively and successfully. Learning to understand what causes the anxiety, and what thought processes underpin it, is important. Taking very small steps to try and do the activities that the sufferer would normally avoid, can also help to tackle those fears.

Panic disorder

This is an anxiety disorder characterised by the sudden onset of panic attacks, sometimes seemingly out of the blue and without an obvious trigger. Anyone who has experienced just one panic attack will know how frightening and debilitating they can be. For someone with panic disorder, where these attacks occur with some frequency, the ripple effects on the way they live their life can be considerable.

Garry shares how he feels during a panic attack:

> During a panic attack I would shake so much I could barely stand up. I had to sit down or lean against a wall to steady myself. Even though I knew it would pass, it was always very frightening.

Most panic attacks last between five and 20 minutes, but they can go on for up to an hour. Some people experience them once or twice a month, while others can be put through their effects a few times a week.[11]

A panic attack is terrifying and those who experience one can have an impending fear of death. It can typically cause a thumping, racing heartbeat, sweating, muscle weakness and a churning stomach. Some or all of these symptoms may be experienced, although the effects vary depending on the individual.

Below is a list of some of the other physical symptoms that people may experience during a panic attack:

- Faintness/light-headedness

- Nausea
- Chest pain
- Shortness of breath
- Trembling
- Hot flushes or chills
- Shaky limbs
- A choking feeling
- Ringing in the ears
- Numbness or tingling
- Feeling disconnected from their body.

Amy, who went through a period of regular panic attacks and severe anxiety, shares her experience:

> I remember when I was 21, not long after my now husband's father passed away and I went to Australia for a holiday on my own (I got really bad home-sickness, and ended up coming home from Australia after six days), I now realise that I was having symptoms of panic attacks and anxiety. At the time I had no idea, and the doctor thought I had an inner ear infection. I was off work for six weeks and I remember I couldn't leave the house due to severe anxiety.

The psychological impact can be even harder to bear, with sufferers worrying they are dangerously ill, that they might die, that they might cause an accident and harm others, or might pass out and cause embarrassment or harm to themselves. These understandable terrors can have an impact on the way they live their day-to-day life, as people with panic disorder can start to dread or pre-empt their next attack, leading them to live in a constant state of understandable fear, which can cause more attacks to occur, leaving them locked in a seemingly unbreakable cycle.

It is worth noting that the symptoms of a panic attack may be caused by another underlying medical condition, such as hypoglycaemia due to insulin resistance, so it is always wise to consult a doctor, both to rule out any other cause and to get support in seeking help if it is a mental health issue.

According to the DSM-5 (*Diagnostic and Statistical Manual of Mental Disorders*), in order to be diagnosed with panic disorder, the sufferer must have experienced more than one unexpected episode on a regular basis.[12] Treatment for panic disorder aims to ease the symptoms and lessen the number of panic attacks experienced. Talking therapies and medication are the main treatments for panic disorder; depending on the severity of the symptoms, one or a combination of both of these treatments will be recommended.[13]

Phobias

A phobia is defined as 'an extreme or irrational fear of, or aversion to, something', and that 'something' can in fact be almost anything, from a fear of enclosed spaces (claustrophobia) to a fear of buttons (koumpounophobia). While often phobias can be trivialised or the focus of cruel, thoughtless jokes, I can assure you there is nothing funny about them. Every phobia has a very real and crippling effect, leaving people living in fear and often stopping them from leading a 'normal' fulfilling life.

Some of the more common phobias include:
- Agoraphobia (fear of crowded spaces)
- Emetophobia (fear of vomiting)
- Mysophobia (fear of germs)
- Claustrophobia (fear of enclosed spaces)
- Acrophobia (fear of heights)

Agoraphobia: Fear of crowded spaces

Agoraphobia come from the Greek word *'agora'* meaning 'marketplace' and *'phobos'* meaning fear. Unlike other phobias, the disorder usually starts in adulthood. It is a type of anxiety disorder in which the person will fear and avoid places or situations that might cause them to panic, feeling vulnerable and exposed with nowhere to escape or hide. Many of those struggling will avoid these situations by rarely leaving their home, which can often leave them isolated and lonely.

Anabelle says of how she started to develop agoraphobia while suffering PTSD (post-traumatic stress disorder):

> I was always on high alert. I didn't trust people. I didn't open up to people. I was often anxious. I had terrible panic attacks, most frequently in public places like the underground. I would panic about the future, especially with the idea of people close to me dying. I was scared of physical contact and would often flinch even if someone was just going to give me a hug. I started to become agoraphobic.

Emetophobia: Fear of vomiting or being close to others who are vomiting

The word 'emetophobia' stems from the Greek word *'emeto'* meaning vomit and *'phobos'*, again, meaning fear. Those with emetophobia try to control their everyday living around their fear. They may frequently wash their hands, not eat in public and constantly check sell-by dates; some may even avoid foods that are not liquid; in addition, many adopt some of the same coping strategies as people who suffer from obsessive compulsive disorder (OCD). They might open doors using their sleeves or not eat anything that has to be eaten using their fingers – for example, sandwiches might only be eaten down to where their fingers have touched. Emetophobia can also frequently be misdiagnosed as an eating disorder, due to the focus and anxiety surrounding food.

Paula, shares her experience of her daughter's emetophobia:

My daughter seemingly lost weight and would only eat certain foods, We were extremely concerned when this happened and took her to the doctors; they diagnosed her with an eating disorder. As her parents we were never convinced this was the issue and, after taking her to see another therapist, it became apparent that she had emetophobia – she was only ingesting liquid food such as soup and meal replacements due to the fear of being sick. We are so grateful that she is now recovered and living her life to the full.

Mysophobia: Fear of germs

Mysophobia, also known as verminophobia, germophobia, germaphobia, bacillophobia and bacteriophobia, is an extreme fear of germs and/or contamination. The main element of this phobia is not just worry about germs, but an obsessive fear over any kind of contamination, including via sickness, vomiting or contagious illness like coronavirus, dirt or bacteria.

In recent years, the use of antibacterial products has become increasingly popular. Some mental health professionals believe that this heightened awareness of 'germs' has increased the amount of those developing mysophobia. It is most frequently associated with OCD but can present in a wide variety of people.

Claustrophobia: Fear of enclosed spaces

The word 'claustrophobia' comes from the Latin word *'claustrum'*, which means 'a closed-in place'. It is the irrational fear of confined spaces. It can be rational to fear being trapped when there is a real threat or danger. However, those who suffer from claustrophobia experience fear even when there is no apparent or real danger in a particular situation. Those affected will often go out of their way to avoid confined spaces, such as lifts, tube trains and rooms without windows; however, avoiding these places may only reinforce the fear.

One study indicated that anywhere from 5-10% of the world's

population suffers from severe claustrophobia; however, only a small percentage of those people actually receive some kind of treatment for the disorder.[14]

James tells us of his experience with his wife and her claustrophobia:

> My wife has suffered from a fear of enclosed spaces since a child; she would rather walk for miles instead of take the underground. It started to affect our time together and we have to look places up before we go to make sure she won't have to get into any kind of enclosed space; this could even be a room that is small.

Acrophobia: Fear of heights

Acrophobia is an extreme and/or irrational fear of heights, even when they are not particularly high up. Most people experience a level of natural fear when exposed to heights; this is known as the 'fear of falling'. However, those with acrophobia can experience extreme panic, and even a full panic attack, which can then lead to the imagined danger or a struggle to get themselves down safely.

Helen, who had a fear of heights for most of her life, says:

> Ever since I can remember I have had a fear of heights, not even being able to go up a ladder without becoming very anxious. I decided to try hypnotherapy when my young son wanted to go on the London Eye for his birthday… I found it really helped, and I was able to control my anxiety.

Specific phobias

It is possible to have a phobia of anything – a person, an animal, specific places, objects, forms of transport and just about anything else.

Whatever the phobia that someone has, the fear is almost always far larger than the thing they are worried about. To someone else, their anxiety around this particular thing, or things, may seem bizarre and irrational, but for the person suffering, the fear is all too real, and can be hugely debilitating and the root of a large amount of anxiety and panic. Symptoms may include sweating, having trouble breathing and/or full-blown panic attacks. This can have a knock-on effect on many areas of the person's life, including work, friendships and relationships, and can therefore affect their entire family and wider circle of friends.

Techniques for tackling phobias include counselling (page 97) and cognitive behavioural therapy (page 86). Another specific therapy for phobias is exposure therapy where the sufferer is exposed to the thing they fear, often starting with very small experiences, which can begin to retrain the brain to recognise that the thing somebody fears the most does not actually pose a threat.

Obsessive compulsive disorder (OCD)

As the name suggests, this disorder is formed of two distinct parts – obsession and compulsion. Intrusive thoughts form the mental aspect of the condition and these thoughts often give way to compulsive (or repetitive) behaviours.

Most of us have worries, doubts and superstitious beliefs of some kind. It is only when our thoughts and actions make no sense to others, become excessive or begin to impact our ability to live a normal life and to affect people around us that it is officially recognised as a condition. Many people have described themselves as 'a little bit OCD' when what they really mean is that they like to keep their house clean and tidy or have a very organised filing system, for example. Neither of these are characteristics of the illness if they are in a manageable form. It is important to recognise the distinction between 'OCD' as a generalised slang term and the medical condition, which can be totally debilitating.

Some people experience intrusive thoughts, but do not have the desire to carry out compulsive actions. However, much of the time the two components will go hand in hand.

Obsessions are involuntary, seemingly uncontrollable thoughts, images or impulses which occur over and over in the mind. A person experiencing obsessions will not invite these thoughts or enjoy having them but cannot seem to stop them from invading their mind. Some people describe these thoughts as being 'like a stuck record' and just as irritating, yet actively trying to stop them can, perversely, make them worse.

Gerry openly shares his lack of understanding of his son's severe OCD:

> I didn't understand why my son wouldn't just stop his quirky behaviours; he would get quite angry towards me if I tried to intervene. When I started to educate myself a little more on what was going on in his mind, I began to understand and had more empathy about the situation.

Compulsions are behaviours or rituals that must be acted out again and again. Usually, compulsions are performed in an attempt to make obsession go away. For example, if you are afraid of germs and cannot seem to think about anything else, you might develop elaborate cleaning rituals. However, the relief is short lived. In fact, the obsessive thoughts will usually come back more strongly.

In its simplest form, OCD occurs in a four-step pattern:

1. Obsession – The mind is overwhelmed with a constant obsessive fear or concern, such as one's house being burgled.
2. Anxiety – The obsession provokes a feeling of intense anxiety and distress, often causing the 'worst case scenario' to be envisaged or imagined, sometimes repeatedly.

3. Compulsions – A pattern of compulsive behaviour is adopted in an attempt to reduce the anxiety and distress, such as checking all windows and doors are locked three times before leaving the house or going to bed.
4. Temporary relief – Compulsive behaviour brings transitory relief from anxiety.

Obsession or anxiety will almost always return after the above cycle has been completed, causing it to start all over again. Compulsive behaviours in themselves can often result in anxiety, as they become more time consuming and start to demand more and more attention. Anxiety can manifest itself in obsessive thoughts and so the condition spirals.

Greg, who has suffered with OCD since he was a teenager, shares his experience:

> OCD is a vicious cycle; I always do what it tells me as it makes me feel better, but it always comes back and makes my life harder and harder to deal with. I try to ignore the thoughts, which I am able to sometimes and it does help, but if I am having a day where I am feeling less strong, I find it easier to do what it tells me.

It is difficult to give a definitive list of signs and symptoms of OCD, since people can find infinite ways to form an obsession and to behave accordingly.

Some of the commonest obsessions are:

*   Fear of being contaminated by germs or dirt, or of contaminating others
*   Fear of causing harm to yourself or others
*   Intrusive sexual, explicit or violent thoughts or recurrent images
*   Obsessive focus on religious or moral ideas
*   Fear of losing or not having things that may be needed

- Order and symmetry – the idea that all physical objects must line up 'just so'
- Special attention to something considered lucky or unlucky ('superstitions').

The commonest forms of compulsive behaviour are:
- Counting, tapping, repeating certain words or doing other senseless things in an attempt to reduce anxiety
- Spending a lot of time washing or cleaning, either the body or the environment
- Repeatedly checking in on loved-ones to ensure that they are safe
- Excessive double-checking of locks, appliances and switches
- Ordering or arranging objects into specific patterns
- Praying or engaging in rituals triggered by religious fear to an excessive extent
- Accumulating junk, such as old newspapers or empty food containers.

Without adequate coping mechanisms, OCD can eat into so much of a person's life that they find themselves unable to do anything else. This can result in extensive difficulties at home, school and work.

Sarah, whose husband suffers from anxiety, OCD and depression, shares how it affects their family life:

My husband was the youngest of three brothers and had a very controlling father from an RAF background. As a result, he has very low self-esteem and is anxious and angry about non-important things. As a wife I manage this like a puppeteer pulling the strings. He cannot be told what to do so it has to be his idea. As his anxiety increases and the feeling of being out of control increases, this leads to increased OCD behaviour, which has a very negative impact on our family.

Post-traumatic stress disorder (PTSD)

Post-traumatic stress disorder, often shortened to PTSD, is an anxiety disorder that is triggered by stressful, shocking or frightening events. When someone has PTSD, they often experience flashbacks and nightmares. They may have problems sleeping and find it a real challenge to concentrate on other areas of their life as they battle complex and disruptive feelings, including anger and guilt.

Charliee, who has recently been diagnosed with PTSD, shares how it affects her:

> Flashbacks are a huge part of PTSD for me; I'll experience them most nights and sometimes they can be so vivid that I feel as though I'm right back in that moment. Often the flashbacks result in self-harm but grounding techniques and meditation really help to bring me back to the moment and remind me that I'm safe.

The disorder was first recognised in war veterans (you may have heard the term 'shell shock') but it is now said that it can be caused by a wide range of events and experiences, from witnessing a terrorist attack to suffering bereavement.

Of course, it is normal to feel a range of emotions after a traumatic experience. However, for people with PTSD, these feelings persist, having a significant impact on their day-to-day life. PTSD is thought to occur in around a third of those who have been through a traumatic experience, although it is not clear why some people experience it and others do not.[15] There is evidence that poor sleep contributes in that we need deep sleep (that is, non-rapid-eye-movement or non-REM sleep) to process the events of the day. If we sleep in what we feel is an unsafe, uncomfortable or stressed state then those events are re-played in an adrenalin-fuelled state and any trauma is amplified rather than processed and discarded.

As with any mental illness, it is important to get support

and help for PTSD as soon as possible rather than leaving the symptoms to escalate to the point where a second illness, such as depression, can take hold. Once the PTSD has been successfully treated, studies suggest that any accompanying symptoms of secondary depression may be greatly reduced.[16]

As with all mental illnesses, I would urge carers to be involved and vigilant as much as possible. You know what symptoms and behaviours are out of character for your loved one, and it is crucial that you are there as an extra pair of eyes and ears to help ensure that they get the correct treatment path for their individual needs and circumstances.

Body dysmorphic disorder (BDD)

Body dysmorphic disorder (BDD) is an anxiety disorder specifically linked to how people view their body. Those with BDD see their physical appearance differently from how other people view them.

They may have obsessive worries for many hours a day about one or more flaws in their appearance – flaws that are invisible or nearly invisible to others. BDD sufferers may also develop compulsive behaviours around the physical appearance, such as obsessively looking in mirrors, using heavy make-up or seeking cosmetic surgery.

These fixations will interfere with their day-to-day life, affecting their work, social life and/or relationships. Their obsessions and routines can also trigger a range of emotions, including shame, guilt and loneliness, and may overlap with other mental illnesses, such as an eating disorder, depression and/or OCD.

Eve shares her experience of suffering from BDD alongside anorexia nervosa:

> When I was diagnosed with anorexia I got diagnosed with BDD too. I was so bad I would buy clothes in a size 16 and be

puzzled when there was space as I'm a size 6/8. It wasn't until I spoke to a counsellor that it made sense that the image I see in the mirror isn't what I associate with me; it's tough to deal with as it can make me feel low and unhappy when I see myself in the mirror still, but those times are less and I remind myself there's more to life than how I look or how much I weigh. I'd rather be happy and love instead.

Sadly, many people with BDD delay seeking help because they are worried that others will judge them. They therefore may battle on alone for a long time before they get the support they need, by which time their BDD may have escalated and their anxiety have reached a level where another illness, such as depression, could take hold.

I would urge anyone who cares for someone with BDD to find out as much as possible about the illness and to offer opportunities to talk without judgement. Simply opening up may be the first step towards accepting that they need support.

Health anxiety

Like many other anxiety disorders, health anxiety is a more extreme, more intrusive, more disruptive continuum of a relatively common concern shared by almost all of us. After all, who hasn't experienced a bad headache or niggling pain and turned to 'Dr Google', where our curiosity can very easily turn into real fear that our symptoms are a sign of something very serious? However, the difference between this kind of common worry and a disorder like health anxiety (also known as hypochondria) is that the latter is characterised by an obsessive preoccupation with being seriously ill that can have a huge impact on the way the sufferer lives their life. Health anxiety is often housed within the obsessive compulsive disorder (OCD) spectrum of disorders, due to its obsessive traits.

Elaine tells us how her health anxiety affects her day-to-day life:

It has impacted everything – how I raise my daughter; it affects my partner because I won't go anywhere for fear of something bad happening or having a panic attack. I have had nine months off work. I won't drive anymore for fear of crashing or having a panic attack. I cannot exercise for fear of having an asthma attack or heart attack.

A common example of this form of anxiety is when the sufferer feels as though their chest is getting tight and may convince themselves that they are having a heart attack. Another example could be, if a person has a headache, they may believe that it is the sign of a brain tumour.

Some of the common signs to be aware of include:

- Frequently checking for any sign of illness and asking friends and family for constant reassurance that they are not ill
- Feeling sure that the doctor has missed something, made a mistake or is not competent
- Checking the internet obsessively for health information
- Acting as if they are ill, avoiding social activities or sports and spending a long time resting or in bed
- Frequently checking that their body is functioning and being more aware of any changes – for example, checking their heart is beating regularly.

Keeping a diary could help those with health anxiety to make sense of their thoughts, and allow them to challenge them with more balanced views. It might help them to remember, for example, that while stomach-aches can be serious, they can also be a sign of stress.

While self-help has a part to play, it is also important to involve the support of a health professional. Sharing concerns with a sympathetic GP could be the most helpful first step to getting appropriate help.

Rachel tells us of how her severe health anxiety developed:

> I have had so much tragedy and death in my young life that death terrifies me. My health anxiety is so severe that since the age of 21 I have attended A&E 200+ times. I'm working on this now and try to get advice from pharmacies, GPs, out-of-hours etc. There is nothing worse than the fear that fuels anxiety that you're going to die.

Separation anxiety disorder

It is a normal part of childhood development, typically around the toddler years, for youngsters to experience anxiety and upset when they are not with their parents or familiar care-givers. Similar worries may occur throughout childhood, but in 3 to 4% of youngsters[17] these fears can escalate, becoming persistent and having a large impact on the child's life, characterised by an exaggerated fear of separation that interferes with developmentally appropriate autonomy. Adults can also experience separation anxiety disorder, worrying excessively that their loved ones, or they, will become ill, be injured and/or be harmed, with these worries leading to excessive fear which spills over into other areas of their life.

In children, separation anxiety disorder may be character-ised by the child having tantrums or getting very upset or even violent, if they are away from their parent or carer, or anticipate that they will be away from them. They are likely to worry about some kind of harm coming to their loved ones, and this may be reflected in a reluctance to go to school or stay away from home. Problems with going to sleep alone or having nightmares may become an issue, and they may also experience physical symptoms, such as headaches or stomach-aches, when worried about where their care-giver is or where they might be going. It is more likely to occur after a difficult life event, such as parents separating or moving to a new area.

Carla tells us of her experience with separation anxiety when she was younger:

> I was always a worried child; I would always worry if someone was out for longer than they said they would be. I would sit up on my window ledge in my bedroom and wait for my mum or dad to come home, thinking that something awful had happened to them. Nothing ever did! When I went to school, I used to take a hair scrunchie of my mum's so it would give me the feeling of being at home and safe. I still suffer with it now; if I get a feeling something bad has happened, I have to phone every member of my family to make sure they are safe; if I cannot get hold of them my mind spirals into awful thoughts. Technology has definitely helped as it means I can get hold of everyone faster or check if they have been online, and it makes me feel better.

In adults, those with separation anxiety disorder have extreme fear that bad things will happen to the people they hold dear in their lives, such as their children, spouse or parents. It may accompany other anxiety-related conditions. Symptoms of separation anxiety disorder in children and adults are similar. For adults, instead of their life at school suffering, they may struggle at work or when out, which may in turn make them withdraw socially. The over-protectiveness towards loved ones may also have a negative impact on their relationships and wider family life. Like children, they may also experience the physical aches and pains or panic attacks that can accompany anxiety.

Acute stress disorder

Acute stress disorder is a debilitating reaction to a traumatic event, such as a death, or witnessing something shocking. It typically occurs within one month of the destabilising occurrence and will last at least three days but could persist for up to a month or may develop in the long term into post-traumatic stress disorder (PTSD).

The symptoms are similar to PTSD, causing people to dis-associate from their surroundings or avoid certain situations, places and/or people that may be connected with the trauma. Nightmares and flashbacks may occur, and they could be more irritable, emotional and/or more detached than they usually are, and may struggle to sleep or relax properly.

Skin picking

Known also by the names 'dermatillomania' or 'excoriation disorder', skin picking occurs – as the title suggests – when someone compulsively picks at their skin, with their nails, fingers, teeth or even an implement such as tweezers or scissors. Sufferers may not even realise they are doing it, but they are likely to make their skin bleed or bruise and will struggle to stop themselves doing it. Skin picking behaviours are more likely to occur when someone is stressed, and they may also show signs of other anxiety disorders. This anxiety disorder affects up to 1.4% of the total population, and of those, approximately 75% are female.[18]

Jan reflects on her experience of how anxiety can affect her:

> I hadn't thought about it before, but I have always picked at the skin around my fingers. I used to get slapped if I bit my finger nails, so I guess this was my replacement. Thinking about it, I do seem to do it more when I nervous or stressed. I had a particularly stressful phone conversation with a member of my family the other day and my arm was bleeding. Without realising it I had picked at a spot on my arm and made it bleed. This is something I've only just really connected with it being a coping mechanism I suppose.

When skin picking starts to have an impact on someone's life, causing them emotional upset or stopping them from doing normal day-to-day activities, or when it causes injuries that do not easily heal, it is important to seek help from a doctor. They should be able to offer advice and signpost support in the same way that they would any mental health issue.

Hair pulling

Also known as 'trichotillomania', or 'trich', this illness causes people to pull out their hair. The urge to do so will be overwhelming and the relief from their negative and overpowering thoughts, albeit brief, only comes when they are doing so. They may pull out hair on their head, or their eyebrows, eyelashes or on other parts of their body.

Rachel shares her experience of hair pulling:

> I have been a hair puller for as long as I can remember. I find when things are bad or I'm under great levels of stress and anxiety I kind of rock and pull my hair out in chunks. It's been really bad the past few years to the point where I can over-pluck my eyebrows, leave bald patches on my scalp and at times even sit with tweezers and pluck leg hairs one by one. When I'm plucking or pulling hair, my mind is silent for a while and the pain from it is like a medicine – as it causes some physical discomfort it takes my mind off the emotional pain I deal with daily.

Anxiety and stress undoubtedly play a part in this compulsion, and it may be linked to specific life events, such as exam pressure or work stress. The lines between other mental illnesses such as OCD and self-harm are somewhat blurred, although what characterises trichotillomania is the specific hair-pulling aspect of the condition.

There are self-help measures that people can take, such as cutting their hair short or wearing plasters or gloves to cover their fingers, but to tackle the anxiety likely to underpin the behaviour it is important to access support from a professional with expertise in this and other anxiety disorders.

Jo shares her experience of both trichotillomania and dermatillomania:

> Skin picking and hair pulling are some of the major ways my anxiety manifests itself. I've been left with bald patches and no eyebrows. With pock-marked skin. There is a feeling of tension that needs to be released caused by the anxiety and this is how I seem to try to get it out, sometimes without even realising I'm doing it. And it in itself can lead to more anxiety about my appearance when I'm seeing people about what they may think of me. It becomes a cycle.

Selective mutism

Selective mutism is a fear of talking to certain people, which is strongly associated with anxiety. It affects around one in 140 children[19] and if left untreated can continue into adolescence and adulthood, having a huge impact on the person's life.

Those with selective mutism are unable to speak to certain people, often anyone outside their direct family or closest friends. They freeze when faced with situations where they are expected to converse, with the expectation of having to speak causing deep panic that renders them silent.

Jan tells us of how she has suffered from bouts of selective mutism over the years:

> Selecting not to speak is something I know I do when I'm afraid or upset. I found it was a very good tool when my mother used to yell and scream at me when I was younger and wanted a reaction from me. I admit I still do it now when I'm overwhelmed.

If it is not treated, selective mutism can lead to loneliness, isolation, poor self-esteem and can potentially develop into social anxiety disorder. The effects can be wide-ranging, with the psychological impacts of spending so long without social interaction being difficult to overcome. Sufferers may also have failed to reach their potential at school or work because of the limitations that the selective mutism places on their life.

Rachel, who has suffered from selective mutism herself and now cares for others experiencing the same, shares her experience:

As a carer for individuals living with acute mental health issues and some also living with a learning disability, I often work with clients living with selective mutism. Working with Individuals with selective mutism can be very challenging at times as you have to learn their ways of communicating; sometimes it may be pointing, grunting, Makaton etc. Some of my clients don't show any form of communication, which can cause a barrier between us and the individual we are caring for. I have experienced individuals I provide care for getting violent towards staff as they want to physically speak and communicate but something inside stops them from doing so and as we don't always know what they want they can get frustrated and act out that aggression.

Adjustment disorder with anxious features

Adjustment disorders are a group of conditions, with different features, that can be triggered when someone has difficulty coping with a stressful life event, such as the death of a loved one or redundancy. The inability to adjust to the stressful event can give rise to severe psychological symptoms and sometimes even physical symptoms. One of the psychological symptoms is anxiety, where people feel overwhelmed, anxious and/or worried; they may also struggle with concentration and memory.

It can be a very frightening and stressful time, but adjustment disorders are generally shorter-lived than some other anxiety disorders and they often respond well to treatment.

Substance-induced anxiety disorder

This is the term given to the type of anxiety which is triggered specifically by the use of alcohol, drugs or medication, whether that is their use, misuse or withdrawal. Most people think of having a drink or taking certain recreational drugs as a mood-booster, something that helps them relax and boosts their confidence. However, these same substances can be the ones that cause anxiety, leaving sufferers prone to persistent worrying, paranoia and/or panic, which is deeper and more pronounced than the transient worries or sleeplessness people may commonly feel after a night out or similar.

Matty, who suffers from anxiety, depression and other mental illnesses as well as previous drug and alcohol misuse, tells us how his past drug use still affects his anxiety:

> Drug use has no doubt affected my mental health for the worst – walking around hyper-aware of everyone and everything, scared to turn a corner because someone I owed money to or the police would be there. Looking back this was highly unlikely, but in my head, they're still there waiting to get me though it's been years since I've used.

Doctors will assess whether the anxiety a patient is experiencing was present before the drug or substance use. If it was, a diagnosis of substance-induced anxiety disorder would not be made, as substance abuse can also co-occur alongside another anxiety disorder. The difference with this is that the anxiety either started before the drinking or drug or medication-taking behaviour or that it continues even after the substance use has stopped.

To conclude

Let me end this chapter with the thought that recovery is always possible. Most people suffering from anxiety will have people around them who can, and most likely will, support them. What is crucial, however, above all else is that the sufferer themselves really wants to recover; it *has* to be driven by them, remembering always that recovery is both achievable and sustainable.

Chapter 3

Recognising anxiety and seeking treatment

Having an understanding of how the mind of someone suffering from an anxiety disorder works and being knowledgeable on the subject are probably the two most powerful tools you, as the carer, can have when approaching a loved one or a friend that you think may be suffering from an anxiety disorder. Even though it is a relatively common illness, anxiety is still woefully misunderstood and sadly, at times, not always taken seriously.

The bridge between being ill and seeking and receiving treatment for sufferers with an anxiety disorder is a precarious one to navigate, not only for sufferers themselves, but also for the people around them. Leading up to and after diagnosis, many parents, partners and/or carers of anxiety disorder sufferers can make themselves ill by worrying, blaming themselves, raking over the past with a fine-toothed comb and frantically trying to pinpoint where they went wrong. Sleepless nights, high levels of stress and even anxiety disorders in themselves can ensue. This is totally counterproductive, because the feelings of guilt can run two ways – sufferers of anxiety disorders tend to have a hugely over-developed sense of guilt, which can be magnified when they see the effect their illness is having on their loved ones and friends. Their solution to these feelings of shame is, usually, to bury themselves further in their illness, and so the situation can become a vicious circle.

Chapter 3

Angela shares her feelings of guilt:

> The most difficult aspect was remaining calm when he refused LOVE or even a touch of the arm; it felt like rejection. He could not even look you in the eye and as a parent you have thoughts of being guilty that you are not doing enough.

By its very nature, the all-pervasive thought process of worrying, stressing and fretting about life can make it hard to ring-fence, recognise and label as 'an anxiety disorder'. Given that a certain level of anxiety is entirely normal, and even a positive way of building resilience and helping people perform better, it can often be difficult to know when it has moved into more concerning territory.

It is also important for parents, partners and carers to be well enough to support the process of recovery. It is essential for all concerned that carers try to maintain their own physical and emotional well-being during this incredibly challenging time. Whether the sufferer is young and still living at home or older and living independently, the people around them will be of the utmost importance in supporting and guiding them towards health and recovery.

Jayne, whose daughter has suffered from severe anxiety since the age of 14, shares how counselling helped her look after her own mental well-being:

> I had weekly counselling for four months at the beginning because I felt unable to cope and my own mental health was really suffering. I found this to be a great support and I really looked forward to meeting with my therapist. After four months I felt stronger and in a better place emotionally to be able to cope with everything that was happening at home. I am so thankful for those therapy sessions and still think of them today.

Recognising anxiety

Unfortunately, there is no quick and easy laboratory test that can give an immediate diagnosis. Focusing on the physical symptoms alone can often lead to missing the emotional signs. Knowing this is the parents'/carers' biggest ally, as an anxiety disorder can often be extremely difficult to recognise and identify in the early stages.

Angela shares her experience with us of her son's anxiety:

> All you can do is LISTEN to your loved one. They don't want you to solve the problem, because YOU can't. I recognised that something was terribly wrong with my son as he gave up rugby, his music; he was apathetic about his studies, life and friends. If you notice a change in your loved one, mention it calmly but not as a NAGGING question. Despite their denials, offer support.

Let's go back to that first step: realising that something could potentially be wrong. While the clues can often be physical as well as emotional, they are usually just that – clues. Piecing together what at first may seem unconnected pieces of a puzzle is often the first step to recognising a mental illness, such as an anxiety disorder.

There are certain patterns and tendencies that may be able to help you to determine that something could potentially be amiss. In my personal and professional experience, a dramatic change in personality and behaviour can be one of the biggest warning signs. Whether your loved one is usually eccentric and quirky or insular and private, you may know them well enough to be able to recognise the differences over and above their usual mannerisms.

Gemma, whose son started suffering from anxiety when he moved schools, shares the changes she saw:

My son started becoming quite introverted and would display outbursts of anger every so often; this was far from the boy we knew; he would usually be quite mellow and nothing would really faze him. He worried about absolutely everything – if we were going to come home, if the house was going to fall down, if he was unwell; we knew there was something wrong.

To give you more of an idea, below are some of the emotional and behavioural changes that may be present in someone with an anxiety disorder. The person may:

- feel worthless and helpless
- feel anxious or worried a large proportion of the time
- seem to be getting little enjoyment out of life or things they used to like doing
- appear to have very low self-esteem, to be overly self-critical and seem to feel weighed down by guilt and self-doubt
- become very distant, preoccupied and uncommunicative
- seem irritable and intolerant of others
- stop wanting to go out, even to places they used to enjoy visiting
- have suicidal thoughts or appear to be harming themselves, whether through a method such as causing themselves physical damage or substance abuse.

Once your attention is drawn to some of the initial personality changes, you may gradually notice other behaviours starting to emerge, which are out of character for that person. As an anxiety disorder is an illness of the mind, and cannot always be seen, the person's disordered thoughts may be more difficult to detect initially. So once again, the person's behaviour and overall demeanour can play a vital part in recognising something is not quite right, thereby potentially leading to early intervention.

Chris tells us of how his boyfriend's OCD became apparent when they moved in together:

When we were first dating, I noticed quite quickly that he was not a great time keeper – he would always be about 20-30 minutes late for arrangements, always seeming rushed and a bit flustered. After moving in to our flat together, I have now realised why he was always late. I started to note that he would spend a long time in the bathroom everyday cleaning himself and the room multiple times. This then started happening in the kitchen and slowly seemed to progress to the whole flat. It really started to affect our relationship. After speaking to him about it he opened up a bit as to the reasons why he was doing what he was doing, and we are now thankfully on a path to seeking help.

Some physical signs and behaviours you may start to notice are listed below. The person may:

- have trouble sleeping, such as waking intermittently
- eat less or more, and their weight may show quite a marked change
- seem to lack energy
- have a dip in their sex drive
- have unexplained aches and pains, such as tingling in their hands or feet, stomach-aches and / or heart palpitations
- seem to do things more slowly or even speak more slowly
- in some cases, display irrational and even delusional thoughts, seeing or hearing things that other people cannot
- break down in tears for seemingly no reason or in an unexpected situation
- seem to find day-to-day life difficult.

Jan shares the symptoms of anxiety she recognises within herself:

When my shoulders and head start aching and tensing up, and especially if I feel really hot and am sweating, then I realise it's probably anxiety. It can be hard to know or recognise sometimes as very often when I'm anxious my mind and

> body 'play tricks' and I get strange symptoms that, if I give in to the anxious and negative thoughts, make me think I have something more serious!

It is important to say here that just because someone is showing some, or all of these symptoms, it does not necessarily mean that they have an anxiety disorder. As a loved one or caregiver, I would advise you to use your own intuition to guide you in identifying whether these symptoms are typical of the person you know or are somewhat out of character for them.

While in some people the symptoms may be quite noticeable as a distinct change from their normal behaviour and/or way of doing things, others may try to hide or mask the signs of their anxiety and how they are feeling; some can successfully do so for a considerable length of time. They may feel misplaced shame or embarrassment about how they are feeling, or they may worry that revealing their symptoms could disadvantage them, perhaps socially, educationally and/or in the workplace. As a result, they may do all they can to disguise how they are feeling.

Garry gives his advice to fellow sufferers:

> It's important to talk to someone, anyone, about your anxiety. I kept it all inside for so long and thus prevented my family and friends from helping me because they simply didn't know.

Recognising anxiety in yourself

Sometimes it can be easier for family members, friends and colleagues to pick up on the signs and symptoms of anxiety than it is for the person suffering these themselves. Recognising the illness in yourself is crucial as it is the first step towards seeking help and getting the right support or treatment to get better.

Holly, who suffers from social anxiety disorder, says of when she recognised there could be a problem:

> I put into Google 'overthinking' and it came up with links to questionnaires which would apparently decipher whether or not you have depression. At the time I did not know about social anxiety or depression and so it was very alarming for me when the results came back positive for depression.

So how then do you know if you have an anxiety disorder? The short answer is that you may not until you actually go to a doctor and describe exactly how you are thinking and feeling. However, if you have been feeling persistently on edge, worrying, anxious, low and lacking in drive and interest in things you once enjoyed for a period of time, it is important to take those feelings seriously and consider in more depth the other ways you may be affected.

Pete shares his thoughts:

> For years, I didn't realise I had anxiety. It was something I thought we all went through and that it was normal and that I simply didn't cope very well. My diagnosis of depression came years before I was diagnosed with anxiety. My anxiety mainly showed through a fear of getting ill. I would recognise a small problem and convince myself I had cancer or another very serious condition and then couldn't stop thinking about the worst possible scenarios. This 'awfulising' is something I look for to recognise when I might be susceptible to anxiety. If I sense I am doing this, I know I need to take some steps to try and head things off.

As I mentioned earlier in this chapter, it is important to be aware of the physical symptoms, such as poor sleep patterns, loss of appetite (or over-eating), no motivation for anything, and lacking in sex drive, which could also be an indication of an anxiety disorder.

Jess, shares the symptoms she is aware of when anxiety takes hold:

It starts as a low-grade unease, difficulty concentrating or sitting still, constant fidgeting, needing frequent breaks from mental tasks. It can build into a real difficulty in being still at all, the need to move as much as possible, to change position, environment, focus. At worst, it becomes an inability to deal with basic daily tasks, and disruption to work productivity. While I'll feel an inability to sit still, I'll not want to leave my room/ house, which obviously increases the pent-up feelings that can crescendo in an emotional break or crying. Usually fun hobbies and activities become uninviting (exercise, music) and I may lose my appetite as well as any social inclination.

Remember that the symptoms can range from mild to severe, so you could be suffering from a mental illness – and could therefore benefit from professional advice and possibly some form of treatment – at any point along this spectrum. Thinking about whether your worrying is impacting on your work or social life may help you see how much it is affecting you. If the worry and unease do not lift, and you feel they have been a part of your life for a considerable amount of time, you should seek the opinion of your GP to find out what steps can be taken. Delaying too long could cause the anxiety to worsen and prolong the time it then takes to recover.

Jo shares her positive experience of seeing her GP:

I had my first real panic attack in the car with my dad. He drove me straight to the GP's surgery and my GP saw me straight away. He talked me through the panic attack and showed me ways to deal with it. He was proactive and made me feel safe in his care. He contacted my mental health team and got me the help I needed to start managing my anxiety.

Please remember that anxiety disorders cut across ages, genders and social divides. Some groups are more suscepti-ble than others; traumatic experiences can also play a part in some cases, and for some people there could be a genetic link involved, but no one should consider themselves immune from anxiety – you can develop this mental illness even when there is no apparent or obvious reason or root cause.

Judith Cocking, a resilience and performance coach, shares a couple of exercises to help recognise and build resilience against anxiety:

The circle of control

This is an incredibly straightforward exercise, but it never ceases to surprise me how useful clients find it. Running a recent workshop on developing emotional intelligence, many delegates cited it as one of the most helpful parts of the course.

When we are faced with too many demands and competing priorities from work and home life, it is very easy to move into overwhelm mode. We lose our perspective, start to worry about everything and flood our systems with cortisol. The circle of control is a tool which allows us to take a step back and consider the things that are genuinely within our control.

Let's take the example of someone who is worried about their job. It is all too easy to get stuck in the cycle of worrying about whether or not the company will be making redundancies, the state of the economy and the lack of appropriate job opportunities in the market. But what can we really do about any of those? Nothing. If we refocus our efforts back to things that we can genuinely influence, we start to regain some control of the situation and ourselves. In this example, we could ensure that we focus on our day job, ensuring that we do it to the best of our ability so we demonstrate our worth, ensure that our CV is up to date, reach out to our network, and start to build our skill set.

When you find yourself getting overwhelmed, take a little time to think about the things you are worrying about and where each element sits in the diagram (Figure 1 opposite). Focus on those that sit within your circle of control and you will find that circle will gradually increase in size.

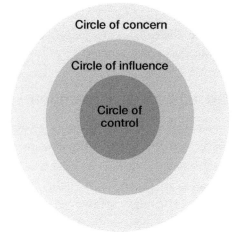

Figure 1

Build your self-regard

Self-regard is the degree to which you value and accept yourself and is the cornerstone of building resilience. Moments of self-doubt are entirely normal but when we reach the point where we find it difficult to identify any positives, it can lead to increased anxiety and an over-reliance on external crutches to make ourselves feel better, including alcohol, controlling what we eat or over-exercising.

To build your self-regard, try a few of these exercises:

- *Once a day take a few minutes to notice your 'inner critic' and challenge it with the question, 'Is that really true?' Ask other people what they see as your strengths.*

- *Create a strengths list. What are you good at? What went well today? What did you enjoy? Add to the list every day.*

- *Reject any 'put-downs' that come your way. A 'put-down' is when someone (including you, yourself) criticises something about who you are as a person rather than something you have done. Every time you say something negative about yourself, counter it with something positive.*

- *Accept compliments from others rather than dismissing them.*

- *Each day allocate uninterrupted time for yourself to do what you want both in work and outside of work.*

The importance of early intervention

The first and most important step towards recovery from an anxiety disorder is that the sufferer must want to get better themselves. As soul-destroying as it is, attempts to rehabilitate sufferers who are not yet ready to acknowledge and deal with the issue are likely to prove fruitless. (However, with the assistance of the right kind of therapy and a positive environment, a sufferer can be stabilised, so that their condition does not worsen. Getting actively better requires the sufferer to engage totally with treatment and the recovery process as a whole.)

The way in which you, as a loved one or carer, act at this point is very important. It is of course tempting to adopt a wait-and-see approach, but the vice-like grip that anxiety can have on a sufferer's mind-set can develop or worsen with astonishing speed. Waiting for more obvious physical signs may mean that you could underestimate the rapid psychological rampage of an anxiety disorder. We know that it is possible to make a full recovery from an anxiety disorder – there is always hope – but we also know the earlier the sufferer is able to access treatment and receive the right help and support, the better chance they have of making a full recovery. According to the NHS, approximately, seven out of every 10 sufferers who have had a course of treatment (two or more sessions) show reliable and significant reductions in their anxiety or depression and around five in every 10 improve so much they are classified as recovered.[20]

Garry says of how important early intervention can be:

Early intervention is vital! I wish I'd seen a professional 40+ years ago! Would probably have saved me a lot of pain and angst.

There are few things more exasperating than watching someone we care about suffer and being unable to intervene. So, what can be done in the meantime? Again, in this instance, knowledge is power. There is a variety of treatments available, and it is important to understand what they entail and how they work. In this way, when the sufferer expresses a desire to get better, their family and friends can leap into action and find the most appropriate source of help as quickly as possible.

Pete shares his views on the impact of early intervention for him:

> This is very important because it enables me to start breaking the thought patterns and ruminations that lead me to catastrophic conclusions. If these develop, they can be really hard to shut down.

To help with this, there is an unbiased guide to some of the treatments available in the next chapter. The speed with which you, as a parent, carer or loved one, might act at this point is also of paramount importance. It is common for the sufferer to yearn for recovery in peaks and troughs, so it is important to place them in a positive and suitable environment while they are in the correct frame of mind and before any seeds of self-doubt are sown by their anxiety disorder which could begin to fester and grow. Remember, they have to really want to embrace this thought process if they are to totally engage with any form of treatment.

At the same time, it is important for carers to show that they are willing and able to help at any time. However frustrating and upsetting it is to see your loved one suffer, it is important to keep the lines of communication open, so they know deep down that you are always there for them. Creating opportunities to talk can be vital. A simple way to do this is to keep pursuing the activities you love doing together. Whether that is taking the dog for a walk, watching your favourite television programme or going for a trip to the shops together, by continuing to maintain those opportunities for emotional closeness, you will not only be giving them the green light to turn to you for help, but you will also be maintaining some much needed normality in what may be an increasingly disordered life.

Jay, my Samantha's fiancé, shares his thoughts on this:

> There are times as a partner you may question yourself on whether or not you are doing the right thing for your partner. Are you helping enough? Are you doing enough or are you doing too much? Am I helping my partner with the condition or am I letting the condition continue without aiding my partner in recovery? This can be a tough battle and a thin line. Only talking to your partner will help ease the tension, talking openly and honestly about what's affecting you and taking the criticism or praise they give back to you.

Starting the conversation

There is no specific time for a worried parent, carer or loved one to wait before they intervene, but if you are unsure about the mental state of your child, family member, partner or someone close to you and you have a hunch that something is not quite right, then it should be investigated further.

Jenny, whose daughter suffers from anxiety, shares her thoughts as a mother:

> Go with your gut always. If you think there is something wrong, ask them and discuss it.

The most effective way to intervene at this point is through communication. It is important to pick the right moment and location: it should be at a time when it is just you and them, otherwise the person may feel 'ganged up on'. It should also be a place where they feel safe; phones, tablets and laptops should all be switched off, so there is nothing to distract you or them. Sometimes people worry that by telling someone, it could make things worse. You therefore need to be very clear from the start that you are there to support and help them, and that you will not do anything without discussing it with them first.

Jenny shares her experience of opening up the conversation with her daughter:

> I mentioned seeing someone and she initially thought it was a terrible idea and that she was a failure in not being able to manage it herself and we acted on this very quickly – or so I thought. She may have been feeling like this for a while and she only decided to open up more when she was ready to.

Communication should take place in a straightforward manner. Do not assume that you know what the problem is; you might be mistaken and could run the risk of talking for ages about something that the person cannot relate to. Let them tell you about their feelings and fears first.

The most important thing, whatever they may say to you, is not to judge them; this may cause them to clam up. Show them that you respect their emotions and also their viewpoint, even if you do disagree with certain things that they may be telling you.

My Samantha says of how finding the courage of opening up to me has helped her:

> Talking to my mum about the thoughts in my head was at first extremely hard, until I realised she had no judgement, just unconditional love. I began to open up to help her understand the thoughts in my head and what they used to say and the reasoning behind them and my actions. She was able to really understand what I was going through and start to help me move forward in my recovery.

Watching for reactions is important. You can tell when you have hit on a sore point or are getting close to an uncomfortable subject by the person's eye contact, body language and how quick they are to defend themselves.

Remain calm. Although you are unlikely to feel calm inside, you must try to stay strong in the situation because, if you are not, the sufferer could start to panic. If you do not act as though there is a solution to their problem and everything will be okay, they may start to despair. They are looking to you as someone to take their pain away.

Examples of how to start a much-needed conversation with them may include:

- 'I have noticed that you are not quite your usual self at the moment… Is something wrong?'
- 'You have been very quiet lately… Is something troubling you?'
- 'Is there anything I can do to make life a bit easier for you?'
- 'Can you describe to me how you are feeling?'
- 'Would you rather write down how you are feeling on a piece of paper for me?'

Acknowledge that the conversation is likely to be difficult for them. Tell them that you are proud of the strength they are demonstrating in telling you about their issues. They might also be reassured if you tell them that there is nothing they could say that will make you stop caring about them or loving them. Tell them it is okay to be frightened and they do not have to put on a brave face, because you will always work it out together.

My Charlotte shares her thoughts:

Having been around mental illness for 15 or so years, and from now working with Mum, I have seen how mental illness impacts the lives of everyone around it, not just the sufferer but also family and friends. One of the most important things I have learnt is to talk. If you think something is wrong with a family member, friend or loved one, always talk with someone you trust; try not to brush things under the carpet, and be as open and honest as you can be.

The general practitioner (GP)

Once you have recognised that there is a problem, whether it be the sufferer themselves reaching out for help or a loved one encouraging them, the first port of call should be the general practitioner (GP). Unfortunately, fewer than one in 10 people have sought help from their GP to deal with anxiety, although this rate is much higher among those who frequently experience anxiety.[21]

Suzie, whose daughter suffers from social anxiety disorder, shares their experience:

My split-second gut instinct (I'm ashamed to say) was to tell her not to be so ridiculous, but something inside me let her carry on talking. After a while, I went into the kitchen, picked up the phone and rang our GP to make an appointment for her. My daughter clearly believed that she was a sufferer and I had no idea where to begin with getting a diagnosis or how to help and so, as far as I could see, my GP was my one and only option.

Tom says of the barriers he faces with his social anxiety:

I haven't actively avoided seeking a diagnosis but the idea of talking to so many doctors and booking/arranging appointments isn't a pleasant thought so I've just continually procrastinated.

At this stage, please remember that no-one's time is ever wasted even if the diagnosis is not an anxiety disorder. The earlier the condition is identified, the earlier intervention can take place, with the hope of a quicker and more effective recovery for the sufferer and their loved ones.

Actively seeking help can be a vital first step forward towards recovery. However, it is important to remember, at this stage, that GPs are not miracle workers or mind readers, nor are they mental health specialists, and whilst some may have substantial knowledge and a special interest in anxiety disorders and other mental health issues, some may not. Sadly, the very limited time slot they are allocated for each patient can sometimes be insufficient to assess all of their patients objectively. In an industry dictated by guidelines and under constant scrutiny, time is one thing most GPs are sadly unable to offer.

Ahead of the GP's appointment, it may be helpful if the sufferer makes a list highlighting their symptoms and how they feel they have changed with time, including details about how these feelings are affecting them on a day-to-day basis. The notes should also include information on distressing and/or upsetting events that have happened either in the past or more recently, as well as details of any other mental or physical conditions or symptoms they may have. In addition, compiling a list of questions to put to the GP could also be helpful. This can include queries about what treatment path they might prescribe and what lifestyle changes may be helpful.

Caitlin shares her positive experience with her GP:

> My GP has been great in trying to avoid medication because of the side-effects, withdrawals etc. But if I've said I need help he's talked me through the options and ultimately it has been my decision. He has had me in for review often to keep track of things too in case anything needs adjusting.

By preparing in this way, it may help the sufferer if they become anxious during their time at the surgery and forget some of the vital facts. A diagnosis is only as reliable as the information the patient provides, so keeping the lines of communication as open as possible with the GP will assist greatly in their diagnosis in moving forward, not only in the initial appointment but in the long term. It might also be extremely helpful to arrange for someone to accompany the sufferer to their appointment. Having an advocate present is beneficial to both parties and can help the sufferer understand and remember the information given to them by the GP, whilst feeling reassured that they are being supported and listened to. With a typical GP appointment lasting around just 10 minutes, it may be useful, if possible, to book a 'double appointment' to ensure there is enough time to cover everything the sufferer is concerned about, without feeling rushed or under unnecessary pressure.

It is really important, at this stage, to encourage the sufferer to be as open and honest as they feel they can be with their GP in the time-frame they have, however frightening, uncomfortable and complicated it may be. Reassure them that they are not alone – according to a survey by the mental health charity MIND, published in June 2018, 40% of GP appointments are related to mental health.[22]

Expectations of GPs can be unfairly high and unfortunately not all appointments will conclude the way the patient or carer would like. The sufferer may feel the GP has not taken their concerns seriously enough. If this is the case, it would be prudent to make another appointment straight away to see another doctor in the practice.

While many people with an anxiety disorder will follow a treatment path directed by their GP (usually medication, talking treatment or a combination of both), in some cases the doctor will decide to refer them on for specialist help from a psychiatrist or local community health team. That is when further delays can occur. Unfortunately, the waiting lists for mental health treatments can be very long. A 2018 study from the Royal College of Psychiatrists[23] found that over half of mental health patients interviewed had to wait at least four weeks to see an NHS mental health specialist, while 6% had to wait a year.

Jess shares her experience of her GP:

> The GP just wanted to get me onto medication. I once asked for situation-specific one-to-one counselling and, although the GP referral came, it was only valid for two weeks and the service I was referred to didn't once answer the phone when I called.

There is no right or wrong way at this juncture; some people may look at seeking private help, to avoid these waiting times. Weighing up the advantages and disadvantages of joining an NHS waiting list as opposed to seeking private alternative help should be carefully thought through. Private treatment costs money and this may prove a stumbling block for many. My advice to parents, loved ones and caregivers would be to read, learn and research as much as you possibly can about the diagnosis. Knowledge is power and will help you make the right choices going forward with and for the sufferer.

Suzie, whose daughter suffers from social anxiety disorder, shares her experience:

> As a parent, I had no idea how to help her with her anxiety. Being 18, she was classed as an adult and I was not given any guidance or involvement with her treatment. I had to go with my gut instinct, online research and my daughter's own guidance. In my mind, she may have been an 'adult' but she was a young adult, still living at home, dependent on us, and about to take exams and move to university. The lack of support I was given was frustrating and the not knowing how to help made me feel useless.

Pete finishes this section with his positive experience with his GP:

> My GP has been very helpful in enabling me to put things in perspective and prescribing medication to help with the

symptoms. I've found medication has worked really well for me and helped with reducing my anxiety. Above all, my GP is just very sympathetic and even when I have an appointment to discuss something else, always asks about my mental health.

Dealing with a diagnosis

Getting a diagnosis of an anxiety disorder can provoke a range of feelings; the sufferer may question why this has happened to them and what the implications may be for them and their future. They may also have to deal with the fact that they may have another mental or physical illness, as anxiety disorders often do not occur in isolation (see Chapter 6). As someone who cares for them, it is vital to remind them that they are not the sum of their diagnosis.

People's reactions to being officially diagnosed with anxiety can vary hugely from sufferer to sufferer. These are some of the most common ways they may feel, although it is by no means an exhaustive list:

- **Relieved** – now they can understand why they have been feeling as they have
- **Shocked** – as they struggle to comprehend what this means for them
- **Hopeful** – that they can find a treatment that will help and make them feel better
- **Angry** – that out of all the people they know, this had to happen to them. (Statistically, it's actually very likely that they also have friends and acquaintances with a diagnosis of an anxiety disorder)
- **Guilty** – that they did something that caused the anxiety disorder
- **Ashamed** – that there is something wrong with them, feeling they are somehow flawed

- **Grieving** – for the life they believe they would or could have had without anxiety
- **Powerless** – as if their illness will control them, rather than them being able to take control of it
- **Embarrassed** – that this is something they should cover up
- **Misunderstood** – and concerned that people will pass judgement on them, publicly or in private without fully understanding what they are experiencing
- **Confused** – they may not fully understand the diagnosis or why a particular treatment path has been recommended
- **Determined** – to manage their anxiety and make sure it no longer controls them.

All of these feelings are absolutely valid and understandable, as is anything else that a person feels when they have been given a diagnosis of an anxiety disorder. In time, as they come to terms with their own illness and the nuanced impact on their own lives, their feelings may shift and change. For some, they will be able to feel more optimistic, whilst for others, the outlook may seem bleaker. As they weather this deluge of feelings, it is important to give them the time and space to explore and accept them, in the hope they will then feel more comfortable to openly discuss them.

Pete explains how he felt when he received a diagnosis:

> Diagnosis was actually very helpful because I realised that it was an illness and not just me. Being able to 'name' the problem was helpful in helping me to learn strategies that help me deal with it. I have found anxiety very, very frightening at times, partly because the symptoms can be very physical, particularly when I've experienced panic attacks.

It can be quite normal to get stuck at the 'why me?' stage for some time. However, after that, there needs to come a plan of action to move forwards. In other words, receiving a diagnosis of an anxiety disorder is the starting point for a longer journey towards finding the right kind of help and support and to start making the changes needed (however small) to be able to begin the road to recovery. As the sufferer embarks on this journey, so too do their loved ones. Learning as much as possible about anxiety, and understanding that it does not detract from the person you care about, are crucial. As they seek help, perhaps from support groups or helplines, caregivers and friends may also find it helpful to seek out others who are in a similar position.

People with anxiety disorders may be advised to write down how they feel, recording their concerns and questions, and noting any changes or patterns in how they are coping. The same can also apply to those who are caring for them. Expressing thoughts and feelings on paper (or electronically) can be really helpful in working through them. Further down the line, a record like this can also serve as a reminder of how far you have all come.

Every sufferer's path to recovery is different, as are their individual experiences of the NHS, private healthcare and any alternative medical professionals they encounter: each person is unique and responds differently. If one treatment proves ineffective, it absolutely does not mean that the patient is 'incurable', it simply means that the treatment is not working for that individual, so maybe it is time to start looking for another – do not be afraid to try different avenues.

Jess shares what a diagnosis of anxiety meant to her:

I've only been diagnosed with anxiety once specific to a particular situation. However, I do recognise the same thought/ behaviour patterns, just less extreme, in myself regularly in other situations. It's unsettling – we like to think we have things in hand and under control, but a diagnosis is also a sledge-hammer that breaks walls of denial or not-knowing and allows exploration of more appropriate coping strategies.

Recognising potential relapse and possible triggers

The reality of an anxiety disorder is that for many people it can remain an unwelcome visitor in their lives for many years. There will be times – weeks, months or years – when life feels brighter and, in some cases, back to 'normal'. However, as with any mental illness, it can have a nasty habit of recurring, especially at times when people leave themselves more open and vulnerable. The good news, however, is that you can take action to reduce the chances of this happening. Should the anxiety start to return, there are ways in which you can identify and reduce the chances of the anxiety making a comeback.

Recognising a relapse of an anxiety disorder is vital in order to act on it and do all you can to prevent it from escalating. While in some cases the sufferer themselves can be astute enough to see the signs, often it is the people around them who are best placed to observe changes that may be significant.

Pippa shares the key changes she noticed in her boyfriend:

I would notice a lot of negative self-talk; he would always wear big, baggy jumpers to cover his body; he would take a long time to reply to messages as he would panic over what he was going to say as he was worried people would judge him if he said the wrong thing.

The symptoms of an anxiety disorder can vary between individuals which makes it essential for every sufferer to understand their own illness and what behaviour or changes may be symptomatic of the kind of anxiety they suffer. That is also true for those around them: knowing the difference between what is 'normal' for their loved one or friend and signs that need to be acted on can really make a difference.

In general terms, listed below are the kinds of symptom or changes that may indicate an approaching bout of mental ill health. Being able to recognise them early enough will help prompt action to prevent them from escalating into something more serious.

- Struggling to sleep or sleeping too much
- Feeling constantly stressed out and in a rush
- Worrying more than usual or feeling on edge
- Having negative thought patterns and noticing the inner critic gaining a voice
- Suffering from headaches or stomach upsets may indicate stress or anxiety taking hold
- Turning to alcohol or drugs to help cope with the difficult feelings
- Getting stressed about an approaching stressful life event.

Once you notice these triggers creeping in, please do not ignore them. They could indicate that those prone to an anxiety disorder need to slow down, give themselves some time and space, and perhaps speak to a therapist or see their GP to tackle the potential problem before it progresses further.

Paul shares his experience of suffering from anxiety from a young age:

> The one main trigger for my anxiety to flare up is not having enough sleep. If I try to do too much I know that the following few days I will suffer for it. Now I am more disciplined with how much I book into my social calendar and making sure I get a good night's sleep; I find I am more able to cope with daily life.

This is where it is important to remember all the things that have helped and made a difference in the past and start putting them back into practice once again. That could be healthy eating, exercise, a regular sleep pattern, talking to someone, indulging in a therapeutic hobby such as art or walking or even, if necessary, seeing the GP for further advice.

At this point it is also helpful to recognise stressful or challenging situations that may be approaching and working out a strategy on how to deal with them, rather than having to deal with the consequences after.

These measures are strategies that someone prone to anxiety should be, if possible, incorporating into their day-to-day life, creating a protective shield against the anxiety.

To conclude

If possible, however difficult things get, try not to allow the sufferer to fall at the first hurdle. It is important to try and all move forward together, making a joint effort to find the right path that works for everyone. There will be ups and downs along the way and it is very much a 'one step forward, two steps back' scenario for a while; it can be a long road but acceptance, understanding and perseverance are key. The sufferer needs all the encouragement you can give them to keep going until they get the right help they need and deserve, so patience and open-mindedness are of the upmost importance. Propping the sufferer up for a little while is okay too, but they have to be able to walk alone at some point and take ownership of their road to recovery. For the process to flourish and be a success they really need to want it 100% for themselves. Being afraid of the unknown is a perfectly normal feeling and reaction when faced with the challenge of tackling a loved one and their mental illness. Please try not to feel daunted by the prospect of what lies ahead, have courage, be strong and stand side by side with the sufferer, standing up to the testing times that are to come by communicating and uniting to confront it head on.

Always remember, recovery is possible.

Chapter 4

A guide to therapies

As discussed earlier in this book, each and every form of anxiety disorder will manifest itself in a different and unique way, because each sufferer is different and unique. In the same way, there is no 'ultimate' treatment. One sufferer may respond very well to a certain treatment, while it may have little or no effect on someone else who has also been diagnosed with an anxiety disorder. For some, a combination of therapies can be the answer. Whichever decision is made, it is essential that the sufferer and their carers choose a course of therapy which fuels and strengthens their desire to recover, as opposed to drowning and eventually killing it.

In order to be proactive during this frustrating time, one step which parents, carers and friends of sufferers can take is to arm themselves with a thorough knowledge of the various treatment options available. Below is an unbiased guide to many of the different therapies and medications available, both within the NHS and outside of it. I have asked specialists within each field, all of whom I know personally, to explain a bit more about their therapy, with the aim of helping you to understand how their individual discipline can help to combat an anxiety disorder.

(You may notice some approaches overlap with others or combine elements from one with another – this is all part of the wide variation in what works for different individuals.)

- Cognitive behavioural therapy (CBT)
- Dialectical behavioural therapy (DBT)
- Medication
- Counselling
- Eye movement desensitisation and reprocessing (EMDR)
- Emotional freedom technique (EFT)
- Neuro-linguistic programming (NLP)
- Havening
- Hypnotherapy
- Psychosensory techniques and principles (Psy-TaP)
- Self-help
- Self-help and support groups.

Cognitive behavioural therapy (CBT)

CBT is one of the most well-known forms of therapy for anxiety. It uses discussion-based therapy to change or reduce unhelpful thoughts, which in turn will reduce damaging and harmful behaviours that are part of an anxiety disorder. CBT also helps people to set achievable, realistic treatment goals and to reinforce all the behaviours that are useful in meeting those goals.

Dr Lucy Viney, clinical psychologist and co-founder of the Fitzrovia Psychology Clinic, explains how CBT can help to treat anxiety:

Humans evolved to experience anxiety because it kept us safe, and for our ancient ancestors – the cavemen – anxiety and fear were related to survival and self-preservation. For example, if a caveman came into contact with a sabre-toothed tiger during his daily walk, he would recognise the danger, which would activate his fight or flight response, enabling him to fight or run away. If he didn't recognise that the sabre-toothed tiger was dangerous, his fear response would not be activated, and the chances of his survival would be much reduced.

In modern society, anxiety becomes a difficulty when the fight or flight response is triggered by events that pose no real threat to us. Because our survival mechanism dates back to our caveman days, our bodies still react today in the same way as our ancestors did thousands of years ago. However, our 'threats' have changed considerably. Our brains respond to anxiety about an exam or having to do a presentation in a similar way that they would when the cavemen encountered a sabre-toothed tiger. It is this overestimation of danger, combined with a belief that we will not be able to cope with the threat, that is key when thinking about treatment for anxiety, and in particular, with the use of cognitive behavioural therapy (CBT).

CBT is the most widely-used therapy for anxiety disorders. The central idea of CBT is that our thoughts – not external events – affect the way we feel. In other words, it's not the situation you're in that determines how you feel, but your perception of the situation. For example, if someone who has a fear of public speaking is told on a Friday afternoon that they are required to do a presentation on Monday morning, they are likely to experience a number of highly anxious thoughts about this scenario. These thoughts might include: 'Everyone's going to think I don't know what I'm talking about,' 'I'm going to blush and everyone will make fun of me,' 'I won't be able to get through it,' 'It's going to be a disaster'. These thoughts will further increase the person's anxiety and impact upon their behaviour. They might become so stressed and anxious that they can't think properly to prepare for the presentation, or worse, they might not prepare at all and call in sick on Monday morning so as to avoid it altogether. Their anxiety about the presentation will remain extremely high, and the next time they are asked to do a presentation, the above scenario is likely to be repeated.

Alternatively, CBT would help this person think differently about their anxieties relating to the presentation, so that they are able to engage in more helpful thought and behaviour patterns which would enable them to manage the situation more effectively. Although the person still feels anxious, a more helpful way of thinking about the situation might be: 'Most people feel anxious about having to do a presentation at short notice, and so I'm sure my colleagues will be able to empathise with my anxiety. I will thoroughly prepare my notes and slides so that I feel as prepared as possible and do my best on the day.' It is likely that this person will be better able to manage their anxiety about the presentation, meaning that they can focus on the preparation, and that once they have got through it, they will feel less anxious about having to do a presentation in the future because they know that they can cope better than they initially anticipated.

As the above example demonstrates, the way we think about an anxiety-inducing situation affects the way we feel and the way we behave. Therefore, a principal aspect of CBT is addressing the way we think. You and your therapist will do this by identifying unhelpful ways of thinking and perceiving particular situations in which you experience anxiety. The second step involves a strategy called 'cognitive restructuring', in which you learn how to challenge these problematic thoughts.

Avoidance and anxiety

It is understandable that If we think something terrible is going to happen, and that we will be unable to cope with it, we are inclined to avoid that situation. The problem is that avoidance maintains anxiety because it prevents us from accessing opportunities where we can experience that we are able to cope with fear-provoking situations better than we had expected. Each time we avoid a situation to minimise anxiety, we make it more likely that we will avoid it again the next time that the feared situation arises.

Therefore, another important element of CBT for anxiety involves 'exposure therapy'. Exposure therapy is a part of CBT that is useful when someone relies heavily on avoidance as a coping strategy for anxiety because it enables them to face their fears in a methodical and structured way. The idea is that through repeated exposures to a situation that causes you anxiety, your anxiety will reduce over time because you learn that you are able to cope with the situation better than expected, and you are therefore able to think and behave differently.

Caitlin, who suffers from generalised anxiety disorder and social anxiety, shares what she has learnt from going through CBT treatment:

I have learnt the following through CBT:
> you can't change other people's actions or emotions
> you can't change your immediate reactions to a situation
> core beliefs typically stem from childhood
> core beliefs absolutely shape how you see yourself
> core beliefs are usually false views of yourself.

I worked with my psychologist to come up with a new, balanced core belief which I reinforce to myself daily via a poster on my wall.

Amy, who went through a period of regular panic attacks and severe anxiety, shares her positive experience of online CBT:

I self-referred myself so there was no need to go to the GP. Then within a week I had had an online consultation and filled out lots of forms for them to be able to assign me a therapist. Then I had eight or 12 weeks of weekly online therapy.

I think it was different to anything I've had before. Having to type it out and try and explain myself helped, and also being able to read back over the conversations after they had happened really refreshed me; I could always refer back to them. I also found the fact the referral was done by me made it easier, and the process was really quick compared to face-to-face therapy options through the NHS. The information given to me from my therapist I still have today, and he again really explained things. I was able to do it in the comfort of my own home, at the same time each week, so I felt relaxed. (Having anxiety and panic attacks I think I would have struggled going anywhere for therapy!)

Dialectical behavioural therapy (DBT)

DBT is an adapted form of CBT developed by Dr Marsha Linehan. It focuses on accepting uncomfortable and unhealthy behaviours and feelings instead of struggling against them. It was developed originally for those diagnosed with borderline personality disorder; however, it has also been found to be an effective treatment for other mental illnesses, such as anxiety disorders. It is a structured form of therapy with the aim of achieving self-acceptance and change by helping the person to regulate their emotions in order to manage and reduce anxiety.

Medication

When it comes to treating anxiety disorders, doctors will usually recommend talking therapies first, such as CBT or counselling. However, if psychological treatments have not proved beneficial by themselves, or are not the right route for an individual, medication will usually be the next port of call.

Before prescribing a particular course of medication, the GP should discuss the different options and explain clearly any possible side-effects, and the length of treatment time expected. Some medication is designed to be taken on a short-term basis, while other medicines are prescribed for longer periods. The doctor should also book in regular appointments to look at how well the medication is working and what side-effects, if any, are being experienced.

The main medications you may be offered to treat an anxiety disorder fall into the following groups:

- A type of antidepressant called a selective serotonin reuptake inhibitor (SSRI)
- A type of antidepressant called a serotonin and norepinephrine reuptake inhibitor (SNRI)
- An anticonvulsant medication called pregabalin, which is

used to treat conditions such as epilepsy, but which can also be helpful in treating anxiety.

- Benzodiazepines, a type of sedative that may sometimes be used as a short-term treatment during a particularly severe period of anxiety.
- Beta blockers, a group of medications that are primarily used to manage abnormal heart rhythms, which can be a symptom of anxiety.

Amy, who went through a period of regular panic attacks and severe anxiety, explains how medication helps her:

> Medication has definitely helped me recently, just to make everyday situations seem more manageable, and has made me feel like I can cope better.

Selective serotonin reuptake inhibitors (SSRIs)

SSRIs are the most common form of medication prescribed for anxiety disorders and work to boost levels of serotonin, a chemical messenger in the brain which carries signals between nerve cells and can boost concentration and outlook, making it easier for people to face up to day-to-day life. SSRIs have names such as fluoxetine, paroxetine, sertraline or citalopram but they are often known by brand names, such as Prozac – a brand of fluoxetine.

A doctor should look at the individual person to work out which medication might best work for them, taking into account factors such as age, other mental health issues, and individual circumstances. It is worth noting that younger people, under 18, are treated with particular caution when it comes to prescribing antidepressants. There is some evidence that use of antidepressants can lead to an increase in suicidal thoughts among young people. As a result, they are viewed as very much a last resort and only prescribed with great caution.

Julie, who has suffered from anxiety and depression for most of her life, shares her experience:

> I have thought about coming off my medication so many times, but it enables me to function on a daily basis and keeps me levelled.

Serotonin and norepinephrine reuptake inhibitors (SNRIs)

If SSRIs do not make a positive difference, someone with an anxiety disorder may be prescribed a different type of antidepressant known as a serotonin and norepinephrine reuptake inhibitor (SNRI), which increases the amount of serotonin and norepinephrine, another chemical messenger, in the brain. These medications have names such as venlafaxine and duloxetine.

Similar to SSRIs, SNRIs increase the levels of certain neuro-transmitters. However, the reason norepinephrine is thought to be vital is because it is known to play a part in the body's stress reaction, which forms the basis of anxiety responses. As with SSRIs, they can take several weeks to start working. With all an-tidepressants, if there is no discernible effect after two months, or the side-effects are particularly pronounced, it is probably wise to ask for an alternative to be prescribed.

Side-effects

As with most medications, each one can have its varied side-effects, so it is always advisable, before starting, to read the information leaflet provided. This will help the sufferer and their carers understand the possible changes that may be experienced, as the drug begins to get into their system, and hopefully starts to work.

Common side-effects of SSRIs and SNRIs include:

- Feeling agitated, shaky or anxious
- Nausea
- Indigestion, diarrhoea and/or constipation
- Dizziness and/or headaches
- Disturbed sleep patterns
- Low sex drive and other sexual problems.

The side-effects should improve within a few weeks, although some can occasionally persist.

Important note: If you are a carer, loved one or the person taking the antidepressants, it is extremely important to keep in mind that there are cases in which a serious side-effect can be suicidal or self-harming thoughts; please contact your GP or medical professional straight away if there is any hint this is occurring.

Those who have been prescribed antidepressants should also be very careful about drinking alcohol, as it can counteract the benefits of the medication.

Serotonin syndrome

This is a rare set of side-effects linked to SSRIs and SNRIs that can nevertheless be potentially serious. This 'syndrome' occurs when the level of serotonin in the brain becomes too high and can also happen when the medication is being taken in combination with another medicine or substance that also raises serotonin levels, such as the natural remedy St John's wort. Symptoms include agitation, shivering, sweating, diarrhoea and muscle twitching and in the most serious cases can lead to seizures, an irregular heartbeat and losing consciousness.

To avoid this, patients should never take two different types of antidepressant together without their doctor's clear guidance. Patients should also make their doctor fully aware of any other natural remedies or treatments they are intending to try in case they are counterproductive to the medication and treatment plan they have already been prescribed.

Louise, who suffers from generalised and social anxiety disorder and OCD, and who is also a nurse prescriber working with patients suffering from chronic pain, shares her experience:

I have come across this in patients who have been on more than one antidepressant. Often the symptoms of increased agitation and distress are present amongst others, such as confusion and sweating. I would usually recommend patients only be on one antidepressant for this reason.

Pregabalin

If SSRIs and SNRIs are not suitable for the person suffering, they may be offered pregabalin. This is a medication known as an anticonvulsant, which is used to treat conditions such as epilepsy, but it has also been found to be beneficial in treating anxiety by stopping the brain from releasing the chemicals that make people feel anxious.[24]

The side-effects of pregabalin can include drowsiness, dizziness, increased appetite and weight gain, blurred vision, headaches, dry mouth and vertigo. Most of these should ease within a few weeks, but a doctor should be informed if the effects persist or are particularly extreme.

Rachel says of how pregabalin helps her to cope with her anxiety:

I'm currently on pregabalin; I've been on it about a month now and find it really helps my anxiety. The first week was tough as I had nasty palpitations but now it's kicked in, I get a lot of relief. It doesn't stop the anxiety completely but definitely helps treat the symptoms and my panic attacks are getting less by the day too. I wouldn't even be able to step out the front door without pregabalin; it's starting to slowly change my quality of life for the better.

Benzodiazepines

Benzodiazepines are a type of sedative that start acting within 30 to 90 minutes and as such may sometimes be used as a short-term treatment during a particularly severe period of anxiety. The most common type is diazepam ('Valium').

Although benzodiazepines can be effective, they can become addictive and should not be used for any prolonged periods of time. A prescription will typically be for a two to four-week stretch.

Side-effects of benzodiazepines can include drowsiness, difficulty concentrating, headaches, vertigo and a tremor.

Driving or operating machinery should be avoided when taking this type of medication, as with alcohol and opiate drugs, which includes prescription painkilling drugs such as tramadol and fentanyl. It is always advisable to check anything you are unsure about with your GP, who will advise you accordingly.

Charliee says of how benzodiazepines help with her PTSD:

It's supposed to only be prescribed short term because of addiction but was agreed that I can be prescribed a set amount each month as they are so beneficial for my sleep. This medication really helps with my flashbacks and I guess it stops me from consciously/unconsciously remembering my trauma whilst I try to sleep. The difference when I take the medication is incredible – I don't have flashbacks, wake up with no anxiety and the need to self-harm is much less.

Beta blockers

Beta blockers work mainly by slowing down the heart beat and are mainly used to treat heart issues, such as angina or a heart attack. Less commonly, these prescription-only drugs may be used to treat the physical effects of anxiety, including sweating and shaking, and may be prescribed to tackle a specific anxiety-inducing event, rather than as a longer-term treatment.

Side-effects can include dizziness, tiredness, cold fingers and toes, nausea and difficulty sleeping. More serious effects, such as shortness of breath, should be reported immediately to a medical professional.

Louise, who suffers from generalised and social anxiety disorder and OCD, shares her personal experience:

> I have personal experience of using beta blockers. I was on them for migraine prevention; while they had little effect on reducing my migraines they did however help with lowering my anxiety levels.

Coming off antidepressants

Sometimes, believing they are well, people 'just' stop taking their antidepressants. Not only can this undermine their effectiveness, but it can also lead to them experiencing some difficult side-effects. Instead, if they do want to come off them, they should reduce the amount they take under the guidance of their psychiatrist or GP. Stopping suddenly can lead to withdrawal symptoms, such as stomach upsets, anxiety, dizziness and in some cases seizures. Even if a recently prescribed medication does not appear to be working, it is important to keep on taking it until the GP suggests otherwise. If there are severe side-effects, seek guidance straight away.

Antidepressants are not, as some people worry, addictive like other commonly abused drugs. Those taking antidepressants will not experience a 'high' or 'euphoria' effect, you also do not get 'cravings' for them or need to keep increasing the dose to get the same effect. However, stopping antidepressant treatment abruptly or missing several doses can cause withdrawal-like symptoms. This is sometimes called discontinuation syndrome: the symptoms that occur can include dizziness, irritability and insomnia. Those experiencing discontinuation syndrome often believe that they are having a relapse as the symptoms can be similar to the mental health issue they were originally prescribed to treat. Work with your doctor to gradually and safely decrease your dose.

My Samantha ends this section with her thought on medication:

> From a young age I have always been anti-medication, as I was always stubborn enough to think I could sort everything out on my own as well as being afraid what effect it would have on me and if I would be able to control it! I then hit the rock bottom of my OCD when it was either sink or swim; I knew I was drowning in the deep end and needed a little help to the surface. I thought to myself 'I have nothing to lose, I am already at my lowest, maybe this time around I need to put my shield down and try it.' From my own experience, the medication I took didn't change my personality, I wasn't out of control, I had just been freed slightly from the burdening voices; by no means did it get rid of them completely, it just pushed them from the front of my head, to the back. I could still hear them but was able to distinguish more what were my thoughts and what were the illness's; it gave me more definition and a clearer path to recovery.

Counselling

The word 'counselling' covers a multitude of different disciplines. Often counsellors will use an element of psychotherapy, CBT and NLP within their method. Most broadly, however, counselling offers an opportunity for patients to talk. Within an anonymous and safe environment, they are afforded the opportunity to speak about anything, while being gently guided with questions by their therapist, which allows them to come to important realisations about the origin and nature of their illness.

Counselling has a number of benefits for those suffering from anxiety disorders. Firstly, it allows them to feel valued.

People suffering from anxiety and other mental health issues often feel isolated and misunderstood. Counselling provides a forum for them to explore their feelings. Secondly, counselling is, by its very nature, tailored to the individual. There is no set format for counsellors, which means that they must, to some extent, treat everyone's case individually. As such, it is crucial in counselling – perhaps more so than with any other type of therapy – to find the right 'fit' in terms of a practitioner. A good counsellor should make their patient feel safe, secure and valued at all times. They should establish a bond of trust with their clients and make it easy for them to discuss potentially painful or difficult issues.

As a mental health counsellor myself, I ensure I have met with a sufferer's parents or carers before I commence working with them, if they are under 18. Many people are surprised that I insist on this; I have always been of the opinion, however, that rehabilitating someone with anxiety, or any other mental health illness, is a group effort and one which will involve constant channels of communication between clients and the people who are most influential in their lives. If a client is over 18 and they have approached me independently, I will usually bring carers into the process a little further into therapy. Under the Data Protection Act, I of course have to obtain the client's permission to share information with carers. Once I have explained the paramount importance of trust and communication, this permission is usually granted. I like the families of my clients to understand my methods and the work I will undertake with their loved ones so they can be as helpful and supportive as possible throughout the recovery process. Recovery can sometimes be a long process, with the sufferer's mind-set changing at each stage, sometimes on a day-by-day basis.

It is important that carers are aware of the changes to help them to gain a real insight into how their loved one is thinking and feeling at each juncture. This is why I prefer to keep them in the loop. Before a client sees me for the first time, I research their interests, whether it is films, music, clothes and/or particular hobbies; this enables me to establish a rapport with them during their initial sessions. It is important for sufferers to feel understood and accepted. It is also important they perceive themselves as a three-dimensional person, rather than as simply 'A mental health issue'. Anxiety disorders can envelope the identity of the sufferer. By talking to my clients about their hobbies and passions, I am demonstrating to them that they are individuals, who are not defined by their illness. This sets in motion the journey towards my client envisaging life without their issue – a huge leap in terms of the recovery process. Encouraging clients to acknowledge their struggles and open up about the factors which might have influenced them is not always easy – it requires time, patience and perseverance.

I tend to work very intensively with my clients initially, seeing them two or three times a week. The challenge to negative emotions and feelings should be worked through as swiftly as possible. This also helps to quickly establish a bond of trust and friendship during this time. Eventually this can be maintained with less frequent sessions.

Juliet shares her experience of working with me towards recovery from anxiety and anorexia nervosa:

What can I say about Lynn? My shining light of hope at the end of a long tunnel that has proven to be my turbulent recovery from anxiety and anorexia nervosa. Her strength and wisdom guide me through the troubled waters that I navigate on a daily basis. She understands my mind on a level that I cannot explain and through that we have fostered a working partnership that empowers me to tackle my fears and face my anxiety head on.

Anxiety to me is a full body experience of crushing panic that builds in my chest, nausea that swirls in my stomach and a pounding head that leaves me unable to think or see straight. Yet whether it be struggles with perfectionism that paralyse me or a catastrophic scenario my mind has created that reaches beyond my control, Lynn is always there to pick me up when I fall, to rationalise with my mind and to help guide me back to myself with a gentle nudge (or sometimes a more needed firm push) in the right direction.

Lynn's approach is one that undeniably works and for that I am incredibly thankful. Her kindness, her compassion and her wealth of experience allow her to work with you as an individual to help untangle the mess of your mind at your own pace, in a way in which you feel supported and loved. Lynn recognises that recovery looks different for us all and through working with her I have come to accept that whilst I may always have anxiety, it is not something that needs to control my life and I can manage it in such a way that I am able to live the life that I want to live without restrictions, adaptations or modifications. Rather, together we have been able to work towards a life that is free from constraints imposed by my mind, one whereby, though I may feel anxious, I am able to do all that I want to do. I feel the fear but with her guidance I do it anyway. And in time those fears have gradually subsided.

I came to Lynn at a time in my life when I truly saw no way out. I felt I was destined to live a limited and restricted life forever, unable to cope with the unknown and uncertainties of the day-to-day. Yet that was not what I wanted for myself. Lynn has been, and always will be, the wind in my sails, steering me towards a better future. Without her I don't know where I would be today.

Eye movement desensitisation and reprocessing (EMDR)

EMDR is recognised by the National Institute for Health and Clinical Excellence (NICE) and the World Health Organization (WHO) as a treatment for post-traumatic stress disorder; it can also be used to treat other types of anxiety.

Kate Guest, registered nurse, coach, speaker and hypnotherapist, explains, what EMDR is and how It can help with anxiety:

Chapter 4

Eye movement desensitisation and reprocessing (EMDR) therapy was reportedly created by Francine Shapiro, a psychologist, in the 1980s, although it is argued to have actually come from John Grinder, the co-founder of NLP for whom Shapiro worked.

Whatever its true origins, EMDR can be extremely effective for treating many mental health conditions. Mainly known for its use in PTSD, it is also now used widely for anxiety and panic disorders, and other conditions such as depression, eating disorders and addictions. In fact, any negative stored emotions from past memories can be targeted with EMDR. EMDR can reduce or deplete the emotional reaction to a memory or event and thus have a positive effect on the associated issue.

It works by causing bilateral stimulation (using visual stimuli which occur in a rhythmic left-right pattern) in the hemispheres of the brain, which enhances memory processing in a beneficial way through resolving traumatic memories stored in the hippocampus (the part of the brain involved in the formation of new memories, and in learning and emotions).

EMDR can be thought of in the same way as 'defragging' a computer. The corpus callosum, the processing highway in the brain, allows communication to occur between the two hemispheres of the brain. The processing results from messages being transmitted between the two. Sometimes during emotional stress, such as in PTSD, this processing is disrupted, and memories are 'locked' in one hemisphere and not processed fully. EMDR allows for the processing, resulting in the memory being intact, without emotional reaction.

Case study

A client of mine in her 30s (Sophie) came to me with depression, anxiety and loss of motivation following a traumatic incident. She had received the usual therapies provided by the NHS, such as CBT and counselling; however, not only did she feel there had been no benefit, she actually felt worse.

Having been off sick for some months, she saw no hope of returning to a better state of mind and thus returning to work, which she dearly wanted to do. She had loved her job and now feared that this prolonged absence for sickness would have lasting negative consequences if she did indeed manage to return to work at all.

We worked together for a number of weeks using EMDR as the main part of the therapy.

Sometimes I would ask Sophie to follow my finger as I moved it in front of her eyes from side to side. I asked her to think about the issue she wanted to release, to be free of, to have a different emotional experience from. Other times I would tap on the back of her hands alternately or click either side of each ear.

I explained that the time needed for this therapy depends on the individual. Normally it takes between three and six sessions and can be combined with other therapies such as hypnosis.

After four sessions, Sophie felt well enough to go on to a return-to-work plan. We agreed to continue for a further two sessions to support her over the first few weeks. That was four months ago. Sophie is now progressing well at work and has tools and techniques that I taught her to use to reinforce positive thoughts as needed in addition to the benefits of the EMDR.

Emotional freedom technique (EFT)

EFT was brought to light in the 1990s by its developer Gary Craig when he published information about the therapy on his website. This therapy involves the use of tapping specific points on the body, in a particular sequence. While doing this, the person focuses on the issue that they want to heal and any associations with that issue that may be hidden.

Deanne Jade, psychologist and founder of the National Centre for Eating Disorders, explains how it can treat anxiety:

Emotional freedom technique, also known as the 'tapping therapy', is one of a range of third-wave somatic treatments for mental health issues.

These issues include destructive beliefs, addictions, self-worth problems, trauma and mood disorders like depression or anxiety.

Elsewhere in this book we learn that anxiety is a normal human experience that can be useful, acting as a warning system alerting us to things that can harm us physically or emotionally. Arousal signals from the brain allow us to become focused, wary and vigilant.

The anxiety signal comes directly from the amygdala, a part of our brain responsible for alarm emotions – freeze, flee or fight. Once stimulated, the amygdala activates chemicals which we feel the effects of in the body: our stomach churns, our breathing quickens, muscles tighten and blood flows to our hands and legs so that we can take rapid action, and our vision narrows, shutting all else out. A bit of anxiety at the right time can be useful, but in some people, anxiety becomes a constant, uncontrollable experience that is paralysing. Chronic and acute anxiety affects many aspects of life. Anxiety can show up as an irrational phobia, such as being out of doors, eating certain foods, being in high places and speaking in public.

Overwhelming anxiety often leads to panic disorder and eventually more problems if people try to escape from it with drugs, alcohol, food or other harmful actions.

Often, we cannot find the source of this anguish, which may lie in our character or in historic personal experiences. When we cannot make sense of our anxiety or loss of control, we may blame ourselves for being so fearful or we accept our limitations as a fundamental truth. A person might say 'I must never speak my mind or people will reject me.' We blame themselves for being fearful and may say 'I shouldn't feel like this' but we do.

EFT works well for anxiety alongside other, more traditional psychological techniques. It was first developed in the 1960s by a psychiatrist called Roger Callaghan. He noticed that a patient being treated for a fear of water lost her symptoms when he accidentally tapped on an acupressure point on her forehead. EFT is an evolution of his original technique. It works by noting the degree of distress that the patient experiences before the procedure takes place and then tapping on energy or acupressure points around the body, while at the same time focusing on the undesired feelings where they are located inside the body; this helps bring up the memories and beliefs that are associated with these feelings. After each round of tapping, the client describes what is going on now, that may be a memory or an emotion and that becomes the focus of the next round of tapping, continuing in this way until the anxious feelings have disappeared. Although this sounds simple, tapping requires the attention of a properly trained EFT therapist who knows how to point the client's attention safely to every single impression that emerges during the tapping process. This is known as bringing to conscious awareness all the aspects of the anxiety response and what lies beneath.

The skill of the therapist is very important; to use the right words, to use metaphor to describe the experience of worry and fear, to notice the changes in how the client holds him or herself, to ensure that all aspects of the embodied anxiety are addressed, and, finally to test that there is no residual anxiety remaining by trying to trigger the former response.

So how does tapping work? It appears to change the energy flows in the body associated with anxiety that are trapped; releasing this energy is healing. The activation of the vagal nerve during a tapping process appears to reprocess emotion and memories into parts of the brain that no longer activate the amygdala. Whatever the reason for the success of EFT, it works astoundingly well and is a valuable tool for all psychotherapists who learn how to do it. We don't want to prevent someone from every feeling anxious again. A certain amount of anxiety helps us to deal properly with dangerous situations. We simply wish to help people calm down when they need to and manage their anxiety when it crops up.

EFT has now been elevated to the domain of evidence-based treatment. It is particularly good for trauma anxiety, where its effects are fast and permanent. Tapping is also a fast, effective treatment for a wide range of anxiety-based health problems such as low self-worth, poor body image, substance cravings and overwhelming emotions. The most remarkable *thing about tapping is that it can short-circuit what would otherwise take months to achieve with traditional talking psychotherapies.*

Neuro-linguistic programming (NLP)

NLP was created by Richard Bandler and John Grinder in California, United States, in the 1970s. It relates to the way we communicate with ourselves. 'Neuro' means 'of the mind', and 'linguistic' is the study of language. Therefore, NLP purely means that you can re-programme the language of your own mind – that is, the way that you think and the words you choose to think with.

Michele Paradise, a Harley Street personal development practitioner, NLP trainer, Havening techniques practitioner and clinical hypnotherapist, tells us of how NLP works:

Neuro-linguistic programming (NLP) is quite a mouthful but a very powerful set of techniques to enable change.

I had the privilege to be trained by Dr Richard Bandler, the co-creator of NLP, and Paul McKenna and to assist them on their courses for 10 years so I saw a lot of change right before my eyes and I know how powerful it is in shifting behaviours, especially around anxiety and old, unhelpful emotions.

As Dr Bandler has said for many years, NLP is not a thing. It is the study of modelling excellence in others, using the newly learned strategies and teaching the client how to think on purpose, not just react to their circumstances.

In 1972 in Santa Cruz, California, Dr Richard Bandler and John Grinder set out to study very successful therapists of the time, such as family therapist Virginia Satir, the world famous hypnotherapist, Milton Erickson and the innovative psychotherapist Fritz Perls, to identify the strategies they used to get great results and teach others how to do it.

What they learned was that we use our five senses to explore the world and map it: the world is so vast and rich that we have to simplify it to give it meaning, and we 'chunk it down' by looking for familiarity and patterns with things and situations through what we see, hear, feel, taste and smell.

For example, every time you see a door in front of you, you have a pretty good idea how it works. You will see a door knob or handle and turn it in a direction that you've turned it many times before to open it. You don't need a set of instructions every time you see a door; they're all pretty much the same and there is a familiar, similar pattern to opening them.

Our brain loves familiarity. It enables us to feel like we know about the situation, even if it's the first time we've encountered it. This is especially true with people. We are more likely to like people who are more like us, not less. You've probably met someone who reminds you of someone in your past and you think to yourself, 'They look like/ remind me of Uncle John.' If you like Uncle John, you are more likely to like them and feel more comfortable around them. If you don't like Uncle John, they will be at a disadvantage with you and it may take longer for you to get to know them.

We do this in all aspects of our life, especially with behavioural patterns. We develop patterns when we need them. Some behaviours are referred to as 'coping strategies' and we run them every time we are in a situation where we need to cope with something that may be stressful. After a while, we have learned them so well that they are now 'anchored' in our unconscious and we don't even have to think about them anymore; they just get 'fired off' when we need them – a bit like being able to open a door without really thinking about it.

Anxiety is a great example of 'firing off' feelings based on things that we frequently can't control and it's always about living in the past or the future, but not in the present. It's about running old behaviours that do not fit the current situation, or catastrophising about the future and living in pain before we even get there. We all unconsciously run films of situations, whether we realise it or not, and wouldn't it be better to run a romcom instead of a disaster film?

Anxiety is always based on a belief – a belief that we're not loveable, not good enough, a failure, not desirable enough and on and on. However, it is just a thought based on something someone might have said to us years before and we're still carrying around to this day. We've built a whole world of belief around it and have 'made' it true for us. We then 'run a behaviour' to help us cope with this belief and sometimes the easiest thing to do is to remove ourselves from interaction with others and literally hide under the duvet.

In order to keep these beliefs alive, we need to run patterns and behaviours that sustain them and this is where NLP is magnificent. Through a process called 'meta modelling', we can easily find out what beliefs and values the client has and how they run the patterns and behaviours around them so that we can teach them a new way to think and behave and change their beliefs forever.

Think back to a time when you firmly believed something to be true, like Father Christmas, the tooth fairy, a haircut that you thought made you look amazing. Now you may not believe any of these to be true anymore and the change in belief probably happened in less than a minute. Maybe someone said something to you or you caught your mother putting money under your pillow and discovered the truth. Whatever it was, the belief changed instantly and you never believed it again.

The really good news is that we're not born with that behaviour; we learned it. Therefore, if we can learn something, we can unlearn something – thanks to the concept of neuroplasticity, which means that the brain has the ability to form and reorganise synaptic connections, especially in response to learning. So, in a nutshell, we have the ability to relearn something and rewire our brain with the right training.

The metaphor I use to describe this is that we're on a very unhealthy 'hamster wheel' in our lives that seems to serve a purpose for that time but we hang onto these behaviours too long and they pass their sell-by date, but we're stuck on that wheel and don't know how to get off, which is where I come in. I metaphorically stick my finger in one of the spokes so that you fall off, wake up and find a new and better way to deal with an old issue.

Through fast and effective NLP techniques and hypnotherapy, I can enable a client to change the way they think, shift their behaviour and live a life with freedom and choice.

A session with an NLP practitioner like myself starts with what I call an 'archeological dig' to find out what the client's beliefs, values and strategies are. A client rarely presents with the real issue. By the time they get to me, they are manifesting a set of symptoms and it is my job to find out how the issue began. The history of the issue can be content free if the client can't remember how it began or the memory is too painful. I then use many and varied NLP techniques until we get the client's desired outcome and finish the session with hypnotherapy so that the unconscious comes on board and allows the client to shift and change.

Anabelle, who suffers from PTSD, shares her positive experience with NLP:

I undertook six years of NLP training/therapy. I spent some of that time working on my own issues and some of that time helping others whilst being an assistant on the courses my trainers undertook. It helped me beyond words. I slowly unraveled where many of my problems had come from and how they had manifested in my older life and learnt many techniques of how to deal with my anxieties and other developed negative behaviours. It wasn't all plain-sailing of course, and I had to really dig deep to find the strength to confront my past and deal with the trauma. Step by step I became stronger and more able to deal with things and really importantly I learnt powerful techniques that have stayed with me all through my adult life.

Havening

As mentioned earlier, Michele Paradise is a Havening techniques practitioner as well as a trainer in NLP and a clinical hypnotherapist. She tells us how the Havening techniques work:

Havening techniques, which were developed by Dr Ronald Ruden, a neuropharmacologist in the USA, make up a psychosensory therapy, which simply means that it is a therapy that connects the mind and body when treating the client. Havening is a process designed to eliminate the consequences of traumatic memories; post-Havening, the response to an emotional trigger is unlinked and/or eliminated. It is extremely effective in removing phobias, stress, anxiety, grief, somatic pain, pathological emotions and many other conditions, including eating disorders.

Havening uses touch, distraction and imagination to create electrochemical changes in the brain to change the emotions around the memory. The client can leave the session with the memory but without the trigger that sets off the associated negative thoughts and emotions.

We are electrochemical beings and when a stimulus enters the body that is distressing to us, it travels up the spinal cord and quickly passes through the 'reptilian brain', also known as the 'autonomic nervous system', which is the life support control of the body. When it is over-stimulated, such as by a traumatic event or memory, our heart beats faster, we become short of breath and our hands begin to sweat, to name a few of the symptoms.

It then travels quickly to the 'mammalian brain' and into the 'limbic system' where the amygdala lives. Think of the amygdala as the third eye. It is an almond-shaped grey–matter structure roughly between the eyes. It is where trauma is stored and gets 'stuck' and sets off the all too-familiar responses such as fight, flight or freeze.

When the amygdala is 'lit up' or activated, it can cause the pre-frontal cortex of the brain to go offline and 'flip its lid' and we then manifest behaviours that are out of character and harmful, or revisit old habits, such as drinking, drug taking, over-eating and under-eating, even if we haven't done it for years. Until the trauma is unlinked and decoded, the amygdala will be activated whenever a similar trigger or memory appears.

Havening is comprised of a series of techniques:

Firstly, activate the traumatic event and measure it on a SUDS (subjective unit of distress) scale of zero to 10, zero being no emotional link to the memory and 10 being a very high emotional link.

Apply the Havening touch, with the client's permission, on the face, shoulders to elbows and hands; this releases delta waves in the brain which are part of your deep sleep and healing state. 'Havening' is from the verb of Haven, which means a safe place; the idea is we put the client in a safe place so they can unlink the negative memory from the amygdala.

The client then counts footsteps in a place of safety, such as a beach or park. They then move their eyes laterally to the right and left and finally hum out loud two verses of a nursery rhyme.

These three distraction techniques enable the client to interfere with the memory whilst being in a healing state. We do repeated rounds of this until we have the SUDS number down to zero or one. Often, the delinking of the traumatic memory from the amygdala can be done in one or two sessions, but every case is different.

There are four components to the perfect storm of trauma, which is referred to as EMLI:

Event—An event that has caused trauma. It can be first, second or third person so we may have experienced it, watched it or read about it or seen it on the news.

Meaning—The meaning that it has for us, which is sometimes difficult for other people to understand why it encodes traumatically.

Landscape—What is the condition of the landscape of the brain? Is it resilient or vulnerable? This will be determined by the person's emotional health and can be affected by their socio-economic situation, their childhood, their current relationship situation and their health.

Inescapability—This is the feeling that you can't leave. You get stuck in the trauma and feel that there is no way out.

Chapter 4

The best way to demonstrate this is to use a client story as an example. Joe (not his real name) a 28-year-old professional, came to see me about his anxiety. He wasn't able to get out of bed in the morning and had lost his job as a result. Through a comprehensive intake questionnaire and session questions, I quickly found out that his mother had committed suicide when he was 10 years old and he had then gone to live with his grandmother and uncle, who both died when he was 16 in a house fire. His trauma was very profound and he bounced from one relative to another until he got married at 25. When I met him, he had layers of trauma that caused him to live in the past and keep replaying the events. This led to anxiety, a bad back and obesity.

1.   *The Event was the trauma of mother's suicide and his grandmother's and uncle's untimely deaths.*

2.   *The Meaning was that he was now alone and felt abandoned, scared and lost.*

3.   *The Landscape of his brain during these traumatic events was definitely vulnerable. His parents were divorced and his father had started a new family with another partner before his mother's death.*

4.   *The Inescapability was profound. He couldn't go back home; his mother would never come back and he was only 10 so couldn't live on his own.*

When I met Joe, I knew exactly what to do to help:

Firstly, I did an 'archeological dig' to find out what the encoding traumas were. This can also be content free if the client finds it too painful to talk about, as I have said.

I then, with his permission, Havened him to delink and down-regulate the traumas from the amygdala.

Finally, I worked with him over several weeks with the three pillars of Havening, which are healing, empowerment and growth. I'm delighted to say that he made a very good recovery and went back to university to finish his degree so that he could get a better job, which he did.

I then taught him how to self-Haven with affirmations to support the healing process. You need no equipment, no complicated algorithms... just your hands.

This is what facilitated Havening looks like in session:

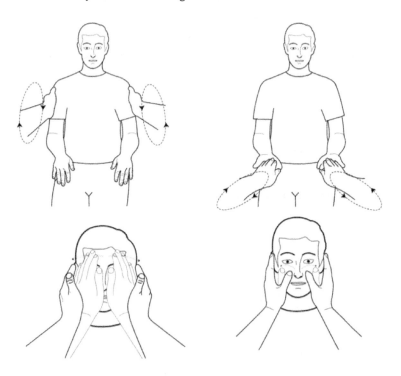

Images ©MicheleParadise

Figure 2: The Havening touches to the arms, hands and face to induce delta brain waves

Joe now knew how to self-Haven so he could 'interfere' and down-regulate any future negative or traumatic events and create a resilient brain landscape. So, in the future, when Joe may feel vulnerable and ungrounded, he can self-Haven with affirmational Havening by saying

positive affirmations whilst Havening. To do this yourself, follow the diagrams above and give self-Havening a go whilst saying something positive like 'I choose to feel safe'. You will quickly notice the feeling of being more grounded and safer.

Hypnotherapy

Largely owing to the way hypnosis is described and presented by the media, there is a great deal of myth and misconception surrounding it. For a large majority, the word 'hypnosis' conjures up visions of magician-type performers persuading unwitting volunteers that they are a chicken/can fly/have an otter in their trousers. We are led to believe that hypnosis involves the total surrender of the will to another person, who is then free to manipulate their hypnotised subject in any way they please. In reality, hypnosis is simply a deep (and very pleasant) state of relaxation. It can be compared to when we awake on a Saturday or Sunday morning and have nothing to leap out of bed for; we tend simply to lie still and enjoy the sensation of being somewhere between sleep and total alertness. We are still able to jump to attention in the event of an emergency, and we are aware of the thoughts that drift in and out of our minds. It is this state which hypnosis exactly replicates.

Dionne Curtis, hypnotherapist, NLP practitioner, TFT practitioner, Psy-TaP practitioner and volunteer hypnotherapist for the MacMillan Cancer Centre, East Surrey Hospital, explains what hypnotherapy is and how it can help with anxiety:

> It may be a surprise to know that hypnosis has been used for many years, in ancient Egypt there were 'Sleep Temples' where people would go to spend a few days in meditation; hypnosis was used by James Esdaile in the mid 1840s at a British medical facility in India during major operations where he reduced the mortality rate from 50% to just 5% – pretty impressive. However, when chloroform was introduced in 1847 it brought the use of hypnosis as anaesthesia to an end.

My introduction to hypnosis came through an NLP course which I took after being diagnosed with panic attacks brought on by stress. I was a director at an international exhibition company, a mother of two young daughters and going through a divorce. Something had to give and apparently that was me – I remember feeling terrified that something was seriously wrong with me and that I was going to leave my girls motherless. I had every test that I could and everything came back normal – my doctor broke the news that what I was experiencing was a panic attack. I found it hard to believe as things like this did not happen to people like me. I was strong and had thrived on the stress of the job; whilst everyone else was getting anxious I was always the calm one finding the solutions. I was offered antidepressants and various other medication, but I have never been good at taking pills – so I decided to learn more about this and find ways to combat it naturally.

It was during my NLP course that I discovered only 10 to 20% of what we do is done consciously – which leaves 80 to 90% which is done subconsciously. I knew then that I wanted to work with the subconscious. I wanted to use that 80 to 90% to change the way I was thinking and therefore change the way I was feeling. I was not prepared for the power and effectiveness of the hypnosis section of the course and could not understand why more people were not using it. This was where my fascination with hypnosis and my love of its use with my clients began.

What has all this got to do with anxiety? Hypnosis forms part of a varied toolbox that I use to treat all forms of anxiety from phobias to panic attacks – untreated anxiety can lead to other mental health problems. I treated a teenager for panic attacks which had developed around taking exams. They had had a bad experience during one exam and began to feel anxious each time they had to sit any kind of test. Each time they faced the situation, the anxiety became worse and quickly escalated to full-blown panic attacks. We needed to go back to what triggered the flight or fight response and change the way that they thought about taking tests – if you change the way you think you change the way you feel.

Here's how they describe what happened during our session:

The reason I went to see Dionne was for my exam anxiety. Before my session I couldn't take a test or an exam without panicking or crying. It started to get close to my end of year exams again and I was getting stressed and panicky. I knew it would start to interfere with my exams and that I had to do something about it; this is when I went to see Dionne. She went through some techniques on how to cope with getting anxious and she also took me back to the root of my anxiety. Ever since then I have been able to take tests and exams with no problem. A couple of times when I got a bit anxious, I just used the exercises Dionne went through with me and I was fine again.

I now have four types of therapy I can offer and use a mixture of all of them, depending on what the client is presenting and what works best for them and their anxiety – one size does not fit all. You never know when anxiety is going to get to you; having different tools that you can use to combat your anxiety as soon as it starts means you never get to the stage where it's controlling you. I have been panic-attack free for over 10 years. Life has not always been easy, however; I am now fully equipped with all the natural, drug-free tools I need to ensure that any anxiety does not escalate.

Bridgette, says of how hypnosis has helped her with her anxiety:

I had a course of sessions of hypnotherapy, and found that it really helped to ease my feelings of anxiety. Whilst it didn't take it away altogether, I feel I have found more peace within myself.

Psychosensory techniques and principles (Psy-TaP)

Kevin Laye, Harley Street-based therapy practitioner, and founder of Psy-TaP, whose current work is endorsed and supported by Paul McKenna, explains to us all about Psy-TaP and how it can treat anxiety successfully:

> Anxiety is a thin stream of fear trickling through the mind. If encouraged, it cuts a channel into which all other thoughts are drained.

— Arthur Somers Roche

Anxiety is often defined as a feeling of worry, nervousness, or unease about something with an uncertain outcome. The key words there are 'worry' and 'uncertain'. One of my statements of worry is, it is like praying for something you don't want... and when people say they are uncertain, ask... 'How certain are you of your uncertainty?' These are little pattern breaks in the rumination cycle and can disarm anxiety quite quickly if timed right.

Anxiety wears many hats, from all-out panic attacks to rumination, to general anxiety disorder (GAD) to social anxiety (SA), and so on. It is also a bit of chameleon and links easily with other mental health issues, like stress, fear, worry and catastrophising, often on problems that only exist in the mind and the imagination.

Interestingly, over the years there has been very little deep research into anxiety from a neurological standpoint, as it is often masked by other things. Treatments range from SSRI-type prescribed medications to mental health interventions like CBT. The latter two examples, however, only manage the symptoms and do not 'fix' the issue.

In my Psy-TaP system we have several rapid, solution- and control-based treatments. The first one literally takes 'one second' to apply. If you feel like you are anxious or about to have a panic attack, take one hand and grip firmly but not too tightly, the index finger of the other hand. If there is fear involved, then squeeze the thumb and index fingers together. If it is more of a 'slow burn' rumination-based anxiety, then squeeze the thumb. All of these are instant one-second interrupts and in most people, most of the time, 'STOP' the issue in its tracks. This empowers you to have control over anxiety as opposed to it controlling you. See the chart below for the fingers to squeeze.

Figure 3: The fingers to squeeze in Psy-TaP

This looks similar to the Japanese Jin Shin Jyutsu system, and there are many overlaps; however, based on our research and modelling, this is the Psy-TaP take on it.

Stress and anxiety are close cousins and often operate interdependently and collaboratively with each other. In Psy-TaP we posit that stress is primarily one thing and that is an elevation of cortisol. Simply put, no cortisol elevation will equal no stress, and at the same time no anxiety either.

Stress, according to the WHO [World Health Organization], will by 2020 be one of the, if not the, biggest, contributors to human morbidity and mortality. Scary prediction.

Now not all stress is bad stress. We have 'Eustress' and that is the thing that gets things done and rises to a peak point of optimum efficiency. It is, however, when we push past this peak that we run into 'Distress', which is damaging to us.

So, what does bad stress do to us?

At a cognitive level, it affects memory, our ability to judge and our concentration to create 'brain fog', indecision and self-doubt (I am certain of the last one).

At an emotional level, it causes or contributes to overwhelm, panic, anxiety, catastrophisation, depression and low mood, fatalistic thinking, cynicism, frustration and anger.

At a physical level, it causes high blood pressure, chest pains, rapid pulse, skin disorders, pain (emotional and physical), depressed immune system leading to illness, coughs and colds etc.

Stress causes inflammation, and most illness has a starting point of inflammation.

At a behavioural level, it causes sleeping too little or too much, feeling demotivated, loss of humour, moving into isolation, self-medication with addictions, food, caffeine, alcohol, smoking, recreational and hard drugs, prescribed drugs and their side-effects.

None of the above is good for you... agreed?

However, rather than focus, as so many do, on the problem, I'd like to offer you a solution to stress and how to choose, if you decide to, to never have to be inappropriately stressed again. Up for it? Do the exercise shown below. That's it, simple.

Use the Lemniscate pattern on the forehead shown in Figure 4 for a count of 20-30 seconds to stimulate your 'third eye'. By stimulating the 'third eye' point we are activating both the pituitary gland and the pineal gland, which will result in oxytocin being released. Oxytocin is 'the' antidote to 'cortisol', the stress chemical, and cancels it out immediately. This is one of the most powerful techniques I have discovered to maintaining a stress-free life. The technique is simple and as such, both we and our clients have no excuse not to apply it. Simple gets done...

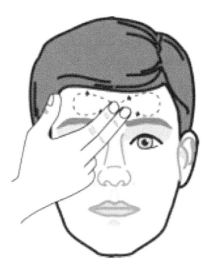

Figure 4: Points on the forehead to tap to stimulate our 'third eye'

This exercise will be the first element of our forthcoming App, designed to handle many areas of mental health issues.

This takes between 20 and 30 seconds; so, if you had to do it 20 times a day, it is 10 minutes of your day to not have stress in your life. This combined with the one-second finger interventions means, we believe, you can have control over your emotions as opposed to being controlled by them. Fast and simple.

Self-help

Senior therapist Sally Baker shares some of her own top tips on changing the way you think, which have been adapted from her own book *The Getting of Resilience from the inside out,* soon to be published by Hammersmith Health Books.

An unhelpful thinking style is when you focus on the negatives in any given situation and ignore the positives. This way of thinking can cause significant increases in your anxiety levels.

Imagine having a seed in the palm of your hand. When you water the seed, it begins to sprout and from that initial green shoot rapidly grows a powerful and all-enveloping vine.

The seed represents a negative thought and the water you give it represents the attention you pay it which reinforces that negative thought.

Very soon the negative thought has grown so much that, just like a tangled vine, from the seed it surrounds you filling all the available space from floor to ceiling and wall to wall.

Negative thoughts allowed to develop in this way quickly dominate until they become all you are capable of thinking about.

Pause and breathe

When you realise that you are focusing on a negative thought and allowing it to grow out of all proportion, it is important to pause and take a breath or two. This helps you to gain a more balanced perspective and to keep your anxiety in check.

When you are caught up in negative thinking it is very common for your breathing to become shallower. This happens without people realising.

An effective way to change your thinking is to change the way you are breathing. To do this you need to assess your breathing. You can do this by taking three gentle in- and out-breaths. While you do this, begin to gain an awareness of the depth of your of breathing on a scale of zero to 10. A zero score means no breath in your lungs and a score of 10 signifies you are breathing deeply and freely. Just take an intuitive guess.

You may be surprised to find your breathing is below a number five, so about half capacity. It is very difficult to feel calm when your breathing is suppressed.

To increase the depth of your breathing you can tap with a soft fist around your collarbone and focus on breathing more deeply for a few moments. The tapping around your collarbone is an energy therapy technique that can help you feel more grounded and secure.

Reaching to touch their collarbone is a natural response for many people when they feel shocked, for instance by hearing bad news. It's an instinctive, self-comforting reaction. Tapping around the collarbone can be used to reduce anxious thinking so that you can feel calmer and more stable instead.

Thinking outside of the box

What if you are experiencing a situation that feels legitimately anxiety-provoking? This is when something has happened that has repercussions which are profound and far-reaching in your life. It could be a health crisis, or losing your job, or the breakdown of a valued relationship – something that feels momentous whichever way you look at it.

It is at times like this that it is easy to fall into ruminative, circular thinking; so it is crucial to be able to gain some perspective instead of spiraling further and further down into negativity and increased anxiety.

In your mind, create a courtroom scenario to explore your anxious conclusion. Just like a barrister, put the evidence for and against your thoughts and ask yourself 'what can I learn from being in this situation?'

It can be helpful to pretend it is even someone else who is going through this challenging experience and not you. Ask yourself how would you advise a person in this situation? Although you may have little compassion and empathy for yourself, you may find you can be kinder and more rational on behalf of someone else. Role-playing can help you look at a situation from a different angle and you may find you are feeling more resourceful and less anxious when you remove yourself from the equation.

Don't forget to be vigilant and interrupt yourself if you begin to get caught up in the suffocating tangle of possible consequences and outcomes. It is useful instead to focus on what you, or indeed another person, could learn from this negative situation. You can then use your insights to feel more resilient and help overcome your anxiety.

Finally, if you are struggling to manage your anxious thoughts you can ask someone you trust for their opinion. Use their perspective on the situation you are in to help give you more clarity and hopefully they can show you that the situation is more nuanced than you initially thought.

Apply the century rule

To interrupt entrenched, anxious ways of thinking sometimes requires shock tactics. So practised are some anxious thinkers that they immediately go into panic mode in the face of adversity and feel as though the end of the world is nigh.

If this sounds familiar to you and describes how you often react, I encourage you to impose the century rule. Ask yourself will whatever you are having anxious thoughts about matter in 100 years? How about in 25 years? Or five years? Or even a week from now?

This reality check can be a powerful intervention to give yourself some much-needed perspective. The truth is that little tends to really matter beyond the moment we are in and you can run the century rule and let go of many, if not all, of the anxious thoughts you are experiencing.

Self-help and support groups

Meeting with others and realising that other people are dealing with the symptoms of an anxiety disorder can be really helpful for some people. Listening to others' experiences can be very therapeutic. Helping people realise they are not alone in their situation whilst, at the same time, talking and sharing feelings and experiences in a safe, non-judgemental setting can also be a valuable release that may actually help ease the isolating effects of the illness.

Self-help groups are not just for talking about feelings; they can also be an opportunity to discuss helpful strategies and therapies, to share knowledge and beneficial experiences with each other. Furthermore, being able to offer help and support to others can be therapeutic in itself, strengthening feelings of self-worth which can, at times, be damaged through anxiety.

Like other therapies, finding the right self-help group, which makes the sufferer feel at ease enough to participate, may take time. Even in the right group, it may take weeks or months of listening and observing before the person feels able to actively participate and speak up. All this is absolutely natural, and the experience should not be rushed.

Families and loved ones of those with an anxiety disorder may feel upset that the person they care for would seemingly prefer to talk to strangers than those closest to them. Understandable as these feelings may be, it can also be very natural to find it easier to talk to someone outside the immediate circle. Instead of feeling threatened, try to support your friend or relative in finding whatever therapy is helpful for them. Continue to make it clear that you are always there for them whenever they want to talk, but also show that you support them in seeking help from others who have their own experience of mental illness.

Self-help groups can also benefit carers and be a safe place to discuss your thoughts and feelings with people in similar situations.

Jayne, whose daughter suffers from OCD, shares her positive experience of a support group near her:

I have become part of an OCD support group and have found that a blessing. I don't feel so isolated and alone now and there is always someone there to listen and offer support and guidance. Everyone is so friendly and welcoming, and they added me to their WhatsApp group which has been great. They are always posting words of support and advice and really seem to care about my daughter and her recovery. It's a relief when you find people who truly 'get it'.

To find self-help groups, talk to your GP or local health authority. Specialist organisations such as SANE, Mind, Anxiety UK and No Panic (see Resources, page 314) can also signpost people to helpful groups, both in-person gatherings and online support. Organisations like this may also have an online community where people can find others going through similar experiences.

To conclude

There is no 'correct' or 'right' path to recovery. You may find either a single treatment or a combination works best. The important thing to remember is that there is, without doubt, a form of treatment available that can help you or your loved one overcome their anxiety disorder. If one treatment is not working, do not be afraid to change tack and try another. It is quite common for sufferers to try various therapies before they find the right treatment for them as an individual.

Your loved one showing a willingness to get better is a huge step forward, and sometimes it can be frustrating and challenging for carers and sufferers when there is a delay in finding an effective treatment. I hope this chapter has assisted you in making sense of some of the terms, buzz-words and theories and that it will help you in making an informed decision about what to try next, always remembering that recovery is possible.

At the back of this book you will find a list of resources and practitioners, all of whom I have personally worked with, researched and/or spoken to at great length about the treatments and methods they offer. I do urge you to get going as soon as possible before the anxiety disorder becomes completely habitual and, if you can afford to, start a treatment that seems right in your case, rather than waiting for state-funded help as this can, sometimes, take a long time to be available.

Chapter 5

Anxiety and well-being

We live in an age where what was once considered alternative treatment is now becoming much more mainstream and widely accepted. I would encourage you, the reader, to be open minded towards all the potential avenues of therapy, both conventional and so-called 'alternative', that are available to you. The methods listed below are not mutually exclusive to conventional treatment but can work successfully hand in hand with it, aiding healing for the sufferer and in some cases the carer as well. It goes without saying that basic self-care is of paramount importance, including the right amount of sleep, exercise and good nutrition. This has been borne out of my own experience both personally and professionally. It is also advisable to talk to your GP before undertaking any kind of therapy.

I have asked specialists within each field, all of whom I know personally, to help give you an understanding of how their individual discipline can help mental well-being for both sufferers and carers alike.

- Exercise
- Sleep
- Nutrition
- Herbal remedies
- Mindfulness
- Self-compassion

- Meditation
- Yoga
- Reflexology
- Acupuncture
- Massage ·
- Applied relaxation
- Essential oils
- Drama
- Music and art
- Apps
- Pet therapy
- Performance coaching for carers.

Exercise

'Exercise is good for the mind, body and spirit.'

Those who exercise regularly tend to do so because it gives them a greater sense of well-being. They tend to have more energy throughout the day, sleep better at night and have sharper memories, and most tend to feel more relaxed and positive about themselves and their lives.

Samantha adds:

> Training has helped me build a strong, fit, healthy body that I am mentally in love with and physically know it is the foundation that will help me conquer the world!

Activity and exercise are especially important for people living with mental ill health, not least because people who have a mental illness can often have a higher risk of physical illness. Similarly, people with a physical illness can be at a higher risk of developing a mental illness, such as anxiety, depression, OCD and/or disordered eating. The body and mind exist in balance, directly impacting one another.

Tan, an experienced personal trainer, adds:

There is such a strong link between physical activity and mental well-being that it simply cannot be ignored. Taking part in regular exercise reduces anxiety and depression whilst improving self-esteem, confidence and overall quality of life. Whether it's going to the gym or being outdoors, with friends and family or a personal trainer, exercise can play a vital role in maintaining health in both body and mind.

Scientists[25] have discovered that exercise causes the brain to release chemicals (including serotonin) which can make you feel good; the most commonly prescribed antidepressants (SSRIs) also work on increasing the serotonin levels within the brain. Therefore, exercise can give you a similar psychological boost but without the side-effects of medication! Regular exercise can promote all kinds of changes in the brain, including neural growth, reduced inflammation, and new activity patterns that aid feelings of calm and well-being. It can also release endorphins, which are powerful chemicals in the brain that leave the person feeling energised and positive. Exercise can also serve as a distraction, allowing the person to find some 'time out' to enable them to break out of the cycle of their negative and distracting thoughts that feed their mental illness.

Susanne says of how exercise helps her:

> Exercise also helped take the edge off of the anxiety. It gave me something to look forward to and pour myself into. It helped take the focus off of the anxiety in the moment.

Mental and emotional benefits of exercise

- **More energy**: Increasing the heart rate several times a week will help the person to have more energy.
- **Stronger resilience**: When faced with mental or emotional challenges in life, exercise can help a person cope in

a healthy way, instead of turning to alcohol, drugs or other negative behaviours that will ultimately make the person feel worse. Regular exercise can also help boost the immune system and reduce the impact of stress.

- **Sleep better**: Even small amounts of exercise at regular intervals can help to regulate sleep patterns.
- **Self-esteem**: Regular activity can improve the mind, body and soul. When it becomes part of everyday life, it can foster a sense of self-worth and make the person feel strong and powerful. They will feel better about how they look and, by meeting personal goals, will gain a sense of achievement.
- **Sharper memory and thinking**: The same endorphins that make a person feel positive can also help with concentration and improve the sharpness of a person's mentality for the tasks at hand. Exercise also stimulates the growth of new brain cells and helps prevent age-related decline.

Jay Hurley, a highly experienced personal trainer, says:

When suffering from anxiety, it can be very easy to be caught in the vicious circle of inactivity. Sometimes the thought of starting an exercise routine can be daunting but it's important to go through the process slowly and comfortably because physical activity or an exercise programme can be hugely beneficial to the sufferer and can help ease the symptoms of anxiety and low mood. It's also important to note that there is a difference between physical activity and an exercise programme. Physical activity is anything you can do that would slightly increase your heart rate. This can be going for a walk/walking a dog, going for a slight jog or even some gardening. An exercise programme can be used in a commercial gym. This can involve a variety of cardiovascular machines, resistance machines and/or strength equipment. There are three main benefits to physical activity or exercise:

Endorphin release

Better self-confidence

Social interaction

When we exercise or do physical activities, a number of chemical responses happen within our body. A range of 'feel good' endorphins are released also known as the 'runner's high'. In bouts of anxiety, this can be a successful and quick way to boost your mood.

Exercise is a great way to improve self-confidence and can lead to an overall sense of achievement. Improving yourself, feeling healthier and stronger, and boosting your energy levels through exercise produces a side-effect of improved self-confidence. It's important to find an activity that you enjoy as you're more likely to stick to it. This could be an exercise class, dance class, gym programme or a sport. Social interaction is a vital tool in the recovery process of anxiety; exercise or physical activity is a great way to involve social interaction into your lifestyle. Suggesting a walk with a friend is a good way to start, or even taking part in a group exercise class together. Gym-based exercise and group classes are also a great way to meet new people and develop a new support system which in turn can also lead to improvements in emotional well-being.

A person does not need to devote hours and hours of their day to exercise, or train at a gym, sweat buckets, or run mile after mile after mile to reap the benefits of it. They can obtain all the physical and mental health benefits of exercise with 30 minutes of moderate exercise five times a week, or even two 15-minute exercise sessions.

Someone suffering from an anxiety disorder or any other mental health issue may find it difficult to take the first step into exercise. Here are some common barriers and some ways in which they can be overcome:

- **Feeling overwhelmed**: When a person feels stressed, anxious or low, the thought of adding another obligation can seem overwhelming and impossible. It is important to remember that physical activity helps us to do and cope with things better. So, try to think of exercise as a priority and find ways to fit small amounts into everyday life.

- **Feeling exhausted**: When a person is tired and lethargic, it can feel like working out will make things worse and is all too much effort. However, it is worth remembering that physical activity is a powerful energiser. Studies[26] have shown that regular exercise can dramatically reduce fatigue and increase energy levels. The best place to start is at the beginning – for example, if a person goes for a five-minute walk around the block or up and down the road, with the idea of increasing the time by a minute or two each time. As they start to feel the benefit from it, it will hopefully not be a chore but an enjoyment.

- **Feeling hopeless**: Even if a person is starting at rock bottom they can still work out. Exercise helps people to get into shape. If you have no experience of exercising, start with a low-impact movement a few minutes each day, slowly building it up gently.

- **Feeling bad about yourself**: Most people are their own worst critic. No matter what your weight, age or fitness level, there are many others with the same goals of getting fit who feel the same. Being with people who are all in the same boat helps. Perhaps take a class with people of a variety of fitness levels. Accomplishing even the smallest of fitness goals will help a person gain body confidence, which can only lead to them feeling better about themselves.

One of the many people I have had the privilege to meet is the wonderful former boxer Frank Bruno. Over the years his own challenges with bipolar disorder have been well documented, about which Frank has been very vocal and emphasised the importance of ongoing exercise as a contributory factor in the recovery process, and as part of everyday life.

> It was hard to exercise when on heavy medication. However, even a small amount every day, building up the time gradually, for example starting by walking then running or going to the gym, is helpful. You don't have to be a body builder – look at it as part of your essential medication. – Frank Bruno

Having used exercise as part of his own recovery, Frank has gone on to start the Frank Bruno Foundation, which provides structured non-contact boxing sessions aimed at relieving the social, emotional and mental distress that adversely affect the mental health of children, young people and adults.

Dave Davies, manager of Frank Bruno, who himself has suffered from anxiety and has family members and clients who have also suffered from anxiety and depression, shares his need for exercise:

> Exercise is essential to me five days a week, every morning for about an hour; mainly on the treadmill walking; it gets me ready for the day and I lose myself there.

Exercise can be enjoyed in many ways: throwing a frisbee for a dog or with a friend, walking around a shopping centre, cycling to work or simply going for a walk. Activities such as gardening or even doing small improvements in the house can be good ways to start moving around more. As well as helping to become more active, these activities can also leave you with a sense of purpose and accomplishment.

Exercise can also have a beneficial social component. Being part of a team or club can help a person to feel they have a sense of identity and belong to a network of people, united by their passion for a particular activity. Working as a team through sport can help to build self-confidence and self-belief as well, all of which has to be a much healthier way to socialise than via the internet.

Sleep

Sleep plays a vital part in good health and well-being throughout a person's life. Getting enough quality sleep at the right times can help to protect their mental and physical health, quality of life and overall safety. According to the National Sleep Foundation; school-age children (6-13 years) need approximately nine to 11 hours' sleep per night, teens (14-17 years) need approximately eight to 10 and adults (18-64 years) need approximately seven to nine hours.

There is a close relationship between mental health and sleep. Many people who experience mental ill health also experience disturbed sleep patterns or insomnia. Over a long period of time, disturbed sleep can actually lead to a mental health condition or make an existing mental illness worse. With lack of sleep, the person may:

- Experience lowered self-esteem through an inability to cope
- Experience social isolation
- Struggle to deal with everyday life
- Experience low mood
- Experience low energy levels
- Develop depression and/or anxiety
- Experience an inability to carry out usual social activities
- Have feelings of loneliness.

Most importantly, being constantly tired can affect a person's ability to rationalise anxieties and banish irrational thoughts. It can feed into negative thinking patterns which are often associated with anxiety and other mental health issues. This can also work the other way around, with anxiety and over-thinking leading to restlessness at night that can make sleep so much harder to achieve.

Holly says of how lack of sleep affected her mental health negatively:

These thoughts would also affect my sleep when my mental health was at its worse; I would just stare into darkness thinking about what people thought of me and replaying social interactions that were embarrassing and could have gone better. This thought process would eventually push me to become very paranoid, something which I still struggle with today.

The night-time hours can be especially daunting for those with an anxiety disorder. There can be a vulnerability associated with sleeping: a dread of the terrors that sleep may leave them more open to, as well as the fear that slumber will undermine the resolve and single-minded focus that they cultivate during their waking hours.

The sufferer may therefore fight against sleep, facing the next day exhausted and even more vulnerable to the dark and irrational thoughts that fuel the illness. So, the continuous cycle of physical exhaustion and mental distortion serves as a huge hurdle to sustained recovery.

While some experts recommend that an adult should have between seven and nine hours of sleep a night, others say that the quality of sleep is far more important than the quantity. For example, if a person has six hours of high-quality, uninterrupted sleep, they will receive more benefit than having eight hours of restless, interrupted sleep. Sleep is not just time out from people's busy routines; everyone needs sleep to help both their mind and body recover from the stresses of everyday life. Sleep is a healing process, one I cannot champion enough for those suffering from anxiety disorders and, indeed, any other mental illness. Sleep has played a vital part in my daughter Samantha's recovery; as she says:

Although sometimes I found it hard to get to sleep as my head was full up and I could not think straight, I would listen to relaxation music which would help me to drown out the thoughts, making it easier to get to sleep. I found that having slept I would wake up feeling more refreshed. Sometimes if I was able, I would have a nap during the day which I found really helped me to think more clearly too. Without sleep I did not have the energy and headspace to cope with and move past the thoughts. Sleep has been a major part in my recovery.

Samantha's experience makes so much logical sense, but sleep is often a forgotten ingredient in the recovery process from a mental illness. Like many people in the general population, those with anxiety disorders easily fall into poor bedtime routines, checking social media late at night or watching TV as the hours tick by, forming habits that undermine good mental health and lead to physical and mental exhaustion in its place.

Getting a good night's sleep is paramount for both the sufferer and their carers alike. There are things that we can all do to help us achieve this:

- If possible, get into a routine of going to sleep and waking up at the same time, although this is not always realistic for everyone, I know.
- Develop a pre-bed routine, which may include having a bath, reading or listening to relaxation music to get the mind into a relaxed state; this should help one to drift off more easily.
- Do not allow iPads, smart phones, television or electronic games in the bedroom. Some people experience disturbed sleep due to the use of technology in the bedroom and blue light from many devices can enhance wakefulness. Going to bed and then spending time on these devices can stimulate the brain, making it more likely they will wake up in the night and then have trouble getting back to sleep, due to feeling the need to check for messages, social media etc.
- Make sure the bedroom is dark, as quiet as possible, and the temperature is comfortably cool (but not cold).

- Alcohol and caffeine can also disturb sleep, as does rich food eaten late at night, so avoid these.

Dave Davies, manager of Frank Bruno, who has suffered from anxiety and has other family members and clients who have suffered from anxiety and depression, says of how sleep is important to him:

> Sleep is so important to me now and I love my bed more than ever before. When I am awake, I need to either read or put the television on otherwise my mind starts working overtime. I will fall asleep very easily in the cinema. I love a power nap in the afternoon or early evening for 20 minutes to an hour and I feel like a new person. Sadly, this does not happen enough.

The benefits of adopting regular and positive sleep habits can be huge. For those with anxiety, having the energy to do things that they love, to connect with others and build a meaningful life away from the illness are the cornerstones of recovery. However, these foundations are so much harder to build if the person is exhausted.

It is also important to be aware that as the sufferer's mind is so active and full, the sleep they get may not always be 'quality sleep'.

Having seen and experienced at first hand how regular, good-quality sleep has benefited Samantha, giving her the energy and strength she needed to be able to challenge and overcome the negative thoughts in her head, I cannot reiterate enough the power and importance of sleep.

Nutrition

I am sure most of us have heard or been told at some point, 'you are what you eat', but we may ask ourselves, what exactly does that mean? The types of foods and drinks we consume determine the types of nutrients in our system and can determine how well our mind and body are able to function.

Gabriella Kinnear-Nock, registered nutritional therapist, explains below in more detail:

> The role of food and nutrition in relation to anxiety cannot be underestimated. Our bodies need certain nutrients to produce the hormones and neurotransmitters that are involved in the feeling of well-being.
>
> There is also a close connection between the gut and the brain, the so-called gut-brain axis. In our gut there are trillions of bacteria living in a symbiotic relationship with our bodies – we cannot survive without them and they cannot survive without us. The gut and its microbes communicate with our brain every second of the day. They control internal inflammation and produce many beneficial compounds that we need for our physical health as well as our mental health.
>
> Although eating healthily will not cure anxiety, it will most certainly reduce the symptoms and make it easier to handle. Diet may also help reduce some of the physical effects of anxiety, such as muscle tension and a racing heart.
>
> The preferred diet for anxiety is an anti-inflammatory diet, such as the modified Mediterranean diet that is rich in lean meats, fruits and vegetables, wholegrains and healthy fats.

Foods to include

> Lean protein: Most of our neurotransmitters, and some of our hormones, are made out of protein. This means that it is very important to make sure that our diet contains plenty of protein. A basic guideline for daily protein intake is: 1 g of protein per kg of body weight. So, if you weigh 60 kg, you need to eat 60 g of protein each day.
>
> Water: This is often underestimated. The NHS recommends drinking 6-8 glasses of water a day[27] which is around 1.5 litres.
>
> Fresh fruit and vegetables: Not only do these contain an abundance

*of goodness in terms of vitamins and minerals, but they also contain the fibre that feed our microbiome bacteria. The fibre is their food and makes them send 'happy' signals to the brain. However, different bacteria like different types of fibre, so it is important to remember that vari*ety is key. *When you shop for fruit and vegetables, try to add one new type each week. Different colours also count, so think 'eat the rainbow'.*

Healthy fats: *Your brain consists of 60% fat. Adding to this, the cell membrane of* every single cell *in our bodies is made up of fat. These cells and membranes need to be maintained, so it is vital to include healthy fats in your diet, for example:*

> *Oily fish such as salmon, mackerel, sardines, anchovies and herrings*
>
> *Nuts and seeds, especially flax seeds/linseed*
>
> *Olive oil*
>
> *Avocados.*

Magnesium-rich foods: *Magnesium has a role in over 300 different processes in the body, from creating energy to the production of dopamine and serotonin. It is known to naturally relax the body and relieve muscle tension. Sources include:*

> *Green vegetables*
>
> *Nuts, especially almonds, cashew nuts and Brazil nuts*
>
> *Seeds, such as flax, pumpkin and chia seeds*
>
> *Legumes, such as black beans, chickpeas and lentils.*

Eggs: *There are full of choline which is an essential nutrient that has a role in supporting brain health, memory and concentration.*

Vitamin D *supports a healthy brain and neurotransmitter function, especially dopamine. It is hard to get enough vitamin D through food. However, we can produce it ourselves by exposing our skin to sunlight for about 20 minutes each day if we are fair skinned. The foods highest in vitamin D are eggs and dairy.*

Avoid anxiety-trigger foods

In general, it is very important to regulate blood sugar as low blood sugar levels can be an anxiety trigger. Avoid going on crash diets and having prolonged periods without food as this can make anxiety worse.

The most effective starting point is to reduce, or eliminate, anxiety-inducing foods: the most important are sugar, caffeine and alcohol.

Tip 1: Replace regular coffee with decaffeinated coffee or green tea. Green tea contains some caffeine, but more importantly it contains the anxiety-lowering substance l-theanine. Alternatively, choose a calming herbal tea such as chamomile.

Tip 2: If you need a treat, the one to reach for is dark chocolate. Rich in antioxidants, it has even been suggested to have an effect on reducing stress and anxiety. But it has to be real dark chocolate, with at least 70% cocoa content.

Tip 3: Reduce your alcohol intake as this is a major trigger for anxiety. That cheeky glass of wine at the end of the day may feel great, but it will increase your anxiety symptoms in the long run.

Jess, explains how eating a balanced diet helps her anxiety and general mental well-being:

> I know that eating healthy food and maintaining stable blood sugar levels helps to balance hormones and thus emotions. I enjoy cooking and eating healthy wholesome meals so it's easy to do this.

Herbal remedies

There are a range of different herbal remedies that are widely used to help relieve anxiety disorders and other mental health issues. However, all too often the evidence for their use is anecdotal rather than scientific. That is not to say that they do not work, rather that they may not have been thoroughly tested and that the onus is on the person with the anxiety disorder and their support network to find the one that works for them. As always, it is important to talk to a doctor to get their guidance on how to navigate the maze of possible herbal remedies.

St John's wort

St John's wort (*Hypericum perforatum*) is a herbal remedy that has a long history of being used for centuries to help treat mental illness. As with all other types of natural remedies and prescribed medication, you should always consult your GP or other medical professionals prior to taking it. (In Ireland you can only get it on prescription.)

The first question to ask with St John's wort is: 'Does it really work?' Most research surrounding it covers its effectiveness in helping those suffering from depression; however, as we know, depression and anxiety can be very closely linked. Like many herbal remedies it has not been through the same rigorous scientific trials as conventional medicines and thus large-scale proof of its efficacy is hard to come by.

St John's wort is thought to work by increasing the activity of the neurotransmitters (brain chemicals) such as serotonin, dopamine and noradrenaline that are thought to play an important part in regulating our mood, having an overall feel-good effect in the brain. As such, it should be used with caution and care.

St John's wort is not currently recommended by the National Institute for Health and Care Excellence (NICE) so doctors in England and Wales do not normally write prescriptions for it. However, your doctor will be able to give advice on whether it is safe for someone to take or whether there is something else in their lifestyle or health profile that could deter them from doing so. This is particularly important to bear in mind given that St John's wort can also trigger side-effects just like any pre-scription medicine, and can interact negatively with many other medicines.

With such a plethora of St John's wort products available to choose from, it is also important to select one that is best suited to your needs. St John's wort products are licensed by the Medicines and Healthcare Products Regulatory Agency (MHRA) under the Traditional Herbal Medicines Registration scheme. Under this scheme, registration is based on the long-standing use of a plant as a traditional herbal medicine, and is not based on clinical trials. Those thinking of taking St John's wort should look out for the 'THR' mark (Traditional Herbal Registration Scheme) on the packaging to get a licensed product.

Taking St John's wort puts the onus on the sufferer and their family and friends to find the right product at the right dose. For someone experiencing anxiety, monitoring the dosage and watching for side-effects can feel like another hurdle to get over. Support from family and friends can be of invaluable help with this.

Jenni, who suffers from anxiety, shares her experience:

> I found the initial week of taking St John's wort really helpful; even if it was a placebo, knowing that I was acknowledging my feelings and doing something about it really helped.

Sammy, who suffers from anxiety and depression, shares her positive experience:

> I couldn't get myself out of the flat for days. I managed an appointment with the GP who suggested I give St John's wort capsules a try. It took away my feeling of chronic fatigue, and gave me the little push to be able to get out and about again, and I slept better. It was the first step in getting involved in life again; I soon after joined the Royal Naval Reserves.

Cannabidiol (CBD) oil

Could CBD oil be a secret weapon in someone's armoury against anxiety? Truthfully, we do not know. What I am aware of is that had I been writing this book five years ago, I might not have even mentioned it. However, such has been the gathering momentum around CBD oil, and in particular its potential impact on mental illness, that it would be remiss not to cover it.

Like many alternative treatments, the problem with CBD oil is that only small-scale studies have been completed on its efficacity and, like other remedies such as St John's wort or valerian, it is often down to the consumer getting a good-quality product in a form that is effective for them that can make all the difference.

So, what do we know? We know that anecdotally many people report that taking CBD oil can have a positive effect on their anxiety. We know that CBD is not psychoactive so, unlike tetrahydrocannabinol (THC), the other most well-known compound in cannabis, you would not get the same 'high' associated with it. The World Health Organization (WHO)[28] claims that CBD oil is *'generally well tolerated with a good safety profile'*.

What we do not have is a raft of research showing its effects. Nor, at the time of writing, do the majority of the medical community actively endorse its use. This uncertainty means that those seeking help with anxiety are left somewhat in the dark, having to find their way around through trial, error and information (or misinformation) on the internet.

Even the rules around CBD are unclear. Although CBD products containing less than 0.2% THC are now legal in the UK (other countries will have their own different laws) as long as they are sold as a health or food supplement, the Food Standards Agency has now ruled that products containing CBD oil must be registered by 2021 or they risk being pulled from the shelves. So, the picture may very well be changing.

Even though the medical community may not generally

endorse CBD products, I would still advise that you talk to a doctor before trying them, not least because CBD may affect other medications. It is also not recommended for those who are pregnant or breastfeeding.

Matty gives us his thoughts on CBD oil and how it has helped him with his anxiety and other mental health issues:

I use Apexxx CBD oil nearly every day. It doesn't take the anxiety and depression away although it's like it's been restricted, almost like a bird with its wings clipped; the clarity and focus after CBD oil helps you really work through your own personal minefields to do with anxious thoughts and, for me, suicidal plans. It's not for everyone but it helps me hugely.

Valerian

Valerian has long been used to help people experiencing sleep issues, particularly when this is linked to anxiety. Like many herbal remedies, the scientific evidence for its efficacy is lacking; however, anecdotally, many people report that it does help them.

Valerian is thought to act on gamma-amino-butyric acid (GABA), a chemical in the brain linked to anxiety. It is thought to help calm the brain and body rather than inducing sleep directly, allowing sleep to occur naturally.

Just because it is a natural remedy, it does not mean it is completely harmless or without side-effects. It is not suitable for children or women who are pregnant or breast-feeding, nor should it be combined with sleeping pills or tranquilisers.

Its relaxing properties may slow down reactions and it should not be taken before someone takes to the wheel or in other circumstances where they need to be alert. It may also react adversely with some mainstream drugs, so – as with all herbal remedies – a GP must be consulted so they can assess whether it is suitable for an individual, taking into account their lifestyle and medical history.

Passionflower

Passionflower is thought to have some calming and sedative actions and there are some small clinical trials that suggest it can be effective in reducing the symptoms of anxiety. However, like most herbal remedies, large-scale scientific evidence is not available. It should be taken with some care and caution and not be used as an alternative to medical treatment unless advised by a doctor.

Jenni, who suffers from anxiety, shares her experience of using an over-the-counter herbal remedy:

> I used the Rescue Remedy spray when I felt my anxiety heightening and when approaching a panic attack, which again seemed to reduce it and I think that's due to taking control back. I had my first panic attack the first week of lockdown (during the Covid19 pandemic in 2020) which is what prompted me to purchase herbal remedies online as I was petrified of it happening again.

Mindfulness

Life, at times can be hectic. Therefore, it can be easy to rush through each day without stopping to appreciate the here and now. Paying more attention to the present moment – to your own thoughts and feelings, and to the world around you – can improve your mental well-being. Some may call this awareness 'mindfulness'.

Catherine Kell, mindfulness and self-compassion teacher and founder of the Self-Compassion Community, explains what mindfulness is:

> *There are many ways of describing what mindfulness is but put simply it is attending to our present moment experience without judgement. Noticing things just as they are, without pushing them away. When we are mindful, we are observing our experience in an attentive way, without*

resistance and this gives us the space to kindly respond to our experience rather than reacting to it in habitual ways. Mindfulness can be very helpful when we feel tangled up with our problems and challenges because it gives us a sense of space between ourselves and our experience.

Many people associate mindfulness with the more 'formal' practice of sitting in mindfulness meditation, which is a very helpful skill to learn. We can also intentionally focus our attention moment to moment outside of sitting meditation, which clients of mine have found particularly helpful when managing their anxiety. In mindfulness courses this is referred to as 'informal' practice. When we are suffering from anxiety, moments of informal mindfulness activity throughout the day can help us ground and anchor ourselves, and restore feelings of calm and safety.

For example, if we are comfortable focusing on our breathing, we can bring the spotlight of our attention to our breath as it flows in and out of our body and begin to mindfully focus on breathing out for longer than we breathe in. This longer out breath will activate a natural bodily response which lowers emotional arousal and can help dissipate anxiety and stress.

Some people prefer to ground and anchor themselves in the body when they feel anxious. We can do this by moving the spotlight of our mindful attention to feeling our feet on the floor, or feeling our body seated on a chair. We can mindfully notice and explore the sensations there. Or we can focus on some mindful movement – either gentle intentional stretching, or taking a mindful walk.

If focusing on breathing feels uncomfortable or unsafe, we can attentively focus on sights and sounds around us. Your teacher will assist you with finding what works best for you and provide more examples. In all cases, the mindfulness activity isn't about fixing, rather it involves noticing when our mind has wandered (and perhaps re-engaged with anxious thoughts, for example) and returning the spotlight of our attention back to our chosen practice. We don't have to strive for anything other than that.

Practising mindfulness regularly is beneficial when we are struggling with anxiety – even in the moments when we are not feeling particularly anxious! This is because our practice is like flexing the mindfulness muscle. And the more we flex that muscle, the more readily and confidently we can access our mindfulness toolkit when our anxiety flares. I see mindfulness as a way of enhancing our resources to take supportive action for ourselves, which is both reassuring and empowering.

Tom talks about how being mindful helps with his mental well-being:

> Hobbies and 'mindful' tasks I've found helpful include ballroom dancing or climbing or playing video games. Those tasks occupy enough of my mind to keep my thoughts on the 'here and now'.

Self-compassion

Catherine Kell, mindfulness and self-compassion teacher and founder of the Self-Compassion Community, also explains the importance of being kind to ourselves when suffering from anxiety:

Self-compassion is about befriending ourselves – taking kind and supportive action for ourselves when we are suffering. Kristin Neff PhD., a leading voice in the field of self-compassion, describes it as:

> *recognising our suffering (mindfulness, which helps us notice our experience as it is happening)*
>
> *recognising that we are not alone (feeling connected to our shared human experience, our common humanity)*
>
> *offering ourselves support and understanding (self-kindness) and taking action to alleviate our pain and suffering.*

Many of my clients who suffer from anxiety have found they have started to feel dislike for themselves, or they have developed a harsh inner voice or negative self-talk. They can become trapped in a cycle of trying to berate and criticise themselves out of their anxious suffering, and unwittingly inflict more harm on themselves in the process. I've seen that self-compassion is a powerful resource for them because it helps them develop a healthier relationship with themselves and see their perceived imperfections or flaws in a new, much kinder light.

This is because self-compassion helps us kindly turn towards ourselves rather than away from ourselves. We learn to treat ourselves the same way that we would treat a dear friend in the same situation.

Studies show that cultivating self-compassion and learning to relate to ourselves with more kindness and understanding can be transformative, and rapidly expanding research demonstrates that self-compassion helps enhance emotional well-being, build inner strength and resilience, and increase happiness and life-satisfaction. Importantly, research also shows that cultivating self-compassion helps people feel less anxious, depressed and stressed.

Meditation

Meditation is the practice of deep thinking or of focusing one's mind for a period of time. While there are many forms of meditation, the ultimate goal remains the same – achieving a sense of relaxation and inner peace, and gaining awareness of feelings so that they can be managed more effectively.

Catherine Kell, mindfulness and self-compassion teacher and founder of the Self-Compassion Community, explains the practice of meditation and how it can help mental well-being:

It's hard to write about meditation without also mentioning mindfulness as the two terms have become so interchangeable nowadays. Meditation and mindfulness share similarities and overlaps but there are differences. Mindfulness is really a capacity of mind and can be done formally through 'directed focus' meditation (mindfulness meditation) as well as infor-

mally, or on-the-spot, which you can do anytime, anywhere. For example, we can mindfully take a walk, or mindfully get dressed, or mindfully pet our dog. So, we can apply or infuse the mindset of mindfulness to our lives in these informal ways as well as sitting in more formal mindfulness meditation. In this sense, meditation is a path to mindfulness.

Meditation in itself is more of an umbrella term for an intentional activity or formal exercise where we set aside an amount of time in which we focus inward to increase a sense of stillness or calmness. There are many different types of meditation which come from different cultures and traditions, including contemplation, visualisation, breath-awareness meditation, guided meditation, unguided (silent) meditation, resting awareness meditation, loving-kindness meditation, mantra-based meditation or reflective meditation, and then many meditation types that combine elements of others. We can meditate to cultivate gratitude, compassion or wisdom, or to get calmer, relax and cultivate a more peaceful state. Research shows that meditation can help us stop over-attending to our thoughts and feelings, and help us find mental quiet, thus helping to reduce feelings of anxiety and assisting us in cultivating a deeper sense of inner peace.

The definitions are not as important to most people as finding what works best for them. Something that works well for someone else may not work in the same way for you and there is no 'best' approach. Mindfulness meditation and other forms of meditation have all shown to be beneficial ways of easing anxiety and are really powerful parts of our well-being toolkit. You can access many different styles and types of meditations in online courses and via apps, many of which are free.

Susanne, who suffers from social anxiety disorder, shares her positive experience of using meditation:

I consider meditation to be the doorway to the present moment. Some people refer to this as mindfulness. Meditation helps me step out of my conditioned mind and directs my attention to what is happening right now. It helps me become still or quieten my compulsive thoughts. During those moments (when I'm still), I'm less self-conscious, less judgemental, less reactive and definitely less anxious. One exercise that helps me achieve this state of mind is to focus intently on my breathing for as long as I can.

Yoga

Yoga is fast becoming a part of many people's everyday routine, with many feeling the benefits of it both mentally and physically. Speaking from experience, both the carer and the sufferer can potentially benefit greatly.

Yoga specialist, Debbie Pennington, tells us more about yoga and how it can benefit anxiety disorder sufferers and general mental health and well-being:

There are many yoga classes to choose from, with titles you may not be familiar with. Most are based on Hatha Yoga, the yoga of Asana (postures) and most start with stillness, move on to gentle movements and end with a lying relaxation. Yoga is ideally practised barefoot so that you can experience a greater connection to the earth below, and so that you don't slip and slide on a yoga mat that you can buy or probably borrow from the teacher. Based in East Sussex, I teach Scaravelli-inspired yoga which is freer and not as regimented as some other types. We work with breathing and movements originating from the spine. Whatever class you choose, if the first one you try isn't right for you, please don't give up; try a different class as they can all be so different.

Take your teacher aside and let them know how you are feeling. This is very relevant to them and you will let out your first sigh of tension.

Practising Scaravelli-inspired yoga, you are invited to be good to yourself, recognising what your body wants on that particular day. Adapt any movement to suit your needs. If you feel anxious about joining a group activity or being barefoot in a communal space, for example, don't worry, as you should not be expected to speak or be made an example of. I often practise with my eyes closed, just a quick peek here and there at the teacher's demonstration; then I can retreat into my own space. Your mat is your 'island'. If you are uncomfortable walking on a hall floor or being close to others, you can rest assured you rarely have to leave your island. Socks can be laid at its edge and this is your sole space. Bringing your own blanket is a good idea too, to wrap yourself up in for the end relaxation and to feel cocooned in a safe place. I'd like to say, however, I'm not trying to encourage a sense of detachment from others.

Hopefully you will be able to tune in to the positive energy in the room, emanating from the people around you filled with love and good intentions. I know that these are some of the worries people who suffer from anxiety have expressed to me and that is what's held them back from joining a class. They are just a surface layer of much deeper feelings of anxiety that the practice of yoga can help with. I've been surprised by the number of people around us who feel this way – people who seem not to have a care in the world but after a while their anxiety reveals itself to me as their yoga teacher. I would say even 80% of my students suffer from anxiety, so you won't be alone on this journey. This is very humbling and is an important lesson to me, reminding me to teach with compassion and consideration. Remember, nobody is looking and judging you in yoga... anything goes! There is a right and wrong way to practise asanas *with safety in mind, but if you truly listen to your body, you can't be wrong.*

So how might yoga help with anxiety? This lies in the question, 'what is yoga?' The movements of asanas *and breathing practices (*pranayama*) are all a preparation for the end meditation – preparing the body through movement and breathing to attain a state of peace and stilling the mind. The whole process should leave you with feelings of calm, happiness and peacefulness. These skills can be applied to daily life – standing in queues, walking, driving, washing up and lying in bed at night. These things all done mindfully, with your whole concentration, can give you a little time out here and there from the gripping tension of anxiety.*

Natalie, who suffers from generalised anxiety disorder, shares how yoga with her daughter helps her:

> I do cosmic kids' yoga with my daughter sometimes and I just find it relaxing. It's done through a story and we laugh and smile if we mess up and exercising just helps. It makes my mood lift. I feel calmer after.

Reflexology

Reflexology is a complementary therapy that is based on the theory that specific areas on the feet correspond with organs and systems of the body. Working these areas can help aid relaxation and allow us to cope better with the stresses that life can bring.

Alison Fuller, hypnotherapist and reflexologist specialising in women's health, explains how reflexology can benefit mental health and well-being:

Would it be helpful to have a way to reduce the impact that anxiety has on your life? In my experience, anxiety is accompanied by overwhelm. When we are overwhelmed we often experience a feeling of being 'unsafe'.

A positive way forward is to find something that allows you to change your current state from one of high-alert into one of calmness, to feel safe. In a nutshell, we need to feel SAFE to feel WELL.

Your intention is to create a feeling of Calmness, Clarity, Confidence and Control (the four Cs). When in a state of calmness you create space for clarity of thought; you begin to improve your feeling of confidence, and you gain a sense of being in control again – taking you into a feeling of wellness.

You can achieve these by seeking anything that instigates a switch from 'fight and flight' into calm. For this I strongly suggest you try reflexology as it brings about a positive state of relaxation – often quite deep.

During a reflexology treatment[29] the vagus nerve, one of the cranial nerves, switches from the anxious state into the relaxed state, often experienced by the recipient as a relaxing of the breath and softening of the muscular body. The switching of 'states' is an involuntary action carried out by the autonomic nervous system (ANS) so the recipient doesn't need to do anything during the session, just simply allow the pleasant sensations that the treatment brings.

The vagus nerve is an important nerve in the body, often termed the 'rest and digest' nerve as it brings about a shift into the natural calm state and is extremely beneficial to the digestive system as well as to the nervous system as a whole.

The body is designed to switch us in and out of fight and flight mode whenever we need to protect ourselves. When there is a state of perceived or potential fear, it switches us into a state of high alert, ready for action.

If the body is constantly, or very regularly, in this high-alert state, then effectively we are in a state of chronic stress and the impact on our wellbeing can begin to take its toll.

When we are in a good state, our nervous and endocrine (hormone) systems work together to help control the function and regulation of our hormones – effectively, we achieve homeostasis, which is stability.

We all have very busy lives these days. We have become 'time poor' and so we steal from our rest, our recovery and our downtime in order to manage and control all the other things that we need to do. Why not try a wonderful reflexology treatment to help you experience control, calmness, clarity and confidence again?

Acupuncture

Traditional acupuncture is based on ancient principles which go back nearly two thousand years; over this time it has been found to have great benefits on mental and physical health and function. The focus is on the individual and not the illness, therefore, two people with the same diagnosis could receive different acupuncture treatments. It is believed, by traditional acupuncturists, that illness and pain arise when the body's *qi*, or vital energy, is unable to flow freely – therefore, the overall objective of acupuncture treatment, is to restore the body's balance.

Gill Bescoby, a registered and licensed acupuncturist, tells us more about acupuncture and how it can benefit a person suffering from anxiety:

Acupuncture is a key component of Traditional Chinese Medicine, dating back well over two thousand years. The process of acupuncture involves the insertion of needles into certain locations along the channels and their collaterals to stimulate the body's healing energy and to balance the opposing forces of yin and yang. It is only recently that acupuncture has been recognised in Western cultures as a safe and reliable method to treat a variety of conditions, benefiting many patients worldwide.

Anxiety is an overall term used to cover a variety of anxiety disorders. The most common are: generalised anxiety disorder, social anxiety, specific phobias, panic disorder, obsessive compulsive disorder and post-traumatic stress disorder. We will focus mainly on generalised anxiety disorder for this brief contribution. Generalised anxiety disorder is a common problem mainly characterised by nervousness/restlessness, panic, irritability and excessive worry that is hard to control, and physical symptoms such as dizziness, tiredness, palpitations, excessive sweating, nausea and sleep dysfunction. These symptoms will inevitably impact greatly on daily life. They could cause the individual to withdraw from social contact and they may find going to work increasingly difficult and stressful.

In Western medicine, anxiety is treated with medication, psychotherapy or a combination of the two. Acupuncture is becoming a popular alternative for treating the condition. Research is ongoing to determine the effects of acupuncture on generalised anxiety disorder. A promising study from 2015 found that acupuncture improved symptoms in people with anxiety who had not improved with psychotherapy or medication. All the participants received 10 x 30-minute acupuncture sessions given over a 12-week period. The results showed a significant reduction in anxiety extending to 10+ weeks after cessation of treatment.[30] *Further research is needed for us to understand the true benefit of acupuncture for anxiety but, so far, the research has shown that it is a safe and viable option.*

From a Western perspective, acupuncture is believed to stimulate aspects of the nervous system to release various neurochemicals (endocannabinoids, dopamine, oxytocin, endorphin, serotonin and GABA to name a few), altering the chemistry of the brain and thereby resulting in better emotional and physical well-being. Acupuncture can be used as a standalone treatment for some patients suffering from anxiety or can be used alongside drug therapy, thus reducing some of the major side-effects of these drugs.

According to Chinese medicine, the health of an individual is dependent on creating complete balance and motivating the flow of energy smoothly and effectively through channels lying just beneath the skin. The flow of energy can be disturbed by many factors, including emotional states such as grief, anger, stress or even excessive joy, and physically through poor nutrition, trauma, hereditary disease or infections. These imbalances, therefore, have to be addressed. When assessing a person within the context of Chinese medicine, we look at how the person is experiencing his or her anxiety and what precipitating factors are involved leading to their present condition. Emotion only becomes a cause of disease when it is excessive or prolonged. As human beings we cannot avoid feelings or emotions, but these have to be kept in check. An acupuncturist will identify this and create a framework to understand the symptoms; developing an individual treatment approach for each patient based on their symptom pattern. An acupuncturist will always look at a patient holistically, taking into account their emotional, physical and spiritual health. To formulate a treatment principle, the pattern of disharmony will have to be identified, allowing a treatment protocol to emerge. The treatment will then include the insertion of sterile, disposable needles into specifically chosen points to correct this disharmony.

Acupuncture is a painless and, most often, enjoyable experience. There will be subtle sensations as energy moves throughout the body. This is usually well tolerated. It is not unusual for a patient to fall asleep or experience deep feelings of relaxation during treatment. At times, emotional release may occur, such as deep sighing or crying. One of the great advantages of acupuncture is the absence of major side-effects.

From a personal perspective within my own clinic, I have treated many patients suffering from anxiety over the 10+ years I have been in practice, with some amazing results. Whilst championing acupuncture, I do feel it is vital to keep the advancement in treating anxiety comprehensive, drawing together and encouraging flexibility in using both Western and Chinese medicine to formulate the best possible treatment for each individual case.

Massage

Massage therapy is a common treatment for the relief of sports injuries, strains and physical rehabilitation. However, its benefits are more than just physical: it can also be an effective way to relieve anxiety, depression and other mental health issues, as well as help to improve sleep quality. Although life stresses are unavoidable, negative feelings and insomnia can be helped with the positive benefits that massage therapy can offer.

Laura Whitcher, a massage specialist, explains this in more detail:

Complementary and alternative medicines are being used more and more as people are trying to find alternative methods to combat mental and physical health conditions. These practices are growing in popularity and are great to be used in combination or alongside more traditional Western drugs and other treatments.

In the past, massage therapy has mainly been used to treat muscle pain, injury and stiffness. Since then, it has progressed and is being used more and more for the treatment of mental and emotional problems, such as stress, anxiety and depression. It is also being used to encourage relaxation which then helps to reduce tension and bring on feelings of calm, as well as slowing down feelings of fear and hopelessness.

'The Mayo Clinic reports a 60-minute massage can lower cortisol, the stress hormone, by up to 30% after just one session. ... In addition to its calming effects, massage therapy can help alleviate the symptoms of anxiety, including muscle tension and sleep disturbances'.[31]

How does it work?

Massage therapy involves warming the muscles by kneading, rubbing and pressing on the different muscle groups. Therapists use their hands and massage oils and follow a certain pattern or routine to work each of these muscle groups. Some therapists will also include aromatherapy oils and soft music to help create a peaceful and relaxing environment.

There are many different kinds of massage offered depending on what is needed by the client. Massages often vary in pressure and muscle group focus. The most common types are: Swedish massage, deep tissue massage, sports massage and Shiatsu (acupressure). With anxiety we would always start with the Swedish massage as this is the most popular form to encourage relaxation of the body and mind. It helps to circulate the blood, increase oxygen flow and encourage the removal of toxins through the lymphatic system.

How does massage therapy help ease anxiety symptoms?

The way massage therapy is used to help anxiety, is to try and slow down the fight-or-flight response, which is normally overactive among sufferers. It helps the body to relax, which will hopefully encourage the person to let go of anxious, stressful and fearful thoughts.

The fight-or-flight reaction is a good thing when needed but with anxiety and constant stress the body continues to release adrenalin which is not what it needs. This heightened stress can cause uncomfortable physical symptoms, such as shortness of breath, increased heart rate, excessive sweating and chest pain. Massage therapy encourages the production of the more 'happy hormones' which in turn encourage a relaxation response, reducing tension, lowering the heart rate and generally making a person feel calmer.

Massage allows mental benefits such as lowering tension, reduces the fight-or-flight response as I've said, and creates a feeling of calmness and positivity. This also includes the physical benefits of less muscle tension, a lower heart rate and the removal of feelings of nausea.

Massage therapy is, then, highly beneficial in helping one to manage anxiety and stress and the related physical symptoms, but it cannot be seen as a 'cure-all'. It is not designed to take the place of any other mental health counselling, talk therapy, physical therapy or anything prescribed by a doctor. Massage is designed to supplement any other therapies that the client is currently receiving.

The therapist also needs to be aware that for most people massage allows for relaxation, but for someone with an anxiety disorder, it can be a cause of panic. With the possibility of claustrophobia, putting their head in the face cradle and the strangeness of the room or massage couch, these clients could suffer further. A thorough consultation would need to be taken and each step explained. A very slow and understanding approach would be required.

Applied relaxation

When we feel anxious, our muscles tend to tense up. There is a school of thought that says if we can relax our muscles more, we can actually reduce the anxiety itself. This therapy focuses on relaxing muscles in a particular way during situations that cause anxiety. Combined with breathing exercises and a recognition of someone's most common anxiety triggers, it can be used to diminish these all-pervasive worries.

While it sounds simple, to be effective the technique should be taught by someone trained in the therapy. They will be able to pass on mind-body exercises that lead to relaxed muscles, deep breathing and ultimately desensitising anxiety sufferers to the triggers that send them into a spin of worry and stress.

It may be most effective when combined with another treatment path such as cognitive behavioural therapy or guided imagery – a technique whereby the person with anxiety is able to close their eyes and imagine the sights and sounds of a place that they find relaxing. Guided imagery allows a sufferer to manage negative emotions, transporting them mentally to a place that brings them happiness and calm. It can also allow them to reframe a difficult situation, visualising a positive outcome rather than imagining the worst.

Essential oils

Ancient Egypt was the true birthplace of essential oils, or 'aromatherapy' as it is known today. The Egyptians cultivated plants for their oils and used them widely for religious purposes, as well as for beauty enhancing, medicinal, spiritual, aromatic and therapeutic practices. Essential oils are still widely used for many ailments in modern society, from repelling mosquitos to soothing aches and pains in the body. They also demonstrate massive benefits as a complementary therapy for mental health issues alongside the conventional treatments.

Corinne Laing, wellness advocate of DoTerra essential oils, talks about the benefits of pure, natural oils and their uses for helping relieve the symptoms of anxiety:

Everybody can experience anxious feelings from time to time. Some of us worry more than others, and excess worry can have an impact on our daily lives. Using essential oils can help us to manage and maintain our well-being, soothe our anxious feelings and calm our worries.

Essential oils can provide a quick and natural way for us to create a calm environment thereby putting ourselves at ease.

There are three ways to use DoTerra essential oils:

1.   Aromatically: *One to two drops of oil in the palms of the hands can help to improve our mood, clear our head and keep us focused. When we inhale natural compounds from essential oils, they hit our olfactory nerve. The olfactory nerve then sends signals to parts of our brain which then in turn sends signals to the rest of our body. This can happen very quickly. We can also diffuse these oils in a diffuser anywhere in our home or workplace to create a calming or uplifting environment.*

2.   Topically: *DoTerra essential oils can be applied directly onto the skin with a carrier oil to help relieve any tension we may have. Over our hearts for emotional topical use to help us feel centred. Then our energy meridians end at the feet, so they are a great place to apply essential oils. We can also make up our own rollerball glass bottles to have with us at any time. Perfect for when feeling stressed, applying the rollerball bottle to our pulse points can help relieve any worries.*

3.   Internally: *DoTerra essential oils are safe to use internally as they are CPTG tested (third party tested) for this purpose. Simply take one to two drops in a glass of water, add to food to enhance flavours, or simply take in a veggie capsule.*

There are many wonderful oils to help emotional well-being. Some of them are listed below.

Recommended DoTerra oils for anxiety:

Lavender – *one to two drops in a glass of water can help to reduce anxious feelings. Lavender's calming aroma can cut through feelings of stress and promote relaxation. Perfect on the soles of the feet at bedtime.*

Bergamot – *is unique among citrus oils due to its ability to be both uplifting and calming, making it ideal to help with anxious and sad feelings. Diffuse in the home, classroom or at work when stress levels or tension are high.*

Wild orange – *diffusing wild orange can energise and uplift the mind and body.*

Copaiba – *can help soothe anxious feelings. Place one to two drops under the tongue to encourage a general sense of well-being during times of stress or nervousness.*

DoTerra Balance Blend – *with its grounding oils, of frankincense and blue tansy, this blend helps balance emotions and establishes a sense of well-being. Apply to the neck and wrists to help ease anxious feelings.*

DoTerra Hope Blend – *has an energising and refreshing aroma which can help lift the mood when applied topically. Apply to pulse points and over your heart to promote feelings of comfort and emotional healing.*

We need to remember that essential oils work differently for everyone due to each oil having its own complex chemical make-up. Aromas interact with parts of our brain that store our personal memories and experiences, so what works for one person might differ for someone else.

Drama

I have seen at first hand how participating in drama has enhanced the sense of self and mental well-being of my own daughter. Samantha began doing drama workshops at our local theatre when she was well into the recovery process but still felt there was 'something missing'. Being a naturally shy person, drama gave Samantha the safe place she needed to explore emotions. It has completely transformed the way she sees herself and her communication skills and has given her the confidence she so desperately needed. In some ways, I would say that it is drama and finally finding herself through it that has helped strengthen her recovery from mental illness.

Samantha says of how drama has helped her:

Drama has given a home to my imagination and a place for my mind to run free; it's where I have always belonged but had never found; this is a feeling that is worth overcoming any mental illness to me.

In drama, we learn how to inhabit another character. If people can channel this skill and use it to create a confident version of themselves, they can practise walking, talking and behaving in positive ways until these become second nature. Those who suffer from low self-esteem can often go on to develop a mental illness. If people do not understand what motivates other people to behave the way that they do, they can end up believing that everything that happens around them is a reflection of them. People with low self-esteem and mental health issues can often feel guilty for no reason at all. Drama helps them to think about why characters might act the way that they do and understand that human beings are complex and not everything centres around them.

Ciaran McConville, director of learning and participation at Rose Theatre Kingston, says:

Acting classes are an investigation into impulse, action and response. Actors are taught to employ the 'magic if' to explore how they might behave within imaginary circumstances. This in turn leads to a dialogue about impulse; how we 'listen' to impulse and then either pursue it or inhibit it, depending on what our character needs to achieve. A committed student develops an imaginative vocabulary around internal conflict and obstacle, using techniques such as Chekhov's Imaginary Centres and Laban's Efforts. Emotional memory might also be enriched as the student explores real-life relationships and experiences to find the reality of imaginary circumstances. All of this can be transformative, if approached safely and sensitively. What's particularly interesting is that acting offers a reason beyond self-therapy. Actors are storytellers. They investigate their own experience to tell a story to others. The deeper that investigation, the more truthful the storytelling and the more powerful the shared experience. I think that purposeful approach can often lead to personal dividends because it doesn't feel like the spotlight is on our intimate self. Rather it's on our 'character'.

For shy people, drama is one of the few times in their lives where they can step out of the label of being a shy person. They are given permission to scream, shout and laugh without fear of judgement. Drama pushes people's boundaries, helping them to realise that they do not have to conform to the label they have been given. It can help them to realise what they are capable of and what they can be. Most of the plays and television shows that are written are about consequences too. Looking at a human story from the outside, people can identify the ways that the characters might have made different decisions to bring about a more positive outcome. They can then apply this to their own lives, realising that they do have the power to influence what happens around them and, more importantly, to themselves.

Charlie Brooks, actor, drama teacher and founder of the online drama school, I Am Pro, says:

> Drama can help with mental illness by themes of inclusion, memory and escapism, by taking on another character. Self-esteem can be promoted by being part of a team, relying on others, progression, and reward from rehearsals to the finished show.

Music and art

Some people find it really difficult to express how they are feeling. They might even feel that what they are going through cannot ever be expressed adequately by talking alone. For these people, a creative outlet might help them to explore and exercise negative feelings and embrace new and positive ones.

My Samantha tells us of why she enjoys writing her poems (some of which are in this book):

> I write poems mainly as a creative outlet for all my thoughts but I also feel I have an important message to share with the world that could possibly help others understand and overcome mental illness. The thoughts often come to me in the night;

perhaps it is my subconscious pulling out the scars it has wanted to get rid of for so long in a way that can possibly prevent others having the same pain.

Art and music therapy have long been shown to increase their effectiveness when used alongside traditional therapy methods like counselling and CBT. These activities often have a cathartic quality in themselves, without needing to be analysed.

Anabelle shares her thoughts on how being creative helped her recover from PTSD:

I have always used my creativity as a means of meditation. Music and photography have played a key role in my well-being. When you write a piece of music or take a photo, when at one with that inner creativity, there is only that moment. All other tensions and worries disappear even just for that short time. I consciously use my creativity now to counteract any stresses that everyday life brings. It's a fantastic coping method and brings a lot of inner joy and satisfaction. That, creativity, coupled with my NLP knowledge, provides me with a great platform to work through problems and also to create a really content life.

In just the same way as drama, art and music are reflections of the human condition. They allow us to explore how we feel and behave and why, in a safe and healthy way. They can also evoke emotions. Some people are often frightened of expressing feelings like sadness and so keep them cooped up. Music and art can connect them to their inner voice. They can be a way of un-ravelling complex or frightening situations and emotions.

Neil Long, radio presenter, voice and confidence coach, says:

Music can evoke strong feelings and memories. This process can, with the latest psychological techniques, be nurtured and created deliberately. This process could be used to create strong associations between self-esteem and a well-loved music track.

If a person is particularly 'into' an artist or band, this also helps them form a sense of identity and connect with others who think in similar ways, decreasing any sense of isolation.

Apps for your smartphone

It may seem contradictory to suggest that someone with an anxiety disorder – often an isolating condition in itself – could seek help from an app, but there are a surprising number of different ways that these could help people with mental illness move forward.

From mood trackers to support apps, all kinds of different help can be found on your phone or laptop. There are apps available to help track exercise – a proven mood booster – and others to help you understand the symptoms of anxiety and how to tackle them. The NHS recommends apps including Catch It, Feeling Good, My Possible Self, and Stress and Anxiety Companion.[32]

Apps such as Headspace, Calm and Happify may be helpful to those who want to learn more about the potential benefits of meditation. In a study looking at workplace stress, nearly a third of those who used Headspace for eight weeks reported a reduction in anxiety.[33]

Podcasts can also be helpful. Both those with anxiety disorders and those who care about them can benefit from listening to the experiences of others and finding out what helped them. The Mental Health Foundation (see page 318) can be a good starting point for finding podcasts to help with specific areas of difficulty and concern.

Using a mental health app should not replace going to a GP and seeking medical help. However, for some, mental health apps can complement other therapies and help to provide the motivation that can often be so hard to muster when someone is suffering from anxiety.

Charliee shares her love for the app HeadSpace:

I love it! I try to use it every night before bed. It helps me sleep and I usually wake up in a more positive mind frame. Because the app is on my phone, I can literally use it everywhere. It's handy when I walk the dogs too, but I've also used it before job or uni interviews as well! One of the 'skills' they teach you is body scanning so it really helps me to get in touch with my body and just take a few minutes to connect with myself – I can usually find out why I feel anxious and then link that feeling with a body part.

Pet therapy

Many people report that spending time in the company of animals can have a positive effect on their mood and can help to relieve some of the symptoms of their anxiety. This could be achieved through actual therapy sessions, known formally as applied animal therapy; however, people who simply spend time with a pet may also reap many rewards.

The impact of pets can be felt in many different ways. Having a dog, in particular, gets people out of the house and taking exercise, which we know is positive for those who suffer from anxiety. Animals require their owners to keep to a routine, which can bring order and consistency to the human's life, giving their day purpose, and making them feel relied on and needed.

Studies have shown that people with pets have lower blood pressure in stressful situations than those without pets.[34] Furthermore, playing with a dog or cat, or simply stroking or cuddling them, can boost serotonin and dopamine, helping the person relax and soothing them when they are stressed or anxious.

The picture with a pet looks very positive, but this does not mean that everyone with an anxiety disorder should have their own animal. Being a pet owner is a big responsibility, which in some people can feel like an extra layer of stress to have to deal with. Having another dependant to care for can also raise anxiety for some. Many people's lifestyle or living arrangements are not suitable for a dog, cat or other pet, and this is another factor to bear in mind when weighing up whether getting an animal will help with anxiety.

Louise, who suffers from generalised and social anxiety disorder and OCD, shares how interaction with her puppy eases her anxiety:

> I find spending time with my puppy helps on many levels. Firstly, as a distraction, focusing on something or someone else can stop you spending too much time in your own head. Secondly, he gets me out for dog walks; the exercise and fresh air help to improve my overall mental health. Cuddles can also help to calm me when feeling anxious; the touch and connection with a pet when you do not necessarily want to connect with people can be very helpful in reducing anxiety levels. Dogs seem to just know when their owner is feeling anxious or upset and offer comfort by just being there when you feel alone.

Performance coaching for carers

Supporting others can be mentally and physically exhausting. As a parent or carer, you probably spend a lot of your time focusing on everybody else, always putting everyone else's needs before your own. However, looking after your own well-being is just as important for you, your loved one and the whole family, as they can only be as strong as you are.

Leanne Poyner, life and performance coach, echoes my thoughts:

> As a carer for someone with any mental illness, there is a huge amount of physical and emotional pressure on you and you will most likely be living your life through the person you are caring for. By this I mean your thoughts will be consumed by them; how they are feeling, what their day is about, and physically this may involve you carrying out many additional tasks in your day to minimise the burden on the individual you

are caring for and make their day that bit easier to cope with.

Therefore, it is essential to ensure that you, the carer, are equally looking after your own mental and physical well-being to enable you to be that tower of strength for the individual. To enable this to happen, you need to take time for you, continue to have dreams, make short- and long-term plans to enable these dreams to become a reality. Performance coaching is key to this process.

A good analogy of how your life may feel at the moment is like a tumble dryer. All your thoughts and feelings are whirling around, with no structure, pattern or control. Performance coaching helps you to stop the tumble dryer, unpack the clothes and fold them into nice organised piles. Working together with your coach, you can then start to identify things that are important to you, what motivates you and what you want to achieve. It could be big or small; the main aim is that it gives you a sense of achievement and it is something that you have control of. The key focus of coaching is that you are setting goals that are dependent on you, not reliant on other people, and that you are in control of. For example, it could be making time to go to the gym three times a week, setting up a small business, seeing your parents more often or taking time to read for 20 minutes before bed each night.

A performance coach will not tell you what to do, will not judge, will not give you the solutions or tell you what your dreams should be. By asking the right questions of you, the coach will enable you to recognise what you really want in line with your values and help you to create your own plan of action that you will work towards in a realistic timeframe set by yourself. The priority of performance coaching is you, and you need to be living your life as fully as you can, to enable you to have the inner strength and drive to help support others.

To conclude

The willingness of a sufferer to engage with alternative therapies shows that they are seeking positivity and a way to combat and conquer their illness. This is one of the most crucial and valuable steps towards recovery.

For the carer, alternative treatments can provide respite in the form of 'time-out' to help renew their strength, emotionally and physically, and to enable them to face the challenges that they deal with in their role as a carer for someone suffering from an anxiety disorder.

I cannot reiterate enough that everyone is different, and if one therapy does not work for you or the sufferer, be open minded and not afraid to try another. This chapter has provided only a brief description of each therapy. Full details of the therapists mentioned above are provided in the resource section at the back of the book (see page 318).

Chapter 6

Anxiety and other psychological illnesses

Astonishingly and sadly, around one in four people in Britain will experience some form of psychological illness in their lifetime; ranging from the more common and well-known mental health issues such as anxiety, self-harm, depression, eating disorders and OCD to lesser known conditions. It is important to remember that this figure is based only on the registered sufferers actively seeking medical help, I am sure; there will be countless others who are suffering in silence, adding to these ever-increasing numbers.

My personal and professional findings, more recently confirmed by a survey I prepared in which numerous people kindly participated via my social media channels, support the suggestion that anxiety may also be interconnected with other mental illnesses, such as depression, eating disorders, self-harm and/or OCD. A staggering 80% of sufferers who responded had at least two co-existing mental illnesses. The results of this survey highlighted how anxiety can frequently co-exist with other psychological illnesses.

Eve, who suffers from social anxiety disorder, shares her experience with suffering from multiple psychological illnesses:

I developed social anxiety, depression, anorexia and self-harm which all kind of go hand in hand together as one fed into

> causing the other until I became drowned by them all and
> felt like I wouldn't ever come through the other side, but it's
> possible as I'm still here fighting every day.

In an ideal world, someone suffering from multiple mental illnesses would be treated as an individual, so allowing the multiple illnesses to be treated together; this would be a different and possibly more effective approach than treating each mental illness separately. Sadly, however, due to an over-stretched and under-funded health system, this is not always possible.

Cheryl shares her frustration from her daughter's experience:

> My daughter has been having therapy for around 12 months.
> It can become very frustrating, but I try my best to support
> the programme she is on. She has been self-harming since
> she was around 13 years old, but also suffers from depression
> and anxiety. As her mother I feel the depression and anxiety
> together are the cause of her self-harming; however, she seems
> to be being treated for the physical self-harming and not the
> deep mixed turmoil in her head.

To help you understand the possible links and connections, I will endeavour to explain the more common mental health issues in greater detail in this chapter together with the indicators when interlinked with anxiety.

Like anxiety disorders, all mental health issues can affect anyone irrespective of their age, gender, sexuality, ethnicity or social background. The effect on each individual can vary, as can the length of time a person suffers from it. Individuals who have milder symptoms of mental illness may not appear visibly ill in a physical sense to the outside world, but the distress and difficulty in mental functioning on the inside can cause great fear and angst. These vivid thoughts and internal feelings can become stronger and much worse if left undetected and untreated, and the sufferer will most likely be ill-equipped to tackle this alone.

If the symptoms are more severe, there may be more obvious external signs. Either way, mental illness is just as serious as any physical condition and deserves the same level of attention, respect and intervention; sadly, it is often misunderstood and dismissed because of the lack of visible evidence to the human eye.

It is important to remember that it is the most natural thing in the world to feel happy and uplifted when something positive happens in our lives, as it is to feel sad, anxious, fearful or angry when something negative or worrying occurs. My mum once pointed out to me that bad days are essential in life if we are to recognise and appreciate the good days. Part of ensuring good mental health and well-being is the ability to recognise the difference between 'natural' emotions and prolonged 'unnatural' ones, possibly indicating a potential issue that needs to be dealt with.

As with anxiety disorders, other mental illnesses can be kept a secret by the sufferer, who could at times feel embarrassed, ashamed and/or lonely. However, because of the elusive nature of these illnesses it is difficult to quantify and measure the actual extent of their impact. Personally, I would be inclined to measure the severity by looking at the impact on the life of the person experiencing the illness and those of the people around them.

Garry gives us his open and honest thoughts:

> I believe that anxiety, depression, eating disorders etc are all part of the same thing – a lack of self-worth and self-esteem. The painful reality is that I don't think I have ever loved myself, or even liked myself. Making people believe in themselves isn't everything, it's the ONLY thing!

Questions you could ask yourself are:
- Can the person concentrate in school?
- Can the person hold down a job?

- Can the person socialise?
- Can the person maintain friendships or romantic relationships?
- Can the person sleep at night?
- Is the person looking after their body and physical health?
- Is the person's unusual behaviour causing disruption within the family or home environment?

All of these factors can be negatively affected by mental illness on quite a significant scale.

Rita says of the changes she saw in her sister:

> My sister used to be quite a happy-go-lucky person, quite open to life and nothing really fazed her. She started to find it difficult to speak to other people, which she used to love; she also found it hard to concentrate on anything – work, conversation, programmes on TV. I knew something was wrong.

Before I begin to describe the signs and symptoms of some of the other psychological illnesses, I would like to reiterate that this is only a general and fairly basic guide. Everyone experiences mental illness in different and diverse ways, making it impossible to encompass each and every sufferer's experience. Parents, friends, partners and carers who regularly spend time with their loved ones will know them better than anyone else, but hopefully the information below will help to determine when the line is crossed between the angst that naturally affects us all and something deeper and potentially more sinister. At risk of repeating myself too much, there is no substitute for intuition, so if you feel that something is amiss, then there probably is good reason for further exploration.

In my experience, there are five main types of common psychological illness: anxiety-based illnesses, including OCD (see Chapter 2), being two of them, so I have described the remaining three – self-harm, depression and eating disorders – and how they may present themselves, below. I have also given brief descriptions of bipolar disorder, borderline personality disorder (BPD), schizophrenia, alcohol misuse and substance abuse which can also cross over with anxiety. Although each has its own and varied characteristic symptoms, they are often intertwined and tend to mimic symptoms from one another.

Depression

Depression is a common condition that can cause lengthy periods of low mood, a lack of interest in the things that the sufferer used to find enjoyable, feelings of guilt and low self-worth, disturbance in sleep patterns, loss of appetite, loss of energy and / or compromised concentration. Depression is very different from just feeling fed up, a bit sad or down in the dumps, which we all feel from time to time, usually due to something specific that affects us on a personal level. A person suffering from depression will experience these feelings too but in addition to this they suffer from the permanent weight of extreme anxiety, negativity, hopelessness and despair. These feelings do not subside, but stay with the sufferer every hour of every day like the darkest of clouds, overshadowing everything they try to do.

There are two types of depression: reactive depression and organic depression. The difference between the two is that the onset of organic depression comes from within the sufferer for no apparent or specific reason, completely unrelated to the external features and circumstances of life. Reactive depression is the complete opposite and can actually have a very rational onset, with logical reasoning such as the death of a loved one or the breakdown of relationships, redundancy or diagnosis of a terminal illness. Reactive depression can pass when the person becomes acclimatised and adjusts to the emotional trigger.

People who suffer from depression are often unaware

that they are in the grip of it unless it is pointed out to them by someone who knows them well enough to recognise the symptoms. Similar to some other mental illnesses, this condition can distort the sufferer's perception of what is and is not normal for them. It is often borne out of low self-esteem, anxiety and/ or another mental illness or in reverse it can be their root cause.

By its very nature, depression is not a logical response to the things sufferers have in their life: it does not take into account their luxuries, possessions, circle of friends, social life or our income, and it can strike anyone indiscriminately at any time. Many successful, popular, wealthy professionals who appear to have 'everything', with the world at their feet, can battle inwardly with depression.

My dear friend Bobby Davro talks of his struggles:

> To the outside world, I am a successful, confident, funny entertainer. However, what would surprise many people is that at some of the highest points of my career, I have suffered from dark times, depression, low self-esteem and a feeling of worthlessness. It is in my experience that antidepressant medication and the like are prescribed too easily, leaving the patient unaware of an alternative therapy that in the long term can be a much better alternative to improve their mental health.

Roughly 50% of depression sufferers, once recovered, may never experience it again in their lifetime, but sadly for the remainder there can be unpredictable recurrences throughout the years, which can make things extremely difficult for them and their families.

Typical psychological symptoms of depression include:
- sleeping a lot or insomnia
- feeling very sluggish or being overly fidgety
- having trouble focusing for any amount of time and experiencing a lack of motivation
- continuous low mood or sadness and possibly feeling

irritable and intolerant of others
- no longer enjoying previously enjoyable activities
- feeling anxious or worried and experiencing low self-esteem
- feeling worthless and hopeless
- having difficulty making decisions
- suicidal thoughts or thoughts of harming others
- feeling guilty and tearful
- having thoughts of death.

Typical physical symptoms of depression include:
- a change in appetite and weight loss or weight gain
- lack of energy and/or slowed movement or speech
- changes to the menstrual cycle (in women)
- unexplained aches and pains.

Again, personally, I will say the most important thing to look for is a change in a person's demeanour. If, for example, a teenager continually says, 'I hate the world', but then regularly goes out to meet up with their friends at the park or goes to play a ball game or takes part in other fun activities, in contrast to the words they mutter, then the chances are, they are probably not depressed. If a loved one or a friend constantly complains about how much they hate their job or asks, 'What is the point?" yet goes to play golf, or socialises regularly, having fun and living in the moment without being constantly preoccupied, then the chances are they are probably not suffering from depression either. However, please remember, prolonged apathy and constant negativity are the building blocks of depression. If the sufferer is constantly feeling that everyone else's life is somehow better than theirs and what is the point of their life and what are they doing with it, then there could be a need for help and medical intervention.

An anxiety disorder and depression

The crossover between anxiety and depression is significant, in large part because the two conditions can feed off and fuel each other. Statistics vary but studies appear to suggest that almost six in 10 of those with generalised anxiety disorder also meet the criteria for major depressive disorder.[35] In around a third, it is thought the anxiety precedes the depression, although a similar proportion report depressive symptoms before the anxiety. In the remaining third it is suggested that the symptoms of the two separate illnesses take hold at around the same time. This can deepen the severity of the symptoms and lengthen the time they last for.

Pete shares his experience with anxiety and depression:

> I've struggled a lot with depression, which, coupled with anxiety, has led to me feeling suicidal on previous occasions. I find that the two illnesses tend to come very close together for me. It is almost as though the one feeds the other.

Although the symptoms of both can overlap (including sleep problems, concentration issues and a feeling of impending doom), treatments and self-help techniques are also likely to be similar for both conditions. To get to the real root of the problem and to tackle it most effectively, it is helpful to understand both and recognise them as separate, though connected, illnesses.

Natalie tells us of the difficulties of living with both generalised anxiety disorder and depression:

> I find one feeds off the other. It's a vicious cycle you are caught in. For example, depression tells you that you are worthless, anxiety increases from that negative thought and you are scared that it's true. Then you feel more depressed/anxious because it's swirling around and around in your head. Worthless. No good. Can't do anything right. Failure. Family deserves better than you.

Self-harm

Self-harm is one of the most prevalent and critical factors in mental illness. As a behaviour, rather than as a clinical diagnosis, self-harm is a key indicator across multiple psychological disorders, including depression. People who self-harm are almost always suffering from a mental illness, sometimes severely so, and even if a precise and clinical diagnosis has not yet been achieved. For people who are regularly self-harming or know someone who is, it is imperative that professional advice and support are sought as soon as possible. Whilst suicide is a comparatively rare event, self-harm is a key diagnostic tool in suicide prevention and it is therefore essential that it is taken extremely seriously. It should never be ignored.

Self-harm occurs when a person chooses to inflict physical harm on their body. It varies from person to person, but it is usually a way of indirectly dealing with difficult or complicated issues in a sufferer's life and is often inflicted by means of cutting, burning or damaging the skin. It can also involve a sufferer putting their safety in jeopardy by voluntarily being in hazardous situations or exercising to the point of pain. The mental health charity, Mind, defines self-harm as 'a way of expressing very deep distress'. Often people do not know why they self-harm. Though many sufferers can go to great lengths to hide what they are doing, it can be a means of communicating what cannot be put into words or even into thoughts and has been described by some as an inner scream.

Eating disorders can also be described as a form of self-harm due to the physical damage inflicted to the body in order to block out what is happening in the mind. As with other mental illnesses, such as OCD, self-harm is inflicted to bring relief to the sufferer, albeit only temporarily, so the cycle repeats and repeats with the behaviours becoming both physically and mentally addictive and, in some cases, more severe.

According to the Mental Health Foundation, the UK has the highest rate of any European country for self-harm and affects 400 in every 100,000 (that is one in 250) of the population – males and females equally. These figures are more likely to be much higher though as many people who self-harm do so in secret and seldom tell anyone. Although anybody can be affected, the majority of people who self-harm are between the ages of 11 and 25 years old.[18] Higher rates of self-harm are evident in people already suffering from borderline personality disorders, depression and eating disorders.

Self-harming can include scratching, pinching, hitting or cutting different parts of the body, hair-pulling, burning or anything which is done deliberately to cause pain, including less obvious forms, such as risk-taking, drug overdose or simply not taking care of their own physical or emotional needs.

In children, harming animals, pets or younger siblings can also be a sign of internal anxiety which, if left undiagnosed, could then lead to other mental health issues such as depression, eating disorders and / or OCD.

Many young people who self-harm say that it enables them to feel something, rather than the numbness which can be associated with depression or other mental illnesses. Whilst teenage girls often use self-harm as a physical expression of familiar yet painful emotions, teenage boys are likely to self-harm because they do not have the emotional vocabulary to express how they feel. The symptoms of self-harm can be very hard to spot in young people, because they will very often conceal them from their parents, teachers and friends. On the other hand, self-harm has recently been noted to be 'contagious' in schools whereby students will emulate each other's inflictions, so it is a good idea to ensure that all friends connected to the person self-harming know that intervention is taking place, giving a strong and clear message that it is a very serious issue and not to be mimicked.

Dominique shares her experience when she noticed her own daughter had started self-harming:

> I started to notice a change in the way my daughter was dressing, and when she lifted her arm and the sleeve of her jumper lifted, I started to notice some marks on her arms. I addressed this straight away with her, and alerted her friends' parents so that they could be on the lookout in their own children.

While generally done in secret, self-harm can be a way of attention seeking, physicalising an internal pain for an outside world to see in a way that demands interaction. It can also be an indicator of suicidal thoughts, allowing the person self-harming to test the water without actually attempting the real thing. It is often described as a pressure cooker of emotions that build up on the inside and self-harming is a way of releasing that pressure. It can be linked to feelings of self-loathing, unworthiness and low self-esteem.

Those who self-harm, young and old, will usually cut parts of their bodies – arms or upper legs most commonly, as this can be hidden under clothing. However, you know your loved one and you will recognise any change in their behaviour which could indicate self-harm; this could include unexplained bruises, hair loss or bald patches, scars, wearing long sleeves or long trousers even in hot weather, giving up sporting activities that require less clothing (e.g. swimming) and generally spending a lot of time alone. Some of the signs of self-harm are explained as 'accidental', with the person self-harming making excuses for the bruises or the scars. So the most important factor to consider here, is the frequency with which they appear and the persistence of the injury. Recognising the difference between a one-off and a recurring pattern is vital.

Some of the physical signs to look out for are as follows. The person may:

- experience bruises on parts of their body
- have cigarette burns on parts of their body
- have cuts on parts of their body
- have excessive hair loss/unexplained hairless patches on the scalp
- exercise obsessively (more than the daily recommended time)
- keep covered with layers of clothing, especially long sleeves, particularly in hotter weather
- experience low mood/tearfulness/lack of motivation or interest
- show changes in eating habits or become secretive about eating – including rapid weight loss or gain
- develop alcohol or drug misuse.

Self-harming has reached a very dangerous era by way of the internet. Where once sufferers perceived their self-harming to be secretive and were ashamed of their self-inflictions, covering up to hide their scars or abrasions, they are now joining online communities and sharing with others their scars like 'badges of honour', their painful and misplaced pledge of allegiance to a very disturbing worldwide club.

Anxiety and self-harm

Self-harm occurs when someone inflicts physical harm on their body in a bid to cope with difficult thoughts, feelings and complicated issues in their life. Unsurprisingly, self-harm may at times be a symptom of the anxiety someone is experiencing.

Not everyone who has anxiety self-harms, and not everyone who self-harms has serious anxiety, but it is crucial to work out the relationship where the two co-exist in order to identify the most effective help.

The close link between the two is understandable. Self-harm is believed to be linked to somehow seeking a release from overwhelming emotions, which is how anxiety can often feel. When people do not talk about those thoughts that make them worried, they may turn to other ways of expressing those difficult feelings, and one of those ways may be self-harm.

People may talk about self-harm being a way to regain control over their runaway thoughts, worries and fears but from an objective point of view, we are able to recognise that far from tackling their anxiety through self-harm, they are actually adding another layer of complexity to their mental state and may actually trigger more anxiety rather than lessen it.

Eve, who has suffered from social anxiety from a young age, says of how the anxiety and self-harm co-existed, and how there is hope for getting out of the vicious circle:

As exams loomed as well and my anxiety ramped up even more, one day I harmed myself unintentionally in a textiles lesson and that was the start down a long bumpy road as I felt relief and not pain. For once I felt grounded and like a bliss had taken over me; I felt strangely better than I had for a while. I would harm myself at home, in school toilets, even one time when I was at my cousin's wedding and couldn't stand being part of the wedding party family. It was a relief to do it but tough to hide too and the fear of being caught spiralled my anxiety and so the cycle continued on and on.

Now at nearly 24 I've been free from self-harming for a few years now and though my anxiety is better, reaching out for help got me here and by reaching out to others for support, it has made me realise there's strength in confiding when you're struggling, and no shame at all.

There's always hope for a better future. It may seem impossible but it is truly achievable.

Eating disorders

Generally, eating disorders are defined as a distorted pattern of thinking about food and everything associated with it. They involve the sufferer abusing food, exercise and their bodies to dangerous levels, however the issues originated, and are characterised by disordered thinking and mental distress. Like self-harming, they are an indication that something is happening in the brain, with the effects on the body being the visual symptoms. Eating disorders can be measured not by a set of weighing scales, but by an assessment of feelings, thoughts and behaviours.

Interestingly, eating disorders can frequently co-exist with other mental illnesses. They have been linked to alcoholism and drug addiction and have strong links with OCD, anxiety, self-harm and, of course, depression.

There are many types of eating disorder and within these types there are literally hundreds of variations and symptoms unique to the sufferer, but the condition usually begins with simply eating too little or too much and the obsession with eating, exercise and body image follows, leading to strict, tailored changes of certain foods in both the behaviour and the lifestyle of the sufferer.

With so many variations of dietary preferences in today's society, such as veganism, vegetarianism, pescatarianism and food intolerances, it is becoming more difficult to define 'normal' eating. For the majority of people, however, food and calorie intake/expenditure do not preoccupy their thinking and their lives. An eating disorder is an illness that permeates all aspects of the sufferer's life from the minute they wake up to the minute they go to bed. However, for some they can even dream about food when they sleep which then effectively dominates their life 24/7. It is a serious health condition that can be both physically and emotionally destructive.

The three most well-known forms of eating disorder are: anorexia nervosa, bulimia nervosa and over-eating, which are all described in brief below, yet the most common actual diagnosis is other specified feeding or eating disorder (OSFED), which means that the sufferer does not completely fit within the official criteria for any one eating disorder in particular.

Anorexia nervosa

The official definition of anorexia nervosa is 'self-imposed starvation'. However, anorexia nervosa is not really about how little a person eats, it is about their desire to control what they eat. The sufferer will normally know exactly how much they will eat in a day, at what times and how many calories they will be consuming. They will often weigh and measure their food and are likely to become fearful in situations where they have to deviate from the food plan they have set for themselves.

Juliet, who suffers from generalised anxiety disorder and anorexia nervosa, shares her thoughts on the control element:

> I also suffer from anorexia nervosa which feeds into the anxiety and vice versa in a very damaging spiral. In an anxious state the only thing that feels controllable is my food, and eating less feels like the only right way to move forward.

The sufferer will go to great lengths to eat according to the rules their illness tells them are necessary. They will often hide their behaviour, lie to their loved ones and engage in morally questionable behaviours which prioritise their condition above anything and anyone else in their lives.

Signs of anorexia nervosa, which will help distinguish it from a diet or phase, are listed below. It is important to note that usually there is more than one sign, although that is not always

the case: The person may:
- avoid food and meal times
- make excuses to avoid eating, such as having 'eaten earlier'
- carefully weigh and portion food
- use continual self-effacing language, such as repeatedly claiming to be 'fat'
- check calories and fat content of food
- keep lists of food consumed
- deny hunger
- continually look for approval and validation
- hide food that was believed by others to have been eaten
- pick out a few specific foods and eat these in very small quantities
- start doing intense and or compulsive exercise.

With the physical signs of anorexia nervosa, the person may:
- show rapid weight loss
- have hair loss on the scalp
- experience dizzy spells/feel faint
- experience constipation and stomach pain
- develop 'Lanugo' soft, downy hair on the face and body
- in girls, periods may stop or not start in the first place
- experience poor circulation and feel cold (particularly in the hands, nose and feet)
- develop dry, rough or discoloured skin
- become dehydrated.

The physical symptoms above usually clear up once the sufferer enters into recovery, but it is important to note that they are at risk of long-term health consequences, such as osteoporosis and infertility.

Rob who, from a young age, has suffered from anorexia nervosa, shares his experience:

I suffered with anorexia for many years when I was younger. It has left me with some physical health issues later in life that affect me on a daily basis. I am now recovered from the anorexia though and am grateful for that.

Bulimia nervosa

Bulimia nervosa is just as serious as anorexia nervosa, yet it can be more difficult to detect from the outside, since sufferers are quite often a 'normal' weight, or even slightly overweight.

People who have bulimia nervosa continually 'binge' eat large quantities of food in a short period of time and then 'purge', finding ways to rid their body of the food consumed, most commonly by vomiting. Sufferers of anorexia nervosa may also 'purge', but it is the consumption of large quantities of food and the desire to rid the body of the calories consumed before any weight is gained that is the defining factor that distinguishes bulimia nervosa.

Some signs of bulimia nervosa may include the following. The person may:

- experience urges to eat large amounts of food
- experience mood swings
- experience anxiety and or depression
- start to vomit after eating
- start acting secretively and be reluctant to socialise.

Effects of bulimia nervosa on the body may include the following. The person may:

- experience a sore throat and/or bad breath
- start using laxatives
- engage in compulsive exercise
- experience dry or patchy skin
- constantly put themselves down
- have feelings of being ashamed or guilty

- in girls, experience irregular periods
- be chronically tired
- experience redness around the knuckles
- develop puffiness of the face and fingers.

Emma tells us how her anxiety and bulimia are interlinked:

> When I am due to go out for a meal or to meet friends, I pre-empt that I will get overanxious; maybe this is part of the problem, but I cannot seem to stop it. My anxiety fuels my thoughts about the food I eat and, in turn, the bulimia.

Overeating

This has only been recognised as an official eating disorder fairly recently, which is an important step forward; when people overeat we do not tend to have as much sympathy for them as those who under-eat or purge themselves, even though the effects on the body and mind can be just as harmful and the underlying emotions just as distressing.

People who suffer from compulsive and overeating disorder, suffer from episodes of uncontrolled eating or binging, followed by guilt and most likely depression, although they do not then purge. In addition to eating large quantities of food, the sufferer will also usually have a 'frenzied' feeling as though they are unable to control their actions. They may continue to eat long after they have become full.

Some signs of binge/compulsive eating include the following. The person may:

- be afraid of not being able to control their eating and/or of not being able to stop eating
- be afraid of eating around others
- experience fatigue
- sporadically use popular diet plans

- hide food in secret places to eat later
- have secretive eating patterns.

Effects of binge-eating/compulsive eating on the body may include the following. The person may:
- put on weight
- believe that life would be better if they were able to lose weight
- put themselves down, especially after eating
- become out of breath after light activity
- sweat excessively
- blame personal failures in social and professional life on their weight
- experience depression/mood swings
- suffer from high blood pressure and/or cholesterol
- experience leg and joint pain
- experience decreased mobility owing to weight gain
- experience loss of sexual desire
- suffer from insomnia
- develop poor sleeping habits.

It is important to note here that it is possible to binge eat or eat compulsively and not be overweight. However, this is still a problem, both physically and mentally. Our health is dictated not by how much we weigh but by how much fat is around our internal organs. It is possible to be a small size and yet have unseen fat around the heart, arteries and other internal organs. Using food as a kind of drug is also not healthy emotionally. There is a difference between this and simply having a 'high metabolism' or 'large appetite'.

Max shares his thoughts on how he feels:

For me, it is a vicious cycle. I feel the need to overeat if anything in my day has not gone to plan; this food makes me feel comforted in the moment but as soon as I am finished, I then feel an overwhelming shame and guilt; I feel so low and hate myself for it. This then leads onto the depression taking over. Once I am in the cycle it is so hard to get out of it.

Other recognised eating disorders are orthorexia (sufferers become obsessed with healthy eating to the extent that it totally dominates their lives), compulsive exercising and bigorexia (gym culture, especially among boys). Orthorexia and bigorexia are relatively new and becoming more widely recognised via the media and charities, raising awareness of mental health issues as their prevalence sadly continues to rise.

Anxiety and eating disorders

It is relatively common to find anxiety disorders in people with eating disorders, as – like many mental illnesses – the two can fuel and feed off each other. One study found about two-thirds of individuals with eating disorders also had one or more anxiety disorder, the most common being OCD and social phobia, with 41% prevalence of OCD and 20% of social phobia.[36]

Someone suffering from anxiety may mistakenly feel that monitoring what they eat or how they exercise might give them back some of the control that feels so out of reach to them. From an objective point of view, actually what they are doing is swapping one troubling set of symptoms for another, placing the eating disorder in control rather than gaining control of their anxiety themselves.

In other cases, the eating disorder may occur first and someone with an eating disorder may experience high levels of debilitating anxiety due to fear surrounding food and the inner workings of their anxiety disorder.

Paige shares her experience of anorexia nervosa and bulimia nervosa as well as anxiety:

I find that my anorexia and anxiety come hand in hand. My anxiety around food arises when I do not know the specifics of the food I am eating, such as what is in food and what it is cooked in. When I start to get anxious, I become very distracted and I cannot think about anything except the food and the worst case scenarios, such as, 'what if the food has been made with butter?' I then start to snap at people and I become very paranoid and will accuse other people of adding extra food onto my plate.

With my bulimia and anxiety, I find that if I have eaten food that I cannot cope with, I will start to get a lot of intrusive thoughts and I will get very anxious and worried that I will put on weight and that I am fat. My mind then tells me that the only way to stop this happening is to make myself sick. My anxiety will stay high if I don't make myself sick and I will continue to get intrusive thoughts.

Borderline personality disorder

Borderline personality disorder (BPD) is a complex and serious mental illness, characterised by very unstable emotional and impulse regulation. People with BPD can have a distorted sense of self and may find themselves overly dependent on their relationships with others. Self-harming behaviour, such as hurting oneself, attempting suicide or abusing substances, can often be part of the illness. Given these manifestations of BPD, it is perhaps not surprising that a significantly higher incidence of anxiety has been found among those with borderline personality disorder compared with the general population. According to the Diagnostic and Statistical Manual of Mental Disorders-IV (DSM-IV), there are nine different criteria that can manifest within someone with borderline personality disorder:

1. Frantic efforts to avoid real or imagined abandonment
2. A pattern of unstable and intense interpersonal relationships characterised by the person alternating between extremes of putting the loved one 'on a pedestal' and devaluing them

3. Identity disturbance – that is, strongly and persistently having an unstable self-image or sense of self
4. Impulsivity in at least two areas that are potentially self-damaging (e.g. spending, sex, substance abuse, reckless driving, binge eating)
5. Recurrent suicidal behaviour, gestures or threats or self-mutilating behaviour
6. Emotional instability due to highly reactive mood (e.g. intense episodes of unease/dissatisfaction, irritability or anxiety, usually lasting a few hours and only rarely more than a few days)
7. Chronic feelings of emptiness
8. Inappropriate, intense anger or difficulty controlling anger (e.g. frequent displays of temper, constant anger, recurrent physical fights)
9. Transient, stress-related paranoid thinking or severe dissociative symptoms (breakdown of memory, perception, awareness or identity).

At least five of these must be present for someone to be diagnosed with the condition. In some ways it is possible to draw very clear parallels between these BPD criteria – including self-mutilating behaviour, self-damaging impulsivity and an unstable sense of self – and the key characteristics of depression.

Anxiety and borderline personality disorder

Due to the complex nature of BPD, it is not surprising that anxiety and panic attack symptoms are common in people with this mental illness, especially at times of heightened stress. Some statistics suggest that anxiety is common to around nine in 10 of those with the disorder.[37]

The large crossover between anxiety and BPD can make it difficult to separate the two conditions. It is helpful though to recognise if anxiety is present, as this can influence a person's treatment journey. It is believed, for example, that when it comes to depression, which is closely related to anxiety, antidepressants may not be as effective in those with BPD as they might be if they had depression alone. Focusing on treatment specifically targeting the BPD may be more effective.[38]

Jo explains how both her anxiety and borderline personality disorder co-exist:

> With BPD, anxiety can be a part of the rapidly changing moods we experience. The fact that we experience moods so intensely and more extremely than others means that the anxiety can come on incredibly quickly and strongly. It can take your breath away but it can also disappear as quickly as it came. What can be close to a panic attack can become nothing within a couple of minutes. There is also anxiety linked to specific things that are there under the surface all the time. BPD comes with a fear of abandonment as a symptom. This can cause great anxiety when dealing with friends and family. It can make relationships difficult.

Bipolar disorder

Bipolar disorder, formerly known as manic depression, is a condition that affects the person's mood, which can swing from one extreme to another. People with bipolar disorder have the low and lethargic spells characteristic of depression, but they also have manic episodes where they feel very high, restless and overactive. Recognising and enjoying the 'normal' spectrum of moods for any consistent period of time is something that often eludes bipolar sufferers.

During depressive episodes, people with bipolar disorder may feel worthless and directionless, taking them to such lows they consider, or even attempt, suicide. During the manic phases they may be bursting with energy and ambitious plans and ideas; however, this may lead to lack of sleep, irregular eating patterns and spending unnecessary amounts of money. It can also be accompanied by symptoms of psychosis, where they see or hear things that do not exist.

The high and low phases of bipolar disorder are often so extreme that they can interfere with everyday life.

Anxiety and bipolar disorder

Anxiety disorders are the most common comorbid conditions to be diagnosed in people with bipolar disorder. It is vital to recognise this as it is believed that having anxiety can make the bipolar symptoms significantly worse, increasing the risk of suicidal thoughts and making it harder to function in everyday life.[39]

Treating patients with both bipolar and anxiety can be challenging as antidepressants may make the symptoms of the former worse.[40] For this reason, it is vital to seek professional help to untangle the anxiety symptoms from those specific to bipolar, and to look at different treatment paths that may be more effective.

Rachel explains how her health anxiety and bipolar are interlinked:

I have suffered anxiety really badly for years, but then I was diagnosed with bipolar last year after years of mood swings, one-minute high for two/three weeks and then lows/severe depression for 10+. I can have a stable period then for months with little anxiety. When I'm manic I don't really have anxiety as I feel I'm superior and better than anyone else; however, during the times of depression my anxiety is through the roof. Having bipolar and anxiety is hard. The anxiety can make me very paranoid, my heart races, I get sweaty all over, struggle to breathe and have even had seizures due to the anxiety being so bad. When anxiety is bad, I have to pick at my skin till I'm left with nasty sores, pull out my hair etc. I tend to rock a lot on those bad days and stay in, away from people, crowds etc…

I'm starting to learn to manage the anxiety slowly through mindfulness, self-sooth and distraction.

Schizophrenia

Schizophrenia is generally a long-term mental illness where someone may have very distinct thoughts and feelings that are extremely vivid to them but may not actually be real. They may hallucinate, be disorganised in how they think and speak, and experience thoughts and feelings that are delusional.

The effects of this can be wide-ranging. Living with schizophrenia may make it hard to cope with everyday life and can lead people to feeling isolated and lonely. Their illness can make them suspicious of others and reluctant to seek help. The delusional symptoms of schizophrenia may make it hard for them to even see that there is something wrong.

Schizophrenia is not always well understood by the general public. Perhaps due to the negative stories that make headlines in the press, people often believe that people with schizophrenia are dangerous. This is very rarely the case with this illness, but can lead sufferers to feeling even more isolated and misunderstood.

Anxiety and schizophrenia

The crossover of schizophrenia and anxiety is, unsurprisingly, high, with around four in 10 patients with schizophrenia having at least one anxiety disorder.[41] Social anxiety can be particularly common. Like any mental illness where anxiety is present, the two conditions need to be identified and treatment adjusted accordingly, under the supervision of a doctor. They will be able to establish whether medication is appropriate or might make the issues worse. They may also recommend talking therapy, such as CBT, which may help the anxiety symptoms.

Alcohol misuse and anxiety

As alcohol is the most commonly taken drug, its link with anxiety is worth looking at in more depth. The connection between the two is alarmingly stark, with data suggesting that around 20 per cent of those with social anxiety disorder, for example, also suffer from alcohol dependence.[42]

The overlap between anxiety and alcohol abuse may be clear, but often it is less obvious which one came first. Some people will drink to blot out their worries or because they think alcohol will help them relax or be more confident. Others may develop anxiety, or find their symptoms worsen, as a result of the mood-altering effects from the alcohol. Either way, the knitting together of the two illnesses makes both more complex and harder to unravel.

To understand the link between drinking and anxiety, it is helpful to know what happens in the brain when someone consumes alcohol. Having an alcoholic drink alters the chemical balance of the brain, which is why, when someone has a drink or two, they may start to feel more relaxed and less inhibited. However, if they continue to drink, the alcohol may soon switch their mood to anger, upset or despair. If this happens on a regular basis, the neurotransmitters in the brain that are essential for good mental health will be affected. Drinking too much also causes the level of mood-boosting chemical serotonin in the brain to fall, which ultimately can make the symptoms of anxiety worse and also lead to a vicious cycle of feeling the need to drink more to find the relief which some people may mistakenly believe alcohol will give them. Furthermore, the after-effects of alcohol – the dreaded hangover – can create a cycle of dread, shame and anxiety. This kind of anxiety is actually a physical symptom of withdrawal from alcohol and, where someone is already anxious, this 'morning after' effect can make the symptoms feel worse. The social impact of drinking – including arguments with loved ones or trouble at work – can also make anxiety worse.

This can then lead to a vicious cycle where, faced with a mountain of seemingly insurmountable worries or concerns about what they did or said, someone may then return to drink to find a way to relax. This sets off the chain of events above once again.

For families and loved ones of those with a mental illness, such as an anxiety disorder, being alert to the signs that someone has an unhealthy relationship with alcohol can be the first clue to their deeper mental health issues. Behind the arguments, emotional dysregulation, accidents or work or university absenteeism that can be some of the effects of unhealthy drinking, there may be a person struggling with a persistent low mood and crushing self-esteem filled with worries. Recognising and understanding that may be the first step towards getting the person the help they need for both illnesses.

Lucy shares the experience of her mother:

> When my parents divorced, my mum went into a really out-of-character routine of drinking alcohol every night. It started with one or two but turned into binges whereby she wouldn't wake up for work, she couldn't get out of bed. Her head was all over the place. My uncle intervened and managed to convince her to get help. She is doing much better now.

So, what can be done? To start to unravel the roots of someone's mental illness, eliminating or considerably cutting down the drinking may be a crucial first step (although, of course, it is much easier said than done and may require considerable support from family and friends as well as professional services). If the person is able to cut down or eliminate alcohol, they can start to feel better and sleep better within just a few weeks.[43] Once that happens, it may be more possible to work out whether the drinking has triggered the anxiety or the other way around. The latter is more likely to be the case if the symptoms of anxiety do not lift, or at least improve, once the drinking has stopped.

In either scenario, tackling both the anxiety and drinking at the same time is likely to be the most successful course of action. This may include talking therapy, complementary therapies and, possibly (and under the strict direction of a doctor), medication. Getting help to stop drinking is not a sign of weakness or failure. Actually, the person's desire to change things should be seen as a sign of strength. With the right intervention it is possible to tackle both the alcohol dependency and the anxiety and make a significant difference to the person's overall mental health and well-being.

Drug misuse and anxiety

Alcohol is not the only substance that can play a part in someone's experience of anxiety. There are other substances that can do so. These can include painkillers, laxatives and also recreational drugs. Essentially anything that alters the chemistry in the brain can exacerbate the risks to someone's mental health, particularly in those who are perhaps more prone to or at risk of this kind of illness.

As with alcohol, the interplay between other drugs and anxiety can be complicated and multi-layered. Some people will take drugs to escape the maelstrom of worries that plague them. However, underneath the 'disguise' of the drugs, these problems still persist and the side-effects or come-down from taking drugs may simply make the situation even worse.

In other cases, heavy drug use can lead to the kind of chaotic lifestyle that creates a fertile base for mental illness to take root. Taking drugs can cause financial problems, relationship issues and/or risk-taking behaviour, all of which can contribute to the onset and deepening of anxiety.

Matty says of his experience with drug misuse and other mental health issues:

Drug misuse causes so much anxiety it's scary. It mainly depends on the substance itself: stimulating substances generally cause anxiety and I get paranoid thoughts that I'm getting arrested, the police are chasing me and I'm going to die... this mixed in with owing money for drugs to some less desirable people can alone cause anxious thoughts.

To this day I can't go to some places in my home-town without the anxiety peaking. I hate feeling sick with worry I'll get spotted by a dealer I may owe money to or just someone who doesn't like me for something I did under the influence.

Getting the right kind of help when drugs are involved alongside mental illness can also be particularly challenging. A doctor will need to try to work out how much the substance itself – or the withdrawal symptoms from it – is responsible for how someone is feeling and how much is part of an illness such as anxiety.

Cocaine, for example, which is now commonly used by many people, may initially cause a high, but once the effects start to wear off, may leave users feeling low and lacking in energy. For many, these feelings will soon pass but it can be much more prolonged in people who use cocaine regularly and could contribute to a mental illness.

If possible, the best way forward would be to try to support the person to get their drug use under control or, better still, stopped, (sometimes easier said than done) and then a doctor can try to tackle the symptoms that remain with the appropriate treatments for that individual. Seeking help from a GP, drugs advisor or helpline is an important first step towards taking back control and getting a true picture of a person's mental state and what further help and support they need.

Anxiety and physical illnesses

Anxiety may be an illness of the mind, but it can also affect physical health or be exacerbated by physical illness and so the interplay between the health of the body and of the mind are inextricably linked. It is important to understand this connection as it can help families, sufferers and doctors understand the root of a person's symptoms and how best to treat them.

When it comes to the relationship between mental and physical health, it can be something of a 'chicken and egg' situation. Sometimes it will be clear when the physical illness triggered anxiety, or vice versa, but often the two are so bound up together that it is virtually impossible to work out which came first. Regardless of that, being aware of the relationship between the two, and acknowledging and understanding it, can be crucial in helping people move forward. Evidence suggests that poor mental health can be linked to poor outcomes in physical health,[44] so it is essential not to ignore the former or to just parcel it up as an inevitable part of a certain illness.

Anxiety can affect anyone, but when it comes to its connection with physical illness it can be broadly categorised into three areas:

1. Where anxiety takes root as a result of the limitations or loneliness placed on someone by a physical illness; when someone feels out of control of their body and the outcome of their illness
2. Where anxiety is a symptom of the illness itself
3. Where an illness or physical symptoms are actually triggered by the long-term toll of anxiety.

A person's mental illness may not fit neatly into any of these categories, as it can seep into so many areas of someone's life, but they do show the different ways that anxiety and illness work together.

So, which physical illnesses are most likely to have a link to anxiety? The list can be almost endless because of all the worries naturally triggered by being ill that can easily spiral out of control. There are, though, some conditions where the connection is particularly stark, including heart disease, chronic respiratory disorders and gastrointestinal conditions. When untreated anxiety is present, the disease itself can be more challenging to treat. At the most extreme level, this can make symptoms worse and may lead to a bleaker prognosis.

Allan tells us about when he suffered from skin cancer and the anxiety this difficult experience brought on:

Prior to suffering from the skin cancer, worrying was not really in my nature; however, since thankfully recovering from it and coming through the other side, I seem to have developed a severe anxiety around every little mark on my body; sometimes there isn't even anything there – my eyes even imagine it, and it puts my mind into a frenzy. The concern has since transferred onto my family too, so I constantly worry about them.

There are also more tangible links between the two. Some conditions, such as an under-active thyroid gland, cause changes in the brain that can actually trigger anxiety or depression. Furthermore, some drug treatments, such as steroids, affect the way the brain works and so may be linked to these two mental illnesses.

It can be hard to seek help for anxiety when a physical illness is present. Firstly, it may be hard to recognise the anxiety when someone is already battling another condition. Secondly, they may also be unwilling to 'burden' the medical team with 'yet another issue'. It can also be very hard to admit that they are struggling.

Friends and family can have such an important role to play here, both recognising if someone is battling mental health concerns and also in reassuring them that to seek help is not a sign of weakness but rather part of their overall treatment plan. Encouraging them to open up and talk about how they feel is an important first step. However, if the feelings persist, they should talk to their medical team or another health professional.

If you know someone is suffering, encourage them to lighten their load, to eat well, take gentle exercise and pursue the hobbies, interests and friendships that have made them happy in the past. No harm can come from doing this and it could provide a vital piece in the puzzle of their recovery.

Eliza, shares her experience of how she suffered from anxiety and depression alongside diabetes for many years:

> For the first 10 years of being diagnosed with diabetes, anxiety and depression had to be the biggest problem for me. I was on the wrong medication for a long time and didn't realise how much the wrong type of insulin had affected me emotionally. Diabetes and anxiety are very linked for me and I believe for many others too. You can live a good life with diabetes but you must control the sugars. No need for crash diets, just balance your life.

To conclude

This chapter demonstrates how all-pervasive anxiety disorders can be. Where there is any kind of weakness, be it mental, physical or emotional, there is the risk that anxiety can move in and take root. For that reason and for the best chance of recovery, it is crucial to be alert to its effects and to act on them as quickly as possible.

However, that is not to say that anxiety disorders are an inevitable consequence of psychological illness. Many people will not be affected and those who follow a healthy lifestyle and look after their own well-being are more likely to have the strongest defence against it. For those who do develop anxiety, maintaining that lifestyle is a key tool in helping them tackle it.

The question of how to deal with anxiety is particularly important when you consider the part it can play in the development of other conditions. Seeking help for the debilitating symptoms that may leave sufferers isolated, anxious and unmotivated is crucial, not only to tackle the anxiety, but also as one defence against wider health issues.

Anxiety disorders do not automatically accompany other illnesses, but they *can* occur alongside some of them. Bearing this in mind and remaining alert to the possibility of anxiety is an important line of defence for sufferers and carers alike.

Chapter 7

Anxiety in the under 25s

Peer pressure

by Samantha Crilly

I have never really fitted in with the 'norm'
Though I spent all my teenage years feeling under
pressure to conform.
I worried so much about what other people thought of me
I failed to be truly happy.
I felt like I was uncool because I didn't do what the 'it'
girls did –
I couldn't possibly just say 'I'm staying in tonight';
GOD FORBID!
I would sit and watch a movie which I should have
technically enjoyed
Yet I was too busy thinking I should be at all the places I'd
tried so hard to avoid,
And even if I did go, I never enjoyed it anyway,
I just wish I could go back in time and tell myself it's okay –
Stop being paranoid about people wondering why you're
not there
Because, truth be told, most of them don't really care –
They are too busy living their own lives to be that worried
about you.
So make sure you pursue whatever you want to do
And to be whoever you want to be
Because that is the only way you will ever be truly free.

We would all like to believe that someone's school days are the happiest days of their life, and for many, even in today's increasingly pressured society, that still does remain the case. However, for a significant number of young people, mental ill health is a reality that will sadly forever taint their experience of growing up, whether dealing with concerns at primary school, coping through adolescence at secondary level, making the hard transition to university or heading out into the 'real world' at the end of it all.

Given that the earlier we identify and help those with a mental illness, the better their chances of recovery are, it is imperative for parents, carers, teachers and friends to have their eyes open to any potential issues that could arise during these life stages.

Juliet tells us of the moment she first became aware of her own anxiety:

> I have always been an anxious person, but I think I first became aware of this when I was in reception class at primary school, aged five. I accidentally drew on another child's school shirt with a whiteboard pen and was so overwhelmed by this 'terrible act' and guilt that I couldn't focus and cried uncontrollably.

Sadly, the statistics are alarming. Some studies show that almost one in eight young people will experience a mental illness before they are 19 years old[45] and almost four in five teachers said that in the preceding year they had seen a pupil struggle with a mental health issue, anxiety being the most common of them all.[46]

With a huge pressure in the UK on Child and Adolescent Mental Health Services (CAMHS) in many areas, there can often be a long waiting list for help and support, leaving many vulnerable young people battling on with issues that could have serious consequences for their ongoing health and happiness. It is devastating to think that young people are not getting the support and help that they need, and the impact this can also have on already over-stretched parents or carers and hard-pressed teachers. If a child's behaviour is giving cause for concern, try not to ignore it and hope it will go away or sit back and accept the possibly long wait for help and support. The longer it goes on, the more likely it is to disrupt your child's life and could potentially develop into something more sinister and long-term.

Carol looks back to the beginning of her son's OCD and anxiety:

> Steven loved his toy cars. I remember he used to line them up in colour order in certain places in his bedroom. If anyone wanted to play with them and moved them out of order, he would become very agitated and upset, to the point that we made sure we didn't touch the cars. In hindsight, I now realise that his behaviour was the start of his OCD, which escalated in his teens.

The under 25s and the Covid-19 pandemic

The coronavirus outbreak created a huge challenge for young people. In general, not taking into account an individual's own mental health issues, the impact may have varied according to their age. For youngsters who may lack the capacity to rationalise and fully understand the implications of the pandemic, the handwashing, social distancing, class 'bubbles' and the like, were bewildering and, at the other end of the scale, could have been terrifying. Even for older children, the impact has been profound. Time spent isolated from teachers and friends may have had a major impact, which will have been worsened if the young person's homelife also feeds their stress and/or anxiety.

For teenagers, concerns about losing out on education, facing disrupted exam preparation, or losing out on expected grades were all hugely upsetting. Add in fears about the shrinking job market and it is all too clear that the current generation of young people have a whole raft of reasons to feel in a state of heightened anxiety.

In a survey by the charity Young Minds in June 2020, a third of 18 to 24 year olds surveyed said they had felt hopeless as a result of the pandemic, with eight in 10 saying that it had made their mental health worse. Just one in 10 said their mental health had improved, perhaps because having to stay at home took them out of a stressful situation at school.[47]

Anxiety in young children

As a parent or carer, if you think or feel something is amiss with your child then you are probably right. As a mum myself, I always say, that there is nothing more powerful than a parent's intuition and love, so do not be afraid to follow and act on your instincts.

When young children feel anxious, they cannot always understand or communicate what and how they are feeling. Some signs you may notice can include:

- becoming excessively irritable, withdrawn, tearful and/or clingy
- having difficulty sleeping
- waking in the night
- wetting the bed on a frequent basis
- having nightmares
- having difficulties socialising with other children.

Eve shares her experience of anxiety from a young age:

In primary school I hated having the attention focused on me. I would look away when asked a question, burning with embarrassment, feeling unable to speak, leave the room and shake violently. It was awful, especially when back then I had no idea what was wrong with me.

The causes of anxiety disorders in young children

Anxiety disorders rarely have one specific cause but are usually a combination of biological, psychological and environmental factors. It may be that a child has a biological vulnerability to mental illness which is triggered when they experience a difficult, traumatic or confusing life event. There are some situations and events that are of particular note, which I will now endeavour to explain in more detail.

Bullying

We tend to think of bullying as someone ganging up on a child in the school playground. Sadly, this is only one aspect of the issue. Bullying can happen in and out of the school environment, in a school club, online or even at the hands of a family member. Whoever it is dishing out the demeaning behaviour, the effects on the person they are targeting can be profound, making them feel isolated, worthless, lonely, anxious, angry and / or lacking in confidence.

Suzie, whose daughter suffers from social anxiety disorder, looks back at the bullying her daughter endured:

> As a parent, the hardest thing for me was hearing about the level of bullying that had gone on in her school years. Whilst I was aware of some things, there was plenty that she had not confided in me about. I had dealt with certain instances as best I could through the school but I think that in the end, they got bored of me. By the end of junior school, they listened to me but ignored me and never took any action. The thought of this upsets her a lot, even to this day, as she says that her Year 6 teacher was well aware of what was going on and very often witnessed the bullying she received but did nothing about it. Had I known half of what I know now, I like to think that I would have been more assertive with the school. At one point, I enquired about moving her but was told it wasn't a good idea as she was in her SATs year. I wish I hadn't been so accepting.

Rightly or wrongly, the guilt and regret that I didn't pick up on what was happening to her and help her are insurmountable. It upsets me even now. If I had moved her, would it have prevented her anxiety? Would she have been a happier child?

The crucial way to tackle bullying is to break the silence that so often surrounds it. Keeping quiet about being targeted will not stop it from happening. If you suspect a child you care for is being bullied, ask them about it and encourage them to talk about it and then to report it, whether to the school, their parent, club leader, youth worker and/or – in the case of online bullying – to the website or social media platform involved.

Melissa, a classroom assistant in a primary school, shares her thoughts on bullying:

One familiar cause is that bullying remains in schools, despite schools prioritising policies and education around this negative aspect of school life. Additionally, the nature and severity of this have changed over time. In the last three years or so, I have seen an increase in incidents of bullying as a direct consequence of children's access to technology. For example, we have had issues with 10-year-olds using WhatsApp to bully, by removing others from certain chat groups. This is a new dimension of bullying in primary schools as more and more young children have their own smartphones. It follows the victim home and then spills over into life at school.

Adam, who suffers from social anxiety, shares his experience of being bullied in school:

At school it [the bullying] improved my studies. I was bullied when I was 15-16 years old so I guess as an act of finding self-worth I threw myself into my studies for A levels. Socially I was awkward at school. I don't think I was a hugely outgoing kid before I went to my boarding school but I became quieter, more reserved and more introverted.

Feeling 'different'

Young people do not need to be actively bullied to be suffering from low self-esteem and/or self-worth, and this could, if left unchecked, trigger a mental illness such as anxiety. For a fragile young mind, simply feeling 'different' may be enough to leave them feeling adrift. It may be something visible that makes them feel at odds with others, such as a physical condition that, in their eyes, makes them different. Alternatively, they may sense a cultural separateness that they cannot ignore. Either way, this otherness can grow from a small seed of disquiet into something that can dominate their life and potentially their mental health.

Eve describes how her anxiety made her feel as a child:

> As a child suffering from social anxiety I felt like the odd one out in a box of milk chocolate. I would be the odd white one misplaced in there and would feel like I was all alone as the others said things about me and wore me down mentally.

Of course, that is not to say that 'difference' is anything to be ashamed of. Quite the contrary, in society today, individuality and diversity are rightly embraced and celebrated. However, for a young child, particularly one with a poor sense of self, 'fitting in' may be something they aspire to and if they feel that they fall short of that, it could trigger difficult feelings that, in those already more vulnerable to mental illness, should be taken seriously.

Jody Lowe, a Year 6 lead, shares his own views from working with young people:

> *I mainly see anxiety relating to physical appearance, being 'cool' and fitting in. Children are so worried about not looking 'the part' or not having the 'right' phone unlike everyone else. Children feel a greater need to 'fit in' and not be the odd one out. Not being the cool kid with the*

latest trainers, phone or school bag is causing huge anxiety for children and a huge increase in bullying and truancy.

Early separation from family

Throughout the childhood years, there are opportunities for children to spread their wings, gain independence and widen their social experiences. However, for some children, the milestones of going to nursery or a child-minder, starting school, moving to secondary school or beginning university can present huge challenges. In younger children it is not unusual for separation anxiety to develop, while it may present as social anxiety in older teenagers.

Like so many aspects of anxiety disorders, nothing is clear cut. While for some children the fear about taking a step into the unknown without the presence of their parents or care-giver(s) can be the clear trigger for the anxiety, for others, the anxiety may actually have a different underlying cause, but beginning a 'scary' new chapter could be the trigger that magnifies it or takes it to the next level.

Care-givers should be on the lookout for children who are angry or upset before the school day starts. They may be slow to get dressed or reluctant to gather their things together, and could also talk about having a headache or tummy-ache. These could be signs of anxiety that need to be monitored.

For older children who may feel isolated and imprisoned by their social anxiety, at the same time as being plagued by the usual awkwardness of the teenage years, it can be a really difficult time. Going away to college or university may seem from afar to be a new opportunity and a chance for a new start – and, indeed, for many this is true – but for others, once the protective shield of family life has been removed, things can spiral out of control. The continued vigilance and love of family are essential. Finding support from a doctor or counsellor is also important. Finding individual self-help measures is also key; whether that is taking a daily walk, keeping a journal, following a hobby or taking exercise, it can be part of a young person's toolbox when it comes to tackling anxiety.

Myrtle says of how her anxiety and depression developed from a young age:

> I was always a shy child; at age eight I was put in a boarding school and that continued throughout the rest of my childhood. This was very emotionally traumatic due to separation from my mum, bullying and feeling alone.

Dealing with change

Change, such as moving house, parents separating, friends moving away or grandparents' health deteriorating, can having a big impact on a child's mental health, particularly if they are prone to anxiety. Other challenges, such as a household burglary or car accident, can also trigger anxiety.

Children may seem to cope at the time but can begin to struggle if one thing happens after another. They may find it particularly hard if they have not processed their feelings over one event or occurrence and then another comes along and knocks them sideways. Even seemingly small 'hiccups' can push their difficult feelings to a new, more serious, level.

Eco-anxiety

For any of us, seeing the terrible bushfires in Australia in 2019 or reading about the melting polar ice caps is incredibly worrying. The scale of the problem seems almost impossible to get our heads around, and the 'Domesday' rhetoric that surrounds it can be hard to handle.

For children this is magnified. Not only are they the generation likely to be most affected by the repercussions of climate change, but they also do not have the brain maturity to process their fears. Unsurprisingly, many look at the size of the issue and simply feel hopeless, and frustrated by the slow way that governments around the world are responding.

According to a large survey of youngsters aged 8 to 16 by the BBC's Newsround programme, nearly three quarters are worried about the state of the planet – including 22% who say they are 'very worried'.[48] Children are reporting that these concerns are affecting their eating habits and their sleep. A fifth say they are experiencing bad dreams as a result.

All of us – adults and children – may need support to process our concerns about the climate. Talking to each other, and listening and respecting each other's views, is an important starting point. Taking practical steps, such as walking instead of using the car, can also make people feel they are at least doing something in their own lives to tackle the issue. Joining a campaign group or working with friends to do something can also help young people feel more in control.

However, if the anxiety is having a real effect on different areas of a young person's life, stopping them from doing the things they once enjoyed or disturbing their sleep, social life or behaviour, it should not be dismissed as an 'understandable' or 'normal' concern. It should be tackled in the same way as any other mental illness, with help sought before it can spiral out of control and become harder to tackle.

Melissa, a classroom assistant in a primary school, shares her thoughts on the much-talked about climate change and the possible impact of this discourse on anxiety in young children:

> Climate change is discussed in PSHE lessons, in assemblies, in Geography, in English, in RE, on theme days, at Guides, in buying choices… it is a constant everyday thing now, and I am sure it contributes to anxiety. It is hard to see how to help with such a gargantuan problem, how to make a difference, how to have any control.

Family issues

Sometimes family problems or traumatic events at home can contribute to the onset of anxiety in young people. It is very hard for the young brain to process some of the difficult feelings surrounding divorce, family disputes, bereavement and/or illness; they could bottle up those confusing emotions, possibly for fear of upsetting other family members or thinking they might somehow be making things worse.

Each of these traumatic events will affect children in different ways and there are individual organisations that can support parents in helping their children to make sense of them. In the UK, organisations such as the NSPCC and Childline (see page 317) carry a wealth of information on their websites about how to help youngsters through these challenging events and times. Both also have helplines where both children and adults will find a sympathetic ear. The key for a parent or carer is not to cross your fingers and hope your youngster emerges unscathed. Instead, try to be proactive in seeking information and support and remain vigilant for signs that a child could be struggling.

Claire, a chaplain in a girl's secondary school, shares her thoughts on this:

> Family issues come up particularly around break-ups. Having a stable home is massively important. This can happen when parents separate, but this is not always the case. Many young people feel responsible for break-ups and can be used as a go-between.

Abuse and neglect

If a child is being physically, mentally or sexually abused, the effects will manifest themselves in different ways, one of which may be decline in their mental health. I think we are more familiar with the idea that someone who has been abused may struggle with a mental illness in later life but, of course, the impact can also be much more immediate.

Charliee looks back on her childhood:

> When I'm in an anxious state, I always hear negative comments that were made to me throughout childhood. It's difficult to pinpoint if that's the reason but I definitely think there is some kind of link between the two!

If you have concerns about a child being abused, the NSPCC website has lots of good advice about what you can do. The most important thing is to keep lines of communication open, taking the child's lead in the conversations you have together. By showing the child or young adult that they can talk to you and that you will listen, you are giving them the green light to open up further as and when they are ready. For further support, at the time of writing this, the NSPCC helpline is on 0808 800 5000.

Kimberly Lucas, personal advisor for social services, says:

> Working with care leavers who have experienced a lot of different types of trauma and mental health, I can see so clearly how young people have slipped through the cracks. The complexity of the individuals who come to my attention often means that they cannot sustain support with their mental health through agencies, often because they cannot remember appointments, or their chaotic lifestyle means that they struggle to engage. Although conversations are being had around mental health and the focus is on early intervention, there is a lack of resources to meet everyone's needs as it is not a case of one-size-fits-all and this leads to many young people being without help after a referral which means they often begin to use negative coping strategies, including substance misuse, which can increase their experiences of mental illness.

Social inequality

Growing up in poverty or in a financially struggling household can have a real impact on a child's mental health, with some research suggesting that children in the poorest households are 'three times more likely to have a mental illness than children in the more well-off households'.[49]

Children whose families struggle to afford many of the things in life that others take for granted can grow up feeling that they are somehow a failure and inadequate and that the future is hopeless. They may feel less able to enjoy time and activities with their peers on an equal footing, leaving them feeling 'different' as discussed already. They may also feel misunderstood by others and marginalised by society as a whole. All these things can leave an early impression on a child's mental health.

Anxiety and learning disabilities

Children who learn differently can be more at risk of mental illness, with up to 40% of young people with learning disabilities having a diagnosable mental health issue.[50]

This is in part due to the fact that the issues that can affect anyone's mental health are felt particularly keenly by those who have a learning difficulty or disability. Social isolation, insufficient support, feeling different from peers, and fears for the future can all play a part.

A further issue may be that symptoms of mental ill health may not be recognised as separate from the learning disability, and some individuals may not be able to express those difficult feelings in the same way as others. For example, challenging behaviour may be seen as part of the learning disability rather than another cause, such as anxiety, being investigated. Even a GP may attribute symptoms to the learning disability rather than raise concerns about mental illness.

Anxiety and autism spectrum conditions

People with autism are more at risk of mental illness, with suggestions that more than four in 10 children with autism have an anxiety disorder, compared with 3% of the general population.[51] This may be in part because of the challenges that many people with autism have interacting with the world around them, which can of course start from a very early age and can be extremely hard for youngsters with autism to understand. In addition, those with autism and other related conditions, who often rely on a predictable routine, can be particularly prone to anxiety if the structure to their life is altered or upset. They can become anxious due to the expectations of others or the fear of uncertainty or change. If this anxiety is not addressed, it can trigger further mental health issues.

People with autism may display their anxiety in different ways, maybe through repetitive behaviour, asking lots of questions, overthinking or getting 'stuck' in a particular thought pattern, getting upset or having a meltdown or withdrawing into themselves.

Many people find it hard to talk about their mental health and this can be even more challenging for people with autism, who may struggle to recognise their feelings initially and find it particularly difficult to communicate them. Even visiting the doctor can be a source of great stress and anxiety to people on the autistic spectrum, and so accessing appropriate help and support can sometimes be an even harder mountain to climb.

Autism is a lifelong condition, so these issues are not simply a concern of childhood. It is, though, important for carers to recognise the increased risk of mental illness in both adults and children on the autistic spectrum so that they know what symptoms to look out for and what help is available. Organisations such as the National Autistic Society (autism.org. uk – see page 318) give more detailed information.

Mel, whose son suffers from autism and anxiety, shares their experience of how the two are connected:

With autism, you have to be a bit of a detective. It's often likened to an iceberg. The behaviours we may see as a family are just the tip of it. The reasons that cause it are often hidden and that's what we have to work out. All too often, the hidden part of that iceberg is down to anxiety. My son will worry about pretty much anything: when his routine changes; when he forgets something for school; when he finds something hard to do; when I am out of the room; when the weather changes. The list is endless. The worries may seem small but for him they are huge, and when they are added together, they can have a big impact on his well-being. He also may struggle to understand and rationalise those concerns, so they can quickly spiral out of control. This then affects the way he interacts with others at home and at school. When he is anxious, he is much more likely to have emotional outbursts which are really debilitating for him and for those around him.

Caring for someone with special educational needs, in our case for my son with autism, can be overwhelming and I try to keep an eye on my own mental health to make sure I take time out and share the load so that I am not swamped by it. There are so many things that cause us day-to-day worries, from ensuring our son is getting the right schooling to doing our best to keep him happy and making him feel valued. There is an endless pile of paperwork to keep on top of, as well as a deluge of other information which I have to go through. He doesn't sleep well, which leaves us all tired, and he is very emotionally dependent on us, which can be draining. There are also the longer-term concerns about his future, which can be very hard even to think about. Even though he is getting older, there is little prospect of being able to leave him at home by himself, so it is hard for me and my husband to take time out for ourselves. All these things could potentially be damaging to our own mental health, and my husband and I try hard to look after each other in this respect, with one of us stepping up if the other is struggling. We are very aware of the fragility of carers' own mental well-being, so we do try to pro-actively look after ourselves while also giving our son all the care and attention he needs.

Talking to your child about mental health

Due to their immaturity, most children suffering from an anxiety disorder will have difficulty in knowing how to talk and communicate about what is going on inside their head. They may be confused, embarrassed and unable to process and understand the content of their thoughts. The most effective way to help them is through communication.

If your child is finding it difficult to verbalise their thoughts, encouraging them to draw or write down how they are feeling can sometimes be used as a different form of communication which can be just as effective as talking. This could help both of you to develop a better understanding of what is going on inside their head.

Another way to help your child open up is to use role play. Pretending to act out a difficult scenario, perhaps with the adult taking the place of the child and demonstrating what he or she would say in certain situations, can help children understand how to react to difficult situations in their life.

Through drawing or acting, or even singing a song or making up an expressive dance, you can give youngsters the confidence to open up about their feelings and emotions that may be connected to or could lead to an anxiety disorder. With this in mind, it is important to pick the right moment and location, and it should be at a time and in a place where they feel relaxed, safe and secure.

'Worry time'

It can often take time and patience for parents to see that behind the obstinacy and moaning there is anxiety and uncertainty. However, getting irritated or angry can often make things worse. It is important for parents to try to talk calmly to children about the things that are worrying them, and to reassure them whenever possible.

Hearing their fears and respecting their feelings will give them the opportunity to open up. If they suffer from anxiety when they are separated from you, telling them about what you have done while they have been at school will help ease some of the 'unknowns' of your time apart. Doing some things together after school – a trip to the cinema, tea in a café or a nice walk together – that they can look forward to, may also help them to see that there is more to their life than simply going to school.

Some families find that having a 'worry box' or 'worry times' can help. These are both cognitive behavioural therapy (CBT) techniques. Worry time is a set time each day when they can talk to you about their fears, rather than letting those worries run away with them all day long. Do this at the same time each day, in the same place, ideally not straight before bedtime.

A worry box can be particularly helpful for young children. Get them to choose and decorate a box (maybe a shoe box) and cut a hole in the top. Then encourage them to write or draw their worries on paper, then post the worries in the box. The worries are then in the box and 'out' of the child's mind. Some families will find it helpful to use both techniques – having a worry box and a set time each day to talk to a child about their concerns.

Nicholas Warburton, Psy-TaP practitioner, shares a simple but effective way to help children combat their anxiety using the three Fs:

'Fingers – Focus – Figure 8'

1. Finger squeeze – Extend the first and second finger on one hand and using the other hand, wrap your hand around the two fingers and squeeze as if you are trying to find the pulse but don't crush them.
2. Focus – While you're still doing the finger squeeze, remember that anxiety is the anticipation of what might happen, not what is happening. Breathe slowly and inhale the positivity, exhale the negativity. Repeat five times.

3. Figure 8 – With two fingers you were squeezing, trace a figure 8 on its side (Infinity loop) on your forehead. Cross over in the centre of the forehead and loop out to in line with the outside of your eyes. Repeat this 20 times or for about 20 seconds.

You'll notice that things calm down, your heart rate slows and your breathing has become deeper and longer. You've got this and you're back in control. You're a three-Fs master!

Anxiety in teenagers

The causes of anxiety in teenagers include the factors already covered when discussing younger children: bullying, social isolation, issues at home, social inequality and learning difficulties, as well as having other mental illnesses as covered in Chapter 6.

There are however further issues relevant to teenagers that could have an impact on their mental health. These can include: pressure to succeed at school, peer pressure, coming to terms with sexuality and relationships, experimenting with drugs and alcohol and dealing with the pressures of social media. All of these are exacerbated by the maelstrom of change caused by puberty.

Caroline shares the start of her daughter's anxiety and depression:

> She had managed to settle into secondary school well and was a happy, well-adjusted 13-year-old, but half-way through her second year at senior school all of this changed. One of her close friends started being unkind to her. It really was just childish things: speaking to her one day and not speaking to her the next; making snide remarks to her in the classroom; a little bit rougher in sports lessons than she needed to be; putting her down in front of others; cutting her out of conversations.

All of this went on over several months and our daughter started feeling displaced at school and insecure about herself. We knew it was being at school that was making her feel low because during school holidays she would bounce back and be her usual self. However, over time this started changing and it was taking longer and longer in the holidays to get her back to feeling herself. She went back to school in September a little anxious but generally in good spirits and the same behaviour started again with this one girl. Sometime over the next couple of months she decided to open up a social media account. She started comparing her life to others on there, was able to see when others from school had got together and she hadn't been invited along. She started feeling insecure about her body. She didn't feel she looked as good as all the other girls. She became very critical of herself and gradually over the next couple of months she went downhill very, very quickly. It hadn't really crossed our minds that she was suffering from anxiety and depression.

Puberty

Teenage angst is a very common issue in pubescent young adults as they struggle to get to grips with the rapid hormonal and physical changes that their bodies are being subjected to. What once seemed to be a stereotypically sociable, relatively happy and engaging child can quickly become subdued, dramatic, over-sensitive, self-conscious, short-tempered and distant. These are all normal shifts in adolescence, as teenagers naturally try to find their own platform and independence, detached from the usual securities of their family unit.

At the same time, huge hormonal and brain changes are underway, often throwing logical reasoning off-kilter and opening the door to confusing and sometimes irrational thought processes. Most teenagers will experience short-lived episodes of angst as they navigate their way through the challenging cross-over from childhood to being a young adult and emotions such as sadness, anxiety and frustration will occasionally come to the fore. Problems at school or with friendships and relationships can often be the main culprits, but usually these periods of anguish only last for a short period of time.

Lottie gives us her personal thoughts:

> I think troubles with friends gave me low self-esteem as I never really had a secure friendship group that was nice to me. I spent a lot of time alone at school and was always judged by other people.

It is incredibly hard to differentiate between what is normal behaviour for a teenager and what is not, but generally any prolonged and repeated episodes of destructive or out of character behaviour could be early warning signs of a more chronic problem, such as a mental health issue.

Pressure to succeed

The pressure to conform to a certain ideal is felt particularly strongly during adolescence and not least because young people can feel that success has to be achieved, no matter what the personal cost. There can be pressure to get good exam results, to achieve on the sporting field, to get into a certain school set or to move onto a particular college or university. Not achieving these things can leave a young person feeling that they are somehow lacking and that they must be to blame.

Jenny shares with us her experience with her daughter:

> My daughter started to worry about everything – she thought that by not doing well in her exams she would ruin her whole life. She had low self-esteem and thought she wasn't good enough, and only by listening to her repeat the same thing on more than one occasion I realised she wasn't coping, and by knowing Lynn and having spoken to her about it before, I knew we needed to do something.

Sexuality and relationships

It is hard to escape the issue of sex in today's society and for teenagers trying to understand their own sexuality, this can feel unsurprisingly overwhelming. Coming to terms with sexuality, relationships and early heartbreak are among the most testing teenage experiences. For those with low self-esteem or who are vulnerable to mental illness, issues around sexuality can add significant extra pressure.

The situation can be exacerbated for those questioning their sexuality or their gender. Although society is becoming more understanding and accepting of sexual diversity, there is little doubt that those who are gay, bisexual, transsexual or gender-neutral face greater challenges to their mental health. In an NHS survey, more than a third of young people aged 14- to 19-years-old who identified as gay, bisexual or with another sexual identity had a mental disorder, as opposed to 13% of those who identified as heterosexual.[52]

Aaron shares his own experience:

My anxiety and depression have been such a bumpy ride. I first noticed these when I was at secondary school; all through college, I just couldn't pin point what was wrong with me. When I went off to university, I came to realise that it was because I was living a life that was not me; I was gay. I just didn't 100% know it, or I didn't want to admit it. I actually found a partner at university which really helped me with my own feelings. The thing I was most worried about was how to tell my parents. I had formulated a scenario in my head that my parents would disown me and I would be left with no one. This caused me to fall into a pit of depression. I saw a therapist at university who really encouraged me to speak with my parents, which finally, after two years, I did. I have not looked back. They were very shocked, but it felt like a massive weight off my shoulders, and my low moods and dark thoughts gradually faded.

Drugs and alcohol

It is natural for teenagers to want to try new things, push boundaries and take risks and, as such, many will experiment with smoking, drinking and taking drugs. Individual families will have their own views on this, but if you are worried about your child, or feel they are using alcohol or drugs as part of a mental health issue, it is paramount not to ignore it.

Parents who can talk openly and honestly about alcohol and drugs, making it part of everyday chat rather than a huge one-off conversation, will be showing by example that their door is always open and that the subject is not taboo. Discussing all aspects of drinking and drug-taking, including how mental health can be affected by drinking too much, or using drugs, will help them to make safe and healthy decisions.

If you fear your child is making unhealthy choices around substance use (including alcohol), do not hesitate in seeking help. Your GP should be a good first stop and they should be able to point you in the direction of an organisation that can help.

As a parent or carer, it is also important to bring your own knowledge about illegal drugs up to date, including the effects of taking them, so that if necessary, you are able to talk from a position of some authority.[53]

Acne

According to the NHS, acne affects around 95% of teenagers and younger adults aged 11 to 30, and in some cases, it can continue into adult life. Around 3% of adults over the age of 35 suffer have acne.[54] Anyone who has suffered from a skin issue will most likely say that it is much more than just skin deep.

A study has shown that a staggering 68% of those monitored who had acne vulgaris, also suffered from anxiety.[55] Other studies have shown the presence of other mental health conditions in patients with acne, including low self-esteem, avoidance, depression, shame, suicidal thoughts and attempts, and difficulties in applying for a job. The outcome of this study signposts how important it is that both professionals and the loved ones around the sufferer monitor mood symptoms in those with acne and initiate treatment if the sufferer is displaying signs of an anxiety disorder or another mental illness.[56]

Carla shares her experience of suffering from severe acne when she was a teenager:

My acne started flaring up from the age of around 11 or 12. It wasn't just a pimple here and there – it was all over my face. I used to wake up every day with five new spots; they were also very painful, and it got so bad I could barely open my mouth to eat. I was on antibiotics on and off for eight years; every time I tried to come off them it came up again almost overnight. It was just awful; people used to stop me in the street and ask what had happened to my face; my heart would drop and I would feel so small and disgusting. I also handed in my notice at work because I was so embarrassed about how awful my skin was. It really affected my confidence and caused me to not want to leave the house. I finally went on a stronger medication; one of the side-effects of the medication was depression… but I was already depressed… so what did I have to lose? It took around three months to work, but as soon as I started seeing a difference in my skin, my mood started lifting. Acne is so much more than just a physical thing; it affected my whole life.

Social media

There are few teenagers who are not in thrall to social media. Fuelled by their desire for approval and admiration from friends (and strangers), as well as a very 21st century 'affliction' known as fear of missing out' (FOMO), many spend hours on social media sites every day from as soon as they get their first smartphone – often around the age of 10 or 11.

While on the one hand, the sense of community and

shared interaction with others can be beneficial, there are also undoubted downsides to heavy social media use, with a link to poor mental health being one of the key concerns. We will explore this in far more depth in Chapter 10, but suffice it to say that teenagers, with their fragile egos and frail self-esteem, are particularly vulnerable to the feelings of inadequacy that all of us, at any age, experience when faced with the seemingly perfect lives that people post online. Furthermore, the time they spend on their devices scrolling through these styled images and carefully curated posts is time they are not spending having the face-to-face conversations that are essential for mental well-being.

Melissa Helliwell, vice principal at Oak Academy in Bournemouth, shares her thoughts on the link between anxiety and social media:

> Anxiety is not a new situation; however, it is something that has evolved exponentially alongside our developing environment, therefore it would be remiss to think that social media has not had a part to play. Our young people are constantly 'plugged in' to a medium that, in many cases, governs their thoughts, personality, and belief systems; practically their life. They can find anything on this platform, ask questions that seemingly no one else has the answers to and often find answers that they had not even considered before or knew existed. Young people do not always have the ability to filter and if this is the case, then their search responses are going to be unfiltered too.

Melissa, a classroom assistant in a primary school, also shares her thoughts:

> There is no doubt in my mind that social media has a part to play in young people developing mental health issues. In primary education, we see children being increasingly bullied through it, in what should be the sanctuary of their own homes. We see children not managing their time on technology, losing too much sleep, sending them towards mental ill health at a young age. I also

think that the huge amount of time children spend looking at other people on social media platforms influences low self-esteem and anxiety levels.

Signs to look out for

When looking for signs of an anxiety disorder (or another mental illness), some valuable things to consider might include:

- Does the person worry excessively?
- Have you noticed a sadness or low mood that does not seem to go away?
- Are they irritable?
- Have they lost interest in things they used to enjoy and go out less with their friends?
- Do they seem to be exhausted a lot of the time?
- Do they have trouble sleeping, or sleep more than usual?
- Has their confidence taken a dip?
- Do they talk about feeling guilty, worthless or hopeless, or seem lacking in emotion?
- Do they talk about hurting themselves or show any signs of self-harm?
- Are they having problems at school or playing up, getting themselves into trouble?

Hattie talks of her experience with her best friend who has recently been diagnosed with anxiety and OCD:

Before my best friend was diagnosed with her OCD and anxiety, I was getting very worried about the way she was acting. She was being very all over the place but at the same time seemed to be sort of trying to take control of things too. She also started to not tell me the truth about some things, which really upset me. She was always late to meet me, and I started to think she didn't want to be friends anymore. I did not want to give up on our friendship and knew something was not right with her, so I spoke to her mum about my concerns. Now she has a diagnosis and is receiving help, I can support her as my friend and hopefully help her return to her old self again.

How to talk to teenagers about mental health

The difficulty in identifying a mental illness in a teenager is that teenagers can seem reluctant to openly communicate with those closest to them, thus making an accurate diagnosis quite challenging. Confronting them head-on and throwing specific questions at them, such as 'Do you have a mental illness?' or 'Have you self-harmed?' may be counter-productive, causing them to clam up, run away or shout back. Instead, creating an environment where they feel trusted, safe and respected is much more likely to help them open up.

This means making mental health a subject that you talk about little and often. It is just as important as physical health and if we can begin to talk about it in the same way as we do other illnesses, it will not be pushed to one side and get worse. It also means that youngsters are less likely to bottle up their problems because they will not have fears about how you may react.

There will be times when you have specific issues to address; where and when you choose to do this is up to you, but go for a place to talk where they feel relaxed and unpressurised. Some parents find that a car journey can be a good place to conduct tricky conversations, allowing youngsters to talk without the full glare of their parents' attention on them. Adults too may feel more at ease in this situation than they might do facing their teenager over the kitchen table or in the naturally defensive environment of the teen's bedroom. Talking on a car journey also makes it harder to slam doors or storm out!

Sometimes something you read in a magazine or see on television will provide the perfect starting point for a conversation. It might be a character in a soap opera highlighting an issue, or a report on the news about the stress young people are under. This is when the media can be used to positive effect as the starting point for a chat about mental health.

Wherever and whenever you decide to talk, start the conversation without accusation or assumption (not least because you may find that you have jumped to the wrong conclusion) and try to ask open questions rather than homing in on specific issues. This might mean opening up the conversation by saying something like, 'You have been very quiet lately... is something troubling you?' or 'You have not seemed yourself recently. Is there anything wrong?' Their answer may not come during that conversation or even soon after, but by opening up the discussion you are showing to them that you are there to help, whenever they feel ready to talk. When they do feel able to open up, the key is to listen. Do not assume that you know what they are going to say or leap in and pretend you have all the answers. Instead, really hear what they are saying about their own situation and equip them to find a way forward with your help.

Abigail talks of when she spoke to her son about his mental health worries:

> The first time I tried to speak to my son, I regret that I think I jumped in too quickly to a conclusion that he wasn't ready for. I then slowly planted seeds so he knew he could talk to me when he was ready. It was an extremely slow and painful winter; however, he then came to me and said he needed to talk and we had a very open and honest conversation and agreed we would look into getting him professional help. I am so pleased I decided to give him the space and time to come to me himself; I do however think if it had gone on much longer, I would have had needed to intervene somehow.

It is important not to judge teenagers, even if you do not necessarily agree with what they are telling you. Even though your mind may be racing and your heart hammering, it is important to stay calm. When they are looking to you for guidance, showing panic will only unsettle them further. Perhaps you can share a situation in your own life where you felt worried or stressed to show them that their feelings are understandable and natural.

It often helps teenagers to feel that they can help themselves, so part of your role may be giving them the tools to do this. Once they start talking to you, help them identify what they can do to help. Say to them: 'When you feel that way, what kinds of things could you do to make things feel better?' and you can perhaps help them think of sports, hobbies or other activities that they find calming or confidence-building. You can also point them towards books, websites, podcasts and health information that they can read and digest in their own time, filling them with knowledge that in time they can use to feel more in control of their own well-being.

I make it sound relatively straightforward but, of course, when teenage hormones are mixed with the maelstrom of emotions that accompany any mental health concern, there will be many twists and turns and cross words along the way. Being aware that teenagers often hit out at those that they love and trust the most – especially when they feel confused, scared and unsure about the future – may help the teenager to understand their reactions and to stay calm during the most testing times.

At the same time, do all you can to increase the teenager's resilience to the pressures they are facing. Help them sleep better, eat well and take regular exercise. Encourage them to spend less time on their electronic devices and get out and about, continue to see family and friends and make time for doing things together, even if it is just taking the dog for a walk or making a cake together.

Sarah, whose husband suffers from both anxiety and depression which has reflected onto their son, shares how she has increased her son's resilience:

> When my husband's anxiety and depression started having an impact on the ability of our son, who started to feel like a victim at school because he became the target of bullies etc, I knew

that I needed to make my son more empowered and resilient. By focusing on my son's well-being and encouraging him to talk to another adult outside the family about his frustrations, that led to my husband 'owning' the need to help himself for the sake of our son.

Finally, if you are the carer, do not forget yourself in all this. The role that you play, as a parent/carer, can be one of a child's most important defences against mental ill health. Make time for yourself and get support from friends, family, loved ones and/or colleagues, and your GP if necessary. Looking after yourself and acknowledging how you feel is vital for you if you are to be able to support your child.

Teachers are well placed to spot the early signs

As I have said throughout this book, anxiety disorders can affect anyone regardless of age, gender, sexuality, social background and/or ethnicity; however, families and carers should be particularly alert during adolescence. It is crucial for us to try to understand how the secondary school years can have an impact, and how head teachers, teachers and support staff are in a pole position to recognise the signs and symptoms. These professionals then can be the ones to observe the potential onset of an anxiety disorder, enabling them to trigger the early intervention which is so key to tackling this and other mental illnesses successfully.

Hope Dear from the Grace Dear Trust tells us why they are concentrating on giving teachers training in recognising mental ill health symptoms:

Grace [Hope's sister] had been suffering from depression and anxiety from the age of 13 but hadn't felt she could reach out to anyone to help her make sense of her feelings. Not knowing why, she suffered in silence for many years. Eventually, when Grace spoke out, we tried to give the best help possible, but unfortunately it was too late.

We are working collaboratively with local schools, to educate and inform teachers of the signs and symptoms of mental illness and what to look out for. As Grace was in school for the most part when she was suffering, we feel that if those around her had been more educated on what to look for, her suffering could have been picked up much sooner than it was.

Of course, teachers are in school to teach and with increasingly stretched budgets and the pressure for their students to perform, their jobs appear harder than ever. However, they are also human beings and if faced with a student who they are concerned may have a mental illness, such as an anxiety disorder, few would I am sure turn their backs. However, they are not experts – and no one expects them to be.

Melissa Helliwell, vice principal at Oak Academy in Bournemouth, shares her thoughts on this:

Schools are no longer only places for education; they are the main hub for all multi-agency support referrals. Increased funding cuts, pressure for progress and achievement, sparse training for all and a lack of time do little to support mental health concerns within some schools.

It may, therefore, be helpful to note the signs of an anxiety disorder that may become particularly noticeable in the school environment. Causes for concern include the following. The teenager may:

- perform less well, dropping grades or struggling to complete their work
- start to miss school more often
- appear lacking in energy
- start to isolate themselves
- struggle to concentrate in class
- show signs of tiredness and irritability
- show signs of low confidence and self-esteem

- set themselves unreasonably high standards
- excessively worry about their schoolwork and grades.

How teachers can help

Not only can school staff play an important part in noticing the signs of anxiety, which can hopefully lead to early intervention, but a trusted teacher can be the person that a student confides in if they are worried about their own mental health. With around three children in every classroom affected by a mental health issue,[57] it is a good first step for a teacher to make sure they are familiar with their school's mental health policy, if indeed there is one. That way they will know what to do if the issue arises with one of their students.

If you are a teacher and a student does open up to you about a mental health issue, the most important thing to do is take the time to listen to them. It may have taken them a long while to muster up the courage to approach you and so it is important to demonstrate that what they are saying matters. If you need to tell someone else about what they have told you, try to let the student know who that person is and explain why you need to talk to them, so that the student will not feel that you have betrayed their trust.

In some cases, it may be necessary to seek extra help outside the school community and that could include a referral to Child and Adolescent Mental Health Services (CAMHS). Each school should have a policy on this and a staff member assigned to make a CAMHS referral if necessary.

Lessons in prevention

A school's role is not just to act when they are concerned or worried about a pupil. It is also to educate, inform and support them throughout their education, helping to nurture their confidence so that they can grow up with a strong sense of self. Good self-esteem and confidence in one's own abilities are powerful defences against a mental illness, such as anxiety, and schools have an important – and wonderful – part to play in strengthening the armour that will protect their pupils throughout their life.

Jody Lowe, a Year 6 lead (lead teacher for the final year of primary school), shares his own views from working with young people:

> Like sex education, this has to be for a purpose and aimed at the right age. Children need help, beyond the curriculum. Children need to be educated in how to cope with the harsh world they live in. Life is so confusing for kids today. Growing up seems harder than when I was a kid. I am 44, not too old. I don't recall my childhood being so fraught with danger – terrorism, racism, cruelty on so many levels. Children need to know what mental health means, what it looks and feels like. Children need to be taught how to spot problems in themselves and others around them.

Melissa Helliwell, vice principal at Oak Academy in Bournemouth, repeats this:

> I personally take an interest in this area of our young people's lives as without understanding this, we cannot help students to achieve their potential or encourage them to understand how valued they are. Many believe that they are not 'worthy' and as a result then hurt themselves in a myriad of different ways; sadly, both physically and psychologically.

There are many opportunities throughout the curriculum to help young people grow a knowledgeable, confident and resilient attitude towards themselves. From personal, social, health and economic education (PSHE) lessons through to physical education (PE), there are many occasions to discuss good mental health and well-being. Through involving pupils in discussions about mental illness, schools can help all young people to be aware of these issues and this can in turn help them to both recognise and understand problems in themselves or in their friends.

Claire, chaplain in a girls' secondary school, shares her thoughts on the raised awareness of mental health issues:

The more we can talk about our feelings, the more we can begin to understand and help. There are too many people, old and young, who feel ashamed about their mental health, and, though that stigma is changing, it's not enough. Hopefully with more awareness more can be done to help prevent people feeling alone and considering suicide. We are quick to seek help when we are physically ill but less so when it comes to mental health. I'd also hope that, the more we understand the kinder we can be – that is lacking at times in our world!

Now, the flip side to this is that some people can be very quick to label themselves, often on the back of a Google search. Young people like to have a label sometimes. They also cannot always distinguish between what it is to have an anxiety disorder and what is simply feeling anxious about something. Students will often tell me they have depression, but they've made that decision rather than seeking professional help. When you talk it through, they are actually feeling down about a particular issue or having a low day, rather than being depressed.

Anxiety at university

The move from school to university can be a difficult one to make, involving leaving home for the first time, meeting new people, facing unknown experiences, and having to take control of their own finances – and own life – for the first time. It is no wonder that this can be a particularly challenging time for those with mental illness or those vulnerable to developing one. A study of university students reported high levels of anxiety, with an alarming 42.8% often or always being worried. Almost nine in 10 (87.7%) said they struggled with feelings of anxiety.[58]

While some students adjust with apparent ease to the transition, others may feel overwhelmed with the new responsibilities they face. Most expect university to be the best days of their life, and if it feels very different, they may find themselves struggling.

Pete tells of how his anxiety grew at university:

> When it first arose, I'd become very anxious about being at university, worrying that I didn't fit in and that I wasn't clever enough to be on the law degree that I was studying. This caused me to feel very anxious about lectures and seminars and also social occasions.

All this can be made worse by the move away from home, and the seismic change that this brings to all areas of their life. Without the support circle of family and established friendships, it can be easy to feel very isolated. Furthermore, students are often drinking too much and may be experimenting with drugs. They are likely to be anxious about money and feeling pressure to justify the huge cost of this investment in their education, and they are also facing the weight of expectation that their time at university should be the best time of their life. All this can make a pretty perfect recipe for anxiety and/or depression.

It can also be very hard to find someone to trust and confide in, within the new and unfamiliar environment. That can mean that those battling a mental illness can often find themselves suffering in silence; their anxiety or dark thoughts steadily gaining control, often without anyone really noticing. Universities have increasing awareness of their responsibilities towards students with mental illness. However, the nature of college and university life where individuals can so easily slip under the radar, makes providing a safety net for the most vulnerable students more challenging.

I would urge parents or carers who have a niggling concern about their loved one not to ignore it, even – or maybe especially – if they no longer live at home. If possible, make regular visits to your child, talk to them often, encourage them to share their worries or concerns and follow your instinct if you feel that something is amiss. Encourage them to take part in university life – to go to lectures, get involved in clubs, hang out in the library or coffee shop, where others are. Locking themselves in their small student room could only make things worse. Also remind them that there is life outside the university walls and urge them to find out what else the city where they are studying has to offer beyond that slightly unreal bubble of student life.

It is also helpful to remember that every university will have a counselling service which is usually free, and which is very used to listening to students facing some of these challenges. Encourage them to seek help or visit their GP to tackle their concerns before they escalate.

Trainee teacher and current university student, Alice, gives her advice:

Often student teachers are put under extra pressure as they have to study full-time for the teaching degree but also spend time at school placements learning about new subjects and plan classes under observation. This can be challenging on your mental health, so it is crucial for student teachers to be able to talk to each other about their difficulties and also take advantage of the mental health well-being services available to them at university.

Finally, remind your student son or daughter that university life often does not live up to the hype, that it is not unusual to feel sad, lonely, homesick and/or excluded. However, at the same time, do not write off those feelings as 'normal' in case that stops them from seeking help. Encourage them to keep talking to you about how they feel and give them the details of the university counselling service so that they know there is somewhere they can go to for help.

Anxiety after education

While going on to further education can be hard, so can leaving school or university for the 'real world'. Without the shared experience that education can give someone, it can be all too easy to feel alone and adrift. Problems can feel unique to them and the battles they face may appear to be ones they must tackle alone. However, while it may feel that way, it is possible to find people who can walk forward with us and help make us feel less alone.

It can be particularly testing for those who are looking for work. Many graduates find themselves living back with their parents, often feeling that they have lost the independence and freedom that they built up away from home. Friends may now be a long way away and it can be easy to wallow in that old mental health adversary, loneliness. Without the structure of school or university, the days can seem directionless. Without a job, it can feel like the months stretch on ahead with no real plan. This emptiness can be very hard to get to grips with.

Even for those who do secure a job, the reality of working life can be very different from the dreams they may have harboured for many years. In place of the great pad and smart wardrobe may be a dingy flat-share and living on a starting salary results in yet more money worries. After years of dreaming about being grown-up, it can often be a shock to find it is not as they had imagined. If you add in the stress of possibly moving to a new city, meeting new people, and probably burning the candle at both ends, it can be easy to understand why these years can be difficult to handle.

As always, the role of family and friends is never-ending. Instead of assuming you have got your loved one 'off your hands', check in on them as much as you can. In these years when they are learning to 'run' without your hand to hold, they may find themselves 'stumbling' or even 'falling over'. Reminding them they are not alone, acknowledging how difficult this time of their life can be, and showing them where they can find help is paramount for nurturing their mental health and helping them deal with difficult feelings. If you have real concerns about their state of mind, encourage them to talk to their GP or seek further professional help, and monitor them as closely as you can.

To conclude

It is essential that everyone involved in the life of a young person or, indeed, anyone suffering from an anxiety disorder, employs compassion, understanding and patience. In this way, home schools, clubs, colleges and universities can become an effective part of the caring network for young people struggling with an anxiety disorder.

Throughout this book I have been careful to emphasise that anxiety disorders do not just affect the young. However, sometimes the underlying issues can begin to develop and form at this crucial age. Schools, colleges and universities are all environments where an anxiety disorder can take root. Where schools can, they should incorporate self-esteem into their programme – and preferably from an outside speaker. I say this not because I believe teachers are ill-equipped to deal with the issues, but because I know that young people will often open up to a stranger, safe in the knowledge that they will never see that person again.

There is much more work being done to break the taboo around mental illness. My Samantha, a recent drama graduate, has joined with friends to develop a funny and thought-provoking sketch show challenging and breaking that stigma. Through her work with 'My Mental Life', she is turning the illness that once tormented her on its head, using humour to educate others. I applaud her and all others working to support those tortured by mental illness, including anxiety disorders. I hope that many more people will take the opportunity to understand how sufferers feel and find out more about what they can do to help.

Chapter 8

Anxiety in the home

My guest: Anxiety
by Samantha Crilly

Sorry I can't make it tonight, I already have a guest,
A different kind of one, unlike the rest.
It is unwanted, if that makes you feel any better?
Anxiety always decides when we can spend
our time together.
Believe me, I'd much rather be with you,
But it never seems to allow our time together til it's long
overdue.
If I can, I'll pop by for an hour,
Although I may not talk much – I'll probably be drained
of brain power.
Still, I'd love to just sit quietly in your company.
Would that be okay? Just you and me?
If my guest comes knocking, we can chase
it away together.
Watch on as it starts to crack under the pressure –
I bet if we did that long enough, it wouldn't come
around anymore.
It'll be walking and whispering straight past my door.
Shall we do that? Take the heat from its flame?
Leave it wondering why it ever came?

Modern everyday life can be incredibly stressful. Every generation that has ever existed and evolved has probably said the same thing; however, that does not make it any less true. Today, the expectations of how family and personal life should be, have been completely transformed from how they were even 30 or 40 years ago.

The planet is forever changing, technology advancing and the population is expanding at quite a pace. We undoubtedly have more freedom of choice and are less confined to the traditional gender roles than in previous generations. Whilst these advances are inevitable and to be embraced within relationships and the home environment, some of the realities of contemporary culture such as technology, diet, consumerism and global events, may prove to be inadvertently damaging.

We cannot control the challenges and misfortunes that come our way but we can control how we deal with them and how we allow them to affect our relationships with those around us.

Jayne, who cares for her daughter who suffers from anxiety, shares her positive view:

> I have also found it helpful to learn to accept the life you have and not compare it to others. Everybody is different and we all have different paths to follow and this is ours.

Generally everything is okay in moderation. We do not have to allow ourselves to be glued to our devices 24/7. We do not have to allow ourselves to make the wrong dietary choices for our brain's well-being and balance. We do not have to allow ourselves to be made to feel inadequate by the riches of others and whilst we would like a better future for our planet, we need to try to understand that it is a global effort and not the weight of the world on one person's shoulders.

How we navigate our lives greatly affects how we manage our relationships with others. Within a family/partnership, it is quite normal to have fraught and challenging times, as individuals all with different personalities and needs jostle to find their own voice and be heard, all under one roof. This is without having someone with an anxiety disorder, or indeed any mental illness, thrown into the mix.

When living and coping with the dreadful effects of a loved one who suffers from anxiety, it can put an enormous strain on personal and professional relationships and the toll it can take on all concerned can be devastating.

Charlotte, Samantha's twin sister, shares her thoughts:

> In my own experience, mental illness affects the whole family, close friends and everyone in the surrounding support group. You are constantly aware, thinking, researching and learning about the illness, trying your hardest to support your loved one in as many ways as you can. We have all given up pieces of our life to enable us to support my sister but we all know if it were the other way around, she would do no less.

Every day within my work, I see the shattering effects that mental illness can have on the sufferer and their loved ones and every day I am continually confronted by the pain and trauma that mental illness can bring to the home environment and everyone in it. I have seen and experienced at first hand how it can rip families apart and drive a wedge through once solid relationships, bringing them crashing to their knees.

I will never forget when Samantha was in the throes of her eating disorder and OCD, my husband Kevin described our everyday family life as if someone had picked our house up each morning and given it a good shake, bringing mindboggling chaos and turmoil with it for the rest of the day, until bedtime once again restored the peace and calm – until the next day and the whole cycle would begin again! Equally I can speak at first hand from my own experience and that of my Samantha's, that with the right support, understanding, patience and uncon-ditional love the damage can, in time, be repaired and family dynamics restored, bringing them closer together, more united and stronger than they have ever been. My family is a real example of this.

I do recognise that when 'anxiety' comes into your lives, trying to live in a united household can seem very much easier said than done. It is true that family life will be disrupted and everybody within it will have to make some changes and sac-rifices to accommodate the on-going recovery of the person suffering from an anxiety disorder.

How people act and react around someone with anxiety can also be an important part of their recovery. Trying to strengthen family relationships and promote a genuine acceptance, under-standing and co-operation within the household and everyone living within it can be a challenging task – especially for the person trying to facilitate it. I have listed below some sugges-tions and ideas to help cope with some of the challenges of living with someone who has an anxiety disorder or who may be at risk of developing one.

Recognise the warning signs

As we already know, an anxiety disorder is a serious mental illness, which, is not always visible or easy to identify. Being alert to any early warning signs can be paramount to the sufferer, as, the sooner your loved one or friend receives the right help, the more positive the outcome is likely to be for all involved – particularly the person with the anxiety disorder.

In my personal and professional opinion, behavioural changes are one of the biggest signs that something is amiss. As busy as family life can be, it is vital not to dismiss any changes that could quite easily be passed off as 'just their personality'. With hindsight, many carers say that their loved one became withdrawn, forgetful, emotional, angry and/or pre-occupied. This is important because it is the outward sign of the turmoil that the person is fighting in their head.

Charliee shares the signs she recognises in herself:

> I'm able to recognise my own anxiety quite early, which is when I'll tend to make excuses so that I can avoid a situation – usually a social event. Being able to recognise warning signs is really helpful but also really unhelpful too because I feel as though it makes it a lot easier for me to not challenge my anxiety. My partner James is also starting to learn which situations are an absolute 'no go' for me and which environments I'm more relaxed in.

Anxiety can develop slowly over time, with the changes in someone's behaviour and outlook happening gradually but with time, it can advance into something much bigger and more sinister, as we have seen.

Some signs to be aware of are:
- Shying away from social situations or activities the person usually enjoys
- Struggling to sleep or sleeping more than usual
- Being unusually intolerant of others
- Showing persistent signs of unease and worry
- Excessive overthinking
- Eating more or less than usual
- Having unexplained aches and pains
- Seeming to be less motivated and lacking energy more than usual.

Pippa, whose long-term boyfriend suffers from anxiety, says:

> I recognised some of the early warning signs when we were together with people that Dominic did not know or at large group events. At one event, Dominic said that he wanted some

food but he did not get any because he didn't want to face the people who were standing around the table of food.

Do not pretend things are fine

The temptation may be to pretend that everything is okay, to dismiss some of these signs or symptoms or at least to decide to keep an eye on them rather than act on them right away. The taboo that sadly still exists around talking about mental health can often come into play here. Some people worry that raising the subject of an anxiety disorder may be somehow intrusive or that they do not know the right words to use. They may be concerned that they themselves do not fully understand mental illness and somehow think they could make things worse if they say or do the wrong thing.

All of this is perfectly understandable. We still have a long way to go to challenge and break this stigma and it is, therefore, no surprise that many people are still uncomfortable talking about mental health. I do think that being able to be open about it, however clumsily, is generally preferable to not saying anything at all.

Not discussing anxiety, or mental illness generally, only reinforces the taboo. It sends out the message that it is something that should not be talked about out loud, and to the person coming to terms with their own mental health struggles, the message they receive can be that it is something to be ashamed of and should be kept to themselves.

The opposite is true. Talking about anxiety disorders removes the stigma surrounding the illness. Raising the subject sends the message that it is okay to talk about it. Having the conversation can remove a large chunk of the shame and embarrassment that may accompany anxiety. By letting someone know they are not alone in their illness, you can reduce the isolation which is so often bound up in it.

Pippa (quoted above) says:

> I found that if I tried to talk to Dominic about things, he would say that everything was fine and that there wasn't an issue. I did not ever pretend that things were fine but I would gently try to approach the subject with him every so often in order to try and help him come to terms with it.

The most important reason for not pretending things are fine is that, if left unchecked and undiscussed, the anxiety disorder could get worse. Mild anxiety could escalate to a higher level, ultimately increasing the more serious risk of it spiralling out of control, leaving the sufferer at risk of developing other conditions, such as depression.

The message here is please do not be afraid to talk about it, to raise the subject, to ask if someone is struggling and to offer your help. Showing you care will not make things worse but may make it easier for someone to seek help, thereby putting them on the path to recovery. For the person who may be wrapped up in their anxiety, unable to see a way out, you – as someone who cares about them – can often give them the priceless gift of hope.

My Charlotte shares her thoughts:

> Having been around mental illness for 15 or so years and from working with Mum, I have seen how mental illness impacts the lives of everyone around it, not just the sufferer but also family and friends. One of the most important things I have learnt is to talk – if you think something is wrong with a family member, friend or loved one, always talk with someone you trust; try not to brush things under the carpet and be as open and honest as you can be.

Say the right thing

It can be really hard to know what to say to someone who is suffering from anxiety. You do not want to ignore the illness but sometimes you just do not know if you are saying the right or the wrong thing.

As my mum explains:

Once I knew of the illness and then understood it was a mental illness, I became very careful and wary – should I say – not to say the wrong thing. Frightened of hindering the healing process that was, hopefully, taking place.

With the help of some of the wonderful people who have taken the time to contribute to my books, I have put together (below) a list of some of the things that could be helpful to say to those suffering from anxiety disorders and others that are best avoided.

What not to say

Whilst all of the responses below are completely understandable, the manner in which they can be said is often not helpful for the mind-set of someone battling an anxiety disorder and they are more likely to make them feel misunderstood. With this in mind, try NOT to:

- apportion blame or anger by saying things like 'Why are you doing this to us?' or 'Look at the effect this is having on the rest of the family.'
- minimise the problem by saying 'What do you have to worry about?' or 'This is all in your head.'
- ask someone to 'Snap out of it' or 'Pull yourself together.' Anxiety disorders can be a complex, deep-rooted issue and cannot be switched off just like that.
- say, as tempting as it is, 'How can you be so selfish?' or

'I cannot see why you can't just ignore it'; we have to remember that anxiety disorders are a serious mental illness and like any physical illness, it is not the sufferer's choice.

- judge them, whatever they confess to you. Tell them 'I respect your viewpoint' even if you do not agree with what they are saying.

- say 'I don't know how to help' as they are looking to you as someone to take their pain away.

All the above phrases can potentially create a barrier between the person experiencing anxiety and the person trying to help them. Getting cross and shouting will only make everyone feel worse, including you. No matter how frustrated and disheartened you may be feeling, it is important to try and put those feelings aside when talking to your loved one. It is vital not to belittle their feelings, as this will seem overwhelming to them and will only exacerbate the angst they are feeling.

Throwing around positive clichés, however well meant, may also not be helpful and can come across as empty and worthless. Instead, try to tie your comments and thoughts to their particular situation, praising them for specific steps they have taken forward or reminding them of their personal attributes that you love and admire so much.

Caroline, whose daughter suffered from anxiety, says:

We're not perfect and we can sometimes slip up and say the wrong thing but learn from it, move on quickly and do it better next time. Don't spend time dwelling on and beating yourself up about it as it can be a very stressful time anyway. When you're in the midst of something like this, it isn't the time for analysing everything you've said and done. Just make sure you're being kind to yourself as well!

What to say

When a family member has an anxiety disorder, communication can, at times, require extra effort and patience. Effective communication has a precautionary role, reassuring family members that they care about each other and appreciate each other's efforts. Good everyday communication can also make it easier to bring up issues, make requests when needed and resolve conflict when it arises. Open, non-judgmental communication should, however, always form the basis of the approach.

It is not always easy to know what to say and how to say it, when talking to someone who is struggling with a mental health issue. Every person has their own preferences, but here are a few ideas that you may find helpful:

- You might ask questions such as 'Can you tell me what is happening?' or 'Do you feel you would rather talk to someone else?'
- Give the person space and time to express themselves, asking 'Would you like my advice or would you rather I just listened?'
- Encourage your loved one by saying something like 'There is nothing you can say that will stop me loving you.'
- Praise them for every small step forward by saying 'This must be hard for you but you are going to get through it' or 'I am so proud of you.'
- Help by taking away their fear by telling them 'You are not alone and I would like to help you in any way I can.'

A lot of the time, simply just listening can be helpful. It is important to talk to the sufferer in the same way you have always done, remembering they are still the same person that they were before the illness.

It can be useful having certain code words between you. These can be words that the person with the anxiety disorder can use to indicate when they want to talk or when they are struggling. They may use these words to talk about their anxiety and how they are feeling without actually naming the illness. Perhaps this is where the 'black dog' or 'dark cloud' associated with depression came from, as it is hard to say the words 'I'm depressed' or 'I need help.'

Create a positive home environment

Those living with or close to someone suffering from an anxiety disorder may well be able to have a positive impact on their well-being. Creating an environment within their home which is conducive to a positive, emotional balance can be pivotal for the person suffering and the family as a whole. This is about both the ambience in the home and the way people interact within it.

One effect of anxiety disorders can be that people lose interest in their surroundings. They may lack the motivation to look after themselves and feel disconnected from their environment. At the same time, they may struggle to get out, losing interest in activities they once enjoyed and instead spending long periods of time behind closed doors. While no one would claim that clearing the clutter around them or keeping the house clean will directly change their anxiety levels, not doing so could well contribute to their negative state of mind.

Caitlin says of how decluttering the house has had a positive impact on her anxiety:

> I am ashamed to say it but our home was cluttered. There were so many things washed but needing putting away and it wasn't getting cleaned properly. My partner and I had a big argument one day about the house and I said it was the way it was because I couldn't cope. My partner told me just to ask for help and I have to say he has been great. We have gutted out two rooms, just one to go and the house is decluttered and tidy again. We both need to spend just 30 minutes every weeknight

doing something together, whether it be putting clean washing away/one hoovering and one dusting. Little and often is key!

There are certainly benefits to having access to natural sunlight. So, opening the curtains or moving a chair outside into the garden may be helpful as part of a wider treatment plan. Surrounding the person with things they love could also have a positive impact. Framed photographs of happier times, candles scented with mood-boosting fragrances, blankets and throws that make them feel secure and comforted and activities that may stimulate their interest, such as art materials, jigsaw puzzles or music, can also be helpful.

Eating a varied and broadly healthy diet is beneficial in the treatment and prevention of anxiety and of course someone's home life is absolutely key to this. Working together with the person who has anxiety to find out what they feel like eating and making this as nutritious and enjoyable for them as possible can be really valuable, especially if they have lost interest in their diet or preparing their own food. Helping them understand the foods that can play a part in lifting their mood, versus those that offer no benefits or may even make them feel worse, can also be really valuable (see Chapter 5 for more information).

It is also important to recognise that those suffering from an anxiety disorder such as agoraphobia, where the sufferer may see their home as their only safe place, may need to be encouraged to take small steps to challenge their fears and not become chained to their home. With the support of a loved one, small steps can be introduced, such as a short walk around the block, visiting a local shop or even a short car journey.

Avoid personal criticism

The way in which you react to your loved one's anxiety can have a big impact on them and how they feel. While their bleak mood and apparent lethargy may be frustrating as well as upsetting, showing exasperation or anger is unlikely to be helpful. It will not 'jolt' them out of their mind-set and instead is likely to fuel feelings of guilt and/or shame.

Try to detach yourself from the way they are acting and the effect that may have on their wider circle of family and friends. Instead, remember it is part of their illness and that the person you love and care for is still very much inside. Hopefully, by doing this, it will enable you, the carer, to connect with the sufferer rather than become alienated from them.

Jessica looks back at when her daughter was suffering from anxiety and mild depression:

> Before I really understood what was wrong with my daughter, I just presumed (very naively) that she was being a 'typical' teenager, not wanting to get up and sleeping for a lot of the day. On many occasions I called her lazy and said she needed to sort herself out. I feel so awful now knowing that this actually reinforced how she already felt about herself, that she was worthless and good at nothing.

Hannah, who suffers from anxiety and other mental health issues, talks about this from a sufferer's angle:

> I've recently begun practising affirmations of a morning on my drive to work, or when on my way to a stressful situation which I know could trigger my anxiety. I don't say the things that I have doubt over; I say the things that I know are true: 'My family loves me', 'I'm good at my job', 'I've made amazing progress.' I spend much of my days being critical of myself, so having those 10 minutes at the start of my day to instil some positivity and self-belief really helps and puts me on track for being that bit kinder to myself that day.

Acknowledge small steps forward

Most people thrive on praise and those with an anxiety disorder are usually no different. The road to recovery from an anxiety disorder can be a long and complex one. It can often feel overwhelming and never ending at times to both the sufferer and their carers. The recovery process may involve medication, therapy and lifestyle changes, as well as a willingness and courage on the part of the person with the illness to follow the path recommended to them. Frequent encouragement and praise will help to give them the strength to take the next step on this journey and this is where friends and family can step in as a supportive back-up team.

It is important to acknowledge seemingly small accomplishments along the way. From the very first step, which may be simply admitting how they are feeling, the reaction of loved ones can be a powerful motivator, encouraging them to keep moving forward and not give up. Through visits to the GP, keeping appointments for therapy and sticking to prescribed medication, recognising each of these steps can help motivate them.

You can also support them by encouraging them to set small goals, breaking down larger tasks into smaller, more manageable steps. For people who struggle to get out of bed, setting goals like having a shower and a healthy meal are accomplishments in themselves that should be recognised and praised. They may then be able to move on to meeting with friends or being motivated to revisit a once-enjoyed activity. Acknowledging these achievements lets them know that their hard work and attempts to recover are worth all the effort they undoubtedly made.

Jayne, whose daughter has suffered from severe anxiety since the age of 14, shares her thoughts:

I was given a piece of advice at the start of this experience and it has stuck with me and helped me cope on many an occasion:

'Take one day at a time. Keep looking forward and celebrate every achievement no matter how small.'

Be as kind as possible

Irrespective of their age or position in the family, allowing the sufferer the time, space and security they need on their recovery path will also enable them to open up and relax a little more around those closest to them. By vocalising and acknowledging to the sufferer that you accept and understand how difficult and challenging things are for them, you empathise and reassure them that there is nothing they could say or do to make you stop loving or caring for them. This will give them the courage and the confidence they need to continue in the right direction.

By keeping the boundary walls down between you and the sufferer, you are perpetuating the recovery cycle and creating an open, non-judgemental environment for them, which is exactly what they need to be able to keep challenging themselves and move forwards. That feeling of working together can be immensely valuable to someone suffering from anxiety. It helps them to feel understood and trusted, giving a gentle boost to their self-esteem, which is so important to recovery.

Dave Davies, manager of Frank Bruno, who himself has suffered from anxiety and who has other family members and clients who have suffered from anxiety and depression, says:

Be patient; be caring; spend the quality time when the sufferer is not anxious putting plans of action and maintenance together for when the sufferer has a 'bad time'.

Encourage self-care

When someone has an anxiety disorder, they may lose interest in both their surroundings and themselves. Smothered by their illness, looking after their own well-being can sometimes feel exhausting, unnecessary and out of their reach. However, looking after themselves is not a luxury. It can in fact be an important part of their recovery plan and, as someone who cares for them, this is one area where your support can have a significant influence.

Encourage them to adopt good sleeping habits, to eat well and to take exercise – anything from walking or cycling to yoga or dance – and perhaps join them in doing so. All of these have been proven to be valuable mood-boosters. Help them make a list of the things they enjoy or that make them feel happy (or have done in the past). Maybe a good book, long bath or their favourite funny film, so that they recognise the things they can pursue to improve their own mood? Encouraging them to set mini goals can help provide a really positive focus and give them something to strive for.

If someone is struggling, you may feel like you should take care of everything for them. While it may be useful to offer to help them do certain things, like keep on top of the housework or cook healthy meals, it is also important to encourage them to do some things for themselves.

Charliee says of her love for self-care:

> When my therapist first spoke to me about self-care, I thought it was rubbish. Now I have a box filled with hand creams, face masks and other things that smell amazing! When my brain is giving me a hard time, it really helps to look after my body. The act of self-care is the best thing I've ever been taught!

Stay in touch with them

Relationships with others are essential for all of us, especially those with a mental health issue. However, having an illness like an anxiety disorder can make it even harder to maintain those crucial bonds. If friends, family, carers and/or loved ones can keep in touch – even if that contact can sometimes feel one-sided – it can make a huge difference to a person who is wading through the weight of their illness. Just knowing that they are being thought about can make a big difference to how someone feels.

It is likely that the person you know who has an anxiety disorder may seem to have withdrawn, and it is easy to mistakenly interpret that as them not wanting contact. However, the opposite is likely to be true. It is the anxiety that prevents them from reaching out, going out or accepting invitations, and they may fear and mourn the isolation that their illness brings. Try not to take it personally if someone seems to rebuff you or does not keep in touch. It is a symptom of their anxiety disorder, not a reflection on the relationship between you and them or how much they value you as part of their life.

Even when it does feel one-sided, sending a message, email or letter to someone or picking up the phone to give them a call is likely to be much appreciated. Reminding them of their strengths or recalling happy times together can give them a real lift and help them remember how special they are. Anxiety destroys self-confidence and self-worth, so hearing that someone genuinely still believes in them can be very powerful, especially at a time when they may not believe in themselves.

Going out and meeting up with a friend suffering from an anxiety disorder requires a good dose of understanding. They may cancel plans, leave early, or simply say 'no' to well-meant invitations. Remember this is a reflection of their illness and not the way they feel about you as a person. Many people like to continue to be invited to things, even if they rarely go because it makes them still feel part of things. However, always be patient and do not force them to come out if they are not ready.

My daughter Samantha's best friend Zoe sums this up beautifully:

In truth, Sam suffering from mental illness does add a complication to our friendship. It is a subject that I try to, but often can't, fully comprehend. There's almost an unspoken agreement between us, I won't always understand what she's going through, and she won't always be able to commit to doing things. We don't have to talk about it, but we can when she wants to. The end result is a best friend who is great in so many other ways and her challenges are an accepted part of that friendship. It's similar to a friend in a foreign country or a friend with a new baby; it can be difficult to maintain a connection sometimes. But stand by a friend with mental illness, because when they are ready, they will be one of the most tenacious, courageous people you will have the honour of being friends with.

Find the humour

Anxiety is certainly no laughing matter, but that does not mean that humour has to be banned if someone is ill. While being able to laugh together when someone has an anxiety disorder can sometimes feel like an impossible task, trying to see the lighter side of certain situations can normalise them and help everyone weather the storm of mental illness. That is not to say that having a joke or a giggle is suddenly going to bring them out of their mindset, but doing something to make your friend or loved one laugh may be helpful in lifting their mood. Just make sure the person with anxiety feels respected and is not left out of the laughter.

Kevin, Samantha's dad, shares how finding the humour helped their relationship:

> Now I laugh with Sam about her quirky ways but what is much more important and such a huge relief is that she can now laugh at herself when she does her weird stuff.

Samantha shares:

> We joke about it (OCD) a lot and laugh together, which we could never do before. Which I think has really helped us to relax with each other and find our way back together.

Pippa shares how she and her boyfriend, both sufferers of anxiety and other mental illnesses, find the humour together:

> As both Dominic and I suffer with mental health issues, finding humour has been a good way of coping. We often make jokes about how I find food difficult at restaurants because of my anorexia but we also laugh at the fact that Dominic finds people difficult at restaurants as he can find it hard to deal with the amount of people that are there and the anxiety this causes him. I find that making light of it can actually take power away from the mental illness and it can make you feel more comfortable and with a bit more control over it.

Keep your family routine 'normal'

It can be easy to let the anxiety take over, to feel like you have to constantly tread on eggshells and centre everyday life on the person who is ill. However, where possible, being able to maintain a normal routine can be really helpful, both allowing the wider family to carry on and also helping the person with anxiety to have some control over their own life.

Establishing a routine with someone who suffers from an anxiety disorder can be a really key part of their self-care. Setting daily targets for getting up, such as having a shower, doing exercise and achieving other small goals, can provide a series of crucial stepping-stones which may well aid their recovery. That said, you cannot force them to do things; they have to want to do them for themselves. There will be times when they need to sleep and when they cannot motivate themselves to set goals let alone achieve them. Allowing them those times without making them feel guilty about it is okay too.

For parents, partners, friends and loved ones, maintaining your own everyday life is also essential. Make time every week to do something you or your family particularly enjoy, together or alone. It could be listening to music, reading a book, going to the cinema or simply going for a walk. Setting aside time to do your favourite activities can help relieve family tensions, whilst, reinforcing the bond.

My Charlotte adds:

> It was so important to all of us to still try and spend some time all together, even just going for a walk or sitting and watching a movie at home together. It gave us all a small sense of normality and kept us going.

Remember, there is life outside of the mental illness, for everyone.

Remember the siblings

Most people count their relationship with their sibling as one of the most important in their lives. It is a unique relationship, often filled with challenges as well as love, and when one child is struggling with a mental illness, it can have a very profound effect on that relationship.

In this situation, some brothers and sisters may feel that all their parents' attention is directed towards the other child, which can give rise to anger, frustration or negative behaviour. On the flip side, a sibling may feel they have to behave perfectly, tip-toeing their way through life so as not to cause their parents more stress. Other common feelings include feeling protective and responsible for their sibling, while also worrying about themselves and fearing what the future holds.

It is important for parents and care-givers not to conceal what is happening from siblings. That will only make them feel excluded or confused, and may lead them to worry more. Regular family discussions or chats (or even just cooking together or going for a family walk) can be immensely valuable, giving everyone the chance to talk about the good things in their life and the challenges. These do not need to be pressurised meetings but can be a fun time when everyone takes their turn to talk.

A relationship with a sibling is life-long. As they grow in age and emotional maturity, a brother or sister can be of real help and support to their anxious sibling. Their unique bond makes them well placed to help their sibling to embrace new experiences, tackle fears and rediscover places and activities they enjoyed – possibly together – when they were younger.

Even younger children can provide a really supportive role, sometimes without even realising it. By just being there, being loving, accepting and ever-present, they can provide tremendous comfort for someone suffering from an anxiety disorder.

Charlotte offers advice from her own personal experience:

My advice to other siblings would be to create a safe and supportive atmosphere for your sibling and understand that they do not want the anxiety disorder, just as much as you don't want them to have it. Show them pieces of life they can have outside of the mental illness, talk about your interests and how your day was (don't always expect a long answer or too much interaction). Be non-judgemental and listen without prejudice, no matter how difficult the situation. Find someone you trust who you can talk to and open up with so it doesn't build up inside you. Lastly, always have hope that the mental illness will slowly leave, and your sibling will come back to you, it just takes time, patience and resilience.

Distraction techniques

Some of the contributors to this book have mentioned a tool they have found helpful called the 'distraction technique'. Essentially, this means giving themselves something else to focus on when they feel the anxiety or panic rising.

There are no hard and fast rules to what the distraction may be (as long as it is positive), as the idea is simply that the brain is taken away from over-thinking and fretting and instead concentrates on something else. It may be a case of counting backwards or focusing on deep breathing (breathing in for four counts, holding in for four and then breathing out for four). Some people turn to a puzzle or colouring, while others may pick up an engrossing book. Some will imagine a place they love and where they feel safe and allow them to get lost in thoughts of that special place and a time when they were there.

These are all positive and healthy distractions, but sadly some sufferers do turn to negative distractions, such as self-harm. This may feel like a release at the time, but it will ultimately only increase the stress, anxiety and upset someone feels. This should never be chosen as a distractive tool and those who do find themselves self-harming or using another negative distraction, should seek help to break that cycle and tackle the underlying causes.

Charliee tells us about the technique that works for her:

The distraction technique I use daily and find most helpful is using hand cream. The strong smell really helps to occupy my mind and distracts me from the initial thought. By massaging it into my hands it gives me something to do and it doesn't look like a strange thing to be doing. The pot is small enough to keep in my pocket so I always have some with me. This

> works especially well if the anxiety is linked with trauma or flashbacks.

Elaine shares the technique that helps her cope with her health anxiety:

> I look around and name five things I can see, four things I can hear, three things I can touch, two things I can feel, and one thing I can taste or describe things I can see around me.

Jan shares the tool that helps her manage her anxiety:

> It may sound corny, but I find visualising and hearing the character from Disney's *Frozen* singing 'Let it go' really helps. Then when I'm feeling better, I sing my recovery anthem 'I will survive' to myself and that usually works.

Offer hope

When someone is consumed by the wave of anxiety it can be a dark, lonely and hopeless place to be. That famous 'light at the end of the tunnel' can feel constantly out of reach, with the darkness so deep that it can feel impossible to find a way out.

If, in someone's bleakest times, you can continue to be a friend and to care for and about them, you may be able to provide that glimmer of sunshine that they may be struggling so hard to find. Telling them that you are there for them today and will be tomorrow, that you believe in them and will never stop doing so, that they are ill but the illness will pass, may just give them the glimmer of hope they need to keep going.

Garry would like to share some hope:

> There is always hope. After suffering from anxiety for my entire life, I didn't start having panic attacks until the age of 44.

> But after about three years, they stopped happening, though arguably nothing in my situation had changed.

Look after yourself

Supporting others can be mentally and physically exhausting. As a parent or carer, you probably spend a lot of your time focusing on everybody else, always putting everyone else's needs before your own. However, looking after your own well-being is just as important for you, your loved one and the whole family as they can only be as strong as you are. You may not be able to take a break every time you need one, but it is important to have some time that is yours, whether it be going for a walk, meeting a friend, doing a relaxation class or simply reading a book or a magazine. By doing this, it will enable you to recharge your batteries so that when you are by the side of the person you care about, you are there with renewed energy and focus.

My best friend Kate who has been by my side the whole time says:

> Being there for Lynn could mean simply being at the other end of the phone, going out for a coffee after work or being understanding if she had to cancel an arrangement. I also tried to remind Lynn of the importance of having a break once in a while, so she could recharge her batteries. Hopefully, she knows that I am always there for her no matter what!

Jess, who herself suffers from moderate anxiety and whose girlfriend suffered from severe anxiety, shares her thoughts:

> Ensure that your loved one understands your limits and that you're happy to help and support as far as these limits allow, but that you can't be stretched beyond them and that reaching them isn't necessarily a sign that you'll leave or abandon your

loved one. Just that any additional required support needs to come from elsewhere.

Dionne Curtis, professional hypnotherapist, NLP practitioner, TFT practitioner, Psy-TaP practitioner, and volunteer hypnotherapist for the MacMillan Cancer Centre, East Surrey Hospital, gives five tips for dealing with anxiety in the home for both sufferers and their carers:

1. **The elephant in the room:** When trying to communicate, sometimes starting the conversation is the biggest step. You can create a way of opening that conversation by following the steps below:

    Step 1: Obtain an object or choose an object – preferably an elephant that can sit on a shelf or in a drawer in the house.

    Step 2: When you or a member of the family has something they need to discuss, take the elephant out of the drawer (or designated storage area) and put it on a shelf (or designated spot) indicating that someone needs to talk.

    Step 3: The family plan a time that day to sit down without any distractions and talk openly and honestly, without judgement and with good intentions only.

    Step 4: Once the problem / issue / matter has been addressed and resolved, the person who requested the talk removes the elephant from the shelf and places it back in the drawer ready for the next time.

2. **Star jump negative thought interrupt:** Getting out of the negative thought (NT) habit can be hard and we all need a

little help to get started. Consciously acknowledging our NTs is a great way to start, as once we acknowledge we are having an NT we can swap it for a positive thought. A fun way to become consciously aware of your NTs is each time you find yourself thinking in a negative way, get up and do a star jump. If you have more than one NT before you notice, perhaps three or four slip through, then do three or four star jumps. Once you have done your star jumps, change your NT into a positive thought – the more you do this the better you become at doing it and you will find you are having fewer NTs and more positive ones.

3. **Visualising the future:** It has been proven that we all move towards our most dominant thought – whatever we believe is our truth – and this is borne out by the information that we receive through all five of our senses that reinforces that belief. By following these easy steps, we can help ourselves build up a picture of who we want to be in our future and move towards achieving that goal.

    Step 1: Find yourself a place where you feel comfortable. You can either sit or stand, that's up to you.

    Step 2: Close your eyes and imagine/visualise yourself **for at least a couple of minutes** free of any form of anxiety. What would you look like anxiety free? How would your posture be? How would you stand? What would you hear? How would you sound when you spoke? How confident would you feel? What would you see as this future you? Allow yourself to look out of the eyes of the future you and notice any changes or differences.

    Do this for five to 10 minutes each day. By visualising yourself as you want to be, you will start to be able to believe this is possible and you will move towards your most dominant thought.

4. **Write down the good things:** When anxiety is in the forefront of our minds it can be easy to overlook or ignore the good things that happen to us each day. By writing down all the good things you will not only have a reference to look at during tougher times but you will also have proof that good things do happen and that they happen to you on a daily basis. Treat yourself to a small 'good things' notebook and every time something good happens, jot it down. Make sure that you record the smallest of good things through to the massive amazing good things – all are relevant and all deserve a place. If you finish your list each night before you go to bed you can review all the good that has happened in your day; remember not all days will be the same – if just one good thing happens each day that's a great place to start.

5. **Create a happy hour:** Create one hour a day for yourself to be happy. Schedule this into your day and pursue happiness during this hour. Switch off any distraction and allow yourself to be happy. You may have a hobby or want to try something new or you may like listening to your favourite tunes or watching a movie; if you love to sing or dance, line up your favourite music, warm up your voice and your body then sing and dance for the entire hour. Actively seek things that make you happy for use during your happy hour – look forward to it and notice how much you enjoy it.

To conclude

There is no definitive, right or wrong way to work together as a unit in the home. Every situation, every sufferer, every family unit and every home environment is different, but by everyone sticking to the basic fundamentals and working closely together, for the benefit of everyone involved, you will all be on the right path.

Chapter 9

Anxiety in the workplace

Anxiety in the workplace is an area of increasing concern, partly because of the effect that someone's working life can have on their overall mental health and partly because of the huge disparity in different companies' approaches and attitudes to mental illness. What is clear, however, is that millions of employees in any one day will be struggling with their emotional well-being. After all, around 16 million people in the UK, at some point each year, suffer from a mental illness.[59]

Those who struggle with an anxiety disorder at school or university may continue to battle this mental illness when they are in the world of work. Others may find that their anxiety disorder actually starts to develop when they are older, possibly as a direct or indirect consequence of their working life. There are many thousands more people at work today who will be desperately juggling the demands of their employment with the stress of caring for a loved one with a mental illness such as an anxiety disorder. All of these people's health and productivity may be being compromised, making it essential that employers play their part in creating a working environment which is both knowledgeable about mental illness and supportive to those who are affected by it.

Mental health in general is currently a hot topic and employers are starting to recognise their responsibility for supporting employees with this kind of issue as much as they would someone with a physical illness. However, it is questionable whether the many words that are spoken on the subject are matched by actual action. The fact that 11% of employees that disclosed a mental health issue faced demotion, dismissal or disciplinary procedures and that 30% of managers report not having any workplace facilities or services that could help well-being and mental health shows just how much still needs to be done.[60]

Evelyn, who suffers from anxiety and borderline personality disorder, shares her thoughts on how it is generally improving:

> Having conversations with HR [human resources] is always a good start as companies are generally becoming a lot more aware of mental health issues in the workplace and needing to be supportive around this.

This suggests that there is still some way to go to educate employers, managers and human resource teams about mental illness. Having a vague working knowledge gleaned from articles in the press or anecdotes from friends is rarely enough. There are so many myths that pervade society about anxiety disorders and other linked mental illnesses that it is not unreasonable to ask companies to have a policy around them and provide regular training for those who oversee teams of employees. After all, 91 million working days are lost to mental illness in Britain each year.[61]

Promoting a respectful and understanding environment at work is also important. Feeling able to open up about a mental illness such as an anxiety disorder, and believing they will be supported for doing so, could be absolutely critical in helping someone you work with get the help they need.

Rachel says of how her current employers have been supportive:

I have had to take a lot of time off work over the years with my anxiety and not just anxiety but my other mental health issues too. Luckily the company I currently work for as a support worker for learning disabilities have been very understanding.

Work stress versus an anxiety disorder

It is important to note that feeling stressed, irritable, upset and/ or demoralised at work can be very common. We all have days when everything seems to go wrong or times when we struggle to get along with our boss or colleagues. Those difficult feelings may even escalate to the point where they have an effect on someone's life, leaving them questioning whether they want to continue in their job or even leading to Sunday night dread and anxiety about going to work the next day. Though these emotions are very real and can be extremely challenging, they do not necessarily equate to an anxiety disorder. Generally, if tackled by changing jobs, improving work-life balance or finding solutions at work, the stress and feelings of anxiety can be lessened.

By contrast, an anxiety disorder seeps into every part of a person's life and becomes persistently overwhelming, leaving them feeling hopeless, adrift and unable to find a light in their darkness. Their nervous and uneasy feelings are unlikely to lift when they finish work and their home and social life are likely to be affected by their bleak mood.

Holly shares her experience of anxiety in the workplace:

Ultimately my anxieties got so bad that every morning I was being sick or feeling unwell on top of feeling guilty every night that I had achieved nothing at work. Before going to work I would be worried that I would be disciplined that day or, even worse, fired. Once I did bring myself to do work, I would always be concerned that what I was doing was not right, as I had no one there to discuss the project with and I avoided my phone as much as I possibly could.

The two are different and that distinction should be made. However, it is also important to recognise that work stress could escalate to become an anxiety disorder if left unchecked or not acted upon and if something else happens in a person's life that they then find themselves struggling to cope with it can also aggravate an existing mental health issue. This can often make it hard to separate the two. Whether problems at work per se can actually cause an anxiety disorder is still under debate, with some arguing that people either have to be predisposed to a mental illness or subject to major stresses in other areas of their life. However, what is undeniable is that work – where we spend so much of our time – is a key piece in the puzzle of our mental well-being.

The causes of anxiety disorders at work

There is little doubt that many aspects of working life can heavily impact someone's state of mind, which can in turn progress into an illness such as an anxiety disorder. From being bullied by a manager to feeling financially trapped in an unfulfilling role, there are many ways that pressures at work can have a negative effect on someone's self-esteem and self-worth. While the list of possible work triggers for anxiety is virtually endless, I will endeavour to discuss some of the main issues below.

Bullying

Bullying can take many forms from overt put-downs to so-called 'gas-lighting', where a person's perception of reality (for example, how they are performing at work) can be insidiously distorted by someone else. Being bullied at work, where your professional credentials are under attack along with your own sense of self, can have a particularly brutal impact, making people feel worthless. By the nature of 'office' politics, often it can feel hard to report to someone, with employees worrying that by doing so they risk further damage to their standing in the workplace.

It can be hard to know what to do to stop a bully at work. It may be helpful to keep a diary of incidents as they happen, so there is a record to refer back to if further action is taken. Talking to a colleague or manager is also important to break the silence that bullying thrives on. Also consider calmly addressing the issue with the bully themselves. Their actions may not be deliberate and they may be shocked by the effect they are having.[62]

Sandy, who suffered from anxiety and depression after an intense phase of bullying at her workplace, shares her experience:

> At first, I tried to brush off the negative comments aimed at me and thought to myself that I was stronger than to retaliate or let them get to me but after a while, without realising, the bullying got more and more emotional and turned into blackmail and got quite nasty. After about six months of this going on and getting myself into a vicious cycle of anxiety and depression I told my husband about it and he spoke to my boss at work. My boss was amazing and looked into it, the person bullying me got a disciplinary and from then on stayed away from me. I feel that it got as far as it did because I let it and let them get away with it.

It can be common for those who are being bullied to feel as though they are in part to blame for the behaviour that is happening to them. They may feel that they are weak, that they deserve the way they are being treated, or that they have allowed it to happen, as we can see in Sandy's case above. These feelings can be borne out of the low self-esteem and lack of confidence that the person being bullied is experiencing.

Low morale in the workplace

Often bullying can develop alongside a culture of generally low morale at work. Like the playground bully, someone who mistreats their colleagues often comes from a place of feeling undermined, undervalued or vulnerable themselves. That does not excuse their behaviour; however, it may suggest that the problem is more to do with the unsupportive or demanding culture of the workplace rather than the unpleasant actions of one individual.

Like a persistent black cloud hanging over you, low morale at work can have real effects on your well-being. Those who find that the pervasive negative culture of their workplace, is having an effect on their mental health should not ignore those feelings, especially if it persists even when they are at home. Instead, they need to take steps both to look after their own well-being (for example, through exercise, diet, taking breaks or even seeing a life coach or counsellor), and to deal with the issues at work, which may mean raising them with a manager or the human resources (HR) department.

Holly shares her experience in an unmotivating and isolating working environment:

> I had found a new role and had ended up working in the company's head office which was known amongst the site teams to be really cold and isolating and that the people working there were not friendly. In addition to this, there were five people including myself working on the project and as I was the administrator, I was the only one in head office. Everyone else was on a construction site. My manager was the director of the project and I saw him twice a week. It was very isolating and I had no one to ask questions.

A wrong-fit role

There are times when a job that looks amazing on paper or seems impressive to others can feel anything but that to the person who is doing it. Feelings of being trapped or at odds with someone's own personal set of values can fester and grow. Couple this with other pressures, such as needing the salary or working parent guilt, and it can soon begin to have a negative effect on their mental health.

Impostor syndrome

Impostor syndrome is a term used to describe the intense feelings of self-doubt to the extent that people feel like a fraud, either in their personal or more commonly in their professional life. The feelings of inadequacy will most likely override any feelings of achievement or external proof of their competence and they will often live in fear of being 'discovered', worrying that they were hired by mistake. This underlying worry can end up driving their everyday lives, causing high anxiety, a lack of ability to switch off from work and fear of not having finished tasks or completed them accurately.

Pete shares his experience working in the legal profession:

> I constantly feared that what I thought was a lack of knowledge would be discovered and that I would be exposed as a fraud. I really struggled with imposter syndrome and this meant that I never had any confidence in my ability which increased my level of anxiety at work enormously. I used to dwell on even the tiniest situations where I might have made a mistake and imagine terrible consequences.

Garry shares his experience of impostor syndrome in the work environment:

> I have always suffered from imposter syndrome. For the last 12 years of my IT career I worked on a contract basis, paid a daily rate. My last contract ran for five years and I was paid an obscene amount of money. But I STILL felt a fraud and expected to be 'found out'.

Working parent guilt or work-life imbalance

Most people spend many hours at work; however, it is vital to have a good balance between working time and leisure time. This balance can feel even more important if work is taking you away from your children, especially if your workload keeps increasing, robbing you of time at home even more. It can be such a hard balancing act, knowing you have to work to keep a roof over your head but still wanting time to spend with people you love or doing the things you enjoy, which are both crucial to good mental health and well-being. For parents in particular, guilt can be an ever-present niggle, which is often misplaced. However, even if unjustified, its effects can be very real, causing people to dread going into work or leaving them really struggling with the dual demands of their career and family.

Ted looks back on when he feels his anxiety and depression started:

> I really enjoyed my job. It earnt us enough money to live, it was great hours and I had been there about seven years; we then got bought out by another larger company and my work life changed. I was having to fit so much more work into my day which meant I was working 12-hour days, leaving at 7 am and not getting home until around 8.30 pm. I missed our children going to school and coming home from school; I was tired and could barely play with them. I often had to catch up with work on the weekends and so missed out on their play dates and sports days. I felt so alone and as if I wasn't really part of the family anymore. I ended up deep into a pit of anxiety and depression, before I even really knew it.

Financial struggles

There may be an assumption that people who work do not have financial pressures but of course, in reality, that is rarely true. To a greater or lesser extent, everyone feels the stress of not having enough money and of ensuring they have enough in the future. Some people may feel they have to stay in a job that they do not like to be able pay the bills. If this situation continues over a long period of time, it can put a very stressful burden on someone's shoulders, eventually affecting other areas of their life. Their relationships with loved ones may start to suffer, they may struggle to sleep, or they may find themselves turning to alcohol or drugs as a release, so in turn putting more pressure on their mental health. It can also be a vicious circle, affecting how well they do their job. The fear of losing that job can further exacerbate their feelings.

The way forward can often seem unclear, but talking about these emotions with loved ones or a professional can help. Concentrating on your own well-being is also essential to weather these difficult times.

Petra, who suffered from anxiety and depression, shares her experience:

> We were young and decided to buy our very first house together. I think we were very naive and stretched ourselves way too far from what we could actually afford. We struggled to get by week to week and I also hated my job but had no other option than to stay there. We didn't even have a family yet and we couldn't afford to look after ourselves. I couldn't see a future or where we would be in six months' time the way we were going. After a very stressful year, my partner and I finally spoke to each other about how we were feeling (both of us pretty anxiety ridden and depressed) and made the decision to down-grade our house. It is the best thing we could have done. Sometimes now I still get dark thoughts, but I am in a better position to fight them off.

Working in certain industries

While anyone can be affected by an anxiety disorder, regardless of what work they do, there is evidence to suggest that working in certain sectors can increase the risk of suffering mental health issues, including suicide. One UK report highlighted the significantly increased risks of suicide for female nurses, women working in culture, media and sport, both male and female carers and teachers and construction workers.[63] As an example of the latter, men working on a construction site are three times more likely to take their life than the average male. Working long hours, often away from home on site for weeks at a time, with fears about job security, can all play a part. Combine this with the traditional macho of the building trade, where asking for help and opening up about emotions does not come naturally, and the reasons behind these statistics become clearer.

In reality, anyone can develop a mental illness in any job, from a farmer to a musician and each industry in an ideal world should have organisations that could help people deal with any issues triggered by their work. Each profession will come with its own set of concerns, whether those are undue pressure, isolation, a machismo or sexist culture or other issues, and specific unions, trade bodies and charities can all be supportive at times of significant stress or worry.

Mason tells us of his struggles being in a 'macho' working environment:

I work in the building industry as a scaffolder. We all know before we start that banter is part of the job. This was all well and good until I felt the anxiety and depression come over me. There were days when I couldn't get up for work and I'd pretend I had been out the night before, so I sounded like I was hard, but the truth is I was suffering from severe anxiety and was depressed. I thought if I told the truth I would get ripped to pieces. It was so hard as I needed to work to keep me going. In the end, I spoke to one of the guys on site that I was closest to and they were really supportive and said that they had also been through it themselves. I still thank him now.

The Covid-19 pandemic

Our working lives were turned upside down by the coronavirus outbreak. Some, such as key workers, were plunged into a highly stressful, frantic working environment. Others found their workload dropped off a cliff, with fears about job insecurity or redundancy reaching unprecedented levels. At the same time, a huge number of people found themselves working from home, often in less than ideal environments. During this challenging time, Nuffield Health reported that around 80% of British people were feeling that lockdown had had a negative impact on their mental health.[64] For those working at home, heightened levels of stress were caused by being isolated from colleagues and workers feeling they could not step away from their computer in case they missed an important email or were perceived not to be pulling their weight.

Working at home can also breed paranoia and anxiety about your position in your company and whether your job is secure. It is little wonder that all this contributed to heightened levels of anxiety during the pandemic. Even returning to the office became fraught, with new ways of working, rules about social contact and fears about transmitting the illness all contributing to extra stress.

Anxiety when you're struggling to work

When talking about work it is really important to acknowledge that an anxiety disorder can render many sufferers unable to take or maintain a job. While for many the routine of getting up and going out to work is a crucial part of their armoury against the illness, for others it is simply not possible to commit to regular work and all the demands and expectations that entails.

There is evidence though that working can help you cope with anxiety and that not working for a long period can sometimes make it worse. Therefore, perhaps finding the right kind of work is paramount. Negotiating shorter hours or flexible working times could be key for those who want a job but cannot cope with the full-time commitment it may involve.

Myrtle tells us how her generalised anxiety disorder and depression have affected her working life:

> I avoid life when I'm anxious and avoidance has been my unhelpful strategy of choice throughout my life. It has impacted my ability to do my job, so I've had long periods of sick leave[?] from work. The longest period of time off I had was around three months. This was due to comorbid anxiety and depression but often depression comes first and then anxiety can be made worse by being off work.

It is helpful to remember that, by law, employers must make 'reasonable accommodations' for workers with disabilities or long-term physical or mental health conditions, such as an anxiety disorder, so you do have the right to ask for help if you want to return to work.

For those not in employment or who cannot return to their previous job, another possible route may be volunteering. This can be a valuable way for people to re-establish a routine and to see how well they are able to cope with having an ongoing commitment to others. Beyond that, it can also be great for self-esteem – especially if it involves helping others – and can give people a focus away from their own challenges. It can also improve their chances of getting a paid job when they feel ready and able.

Matty talks about how voluntary work helped him in a positive way:

> I unfortunately can't work in a 'proper job' but do have voluntary work every week with 150 to 200 disabled people a week for a special needs/disabled disco and club.

I often find my depression means I don't want to go, get out of bed or sometimes even get ready to go and I will put it off until the very last minute, but in reality it's really helped me to get out of a semi-selfish state by helping other people that are worse off than me.

Voluntary work, along with a few other things, has really helped me become a stronger person and I personally recommend it to anyone even though I didn't want to go there to begin with.

Spotting an anxiety disorder at work

Many people spend eight hours a day, five days a week at work. That is more time than some of them spend with their families. It means that colleagues are well placed to identify and possibly help those suffering. However, even if someone suspects that a person they work with may be struggling with anxiety or any other mental illness, they often do not know what to do about it.

I have already covered in earlier chapters the signs and symptoms of an anxiety disorder. These all still apply. At work, however, there are a few other things that colleagues can also look out for. These include:

- Excessively worrying about their work and looking for constant reassurance
- Poor job performance or increased absenteeism
- Difficulty concentrating at work and/or making decisions
- Lethargy, constant tiredness and/or poor time keeping
- Frequent mood swings, self-esteem issues, problems with food or compulsive behaviours
- Becoming more emotional or over-reacting to what others say
- Withdrawing from social activities, such as not joining colleagues for after-work get-togethers when they used to.

Jess shares how her work is affected when her anxiety gets really bad:

> I began missing safety checks at work, dropping quality of work and struggling to keep up with work load. It meant that I went from being a high performer to someone who was a poor performer and eventually my ability to perform my job was called into question.

The effect an anxiety disorder has on someone's working life can be immense. They may find it hard to concentrate on their work or interact with colleagues. However, for some, having a routine and being in a different environment from their home can work in a positive way towards aiding recovery.

Tom shares how his social anxiety can impact his working life:

> When I'm in an anxious patch and physically sick every morning before work, this impacts my attention and accuracy at work. I was so afraid of being found out that I hid within myself instead of seeking help and informing my boss/colleagues until it was too late. I cannot talk about it without crying. I find that so shameful I try to avoid it at all costs, even though the crying is the thing that eases my anxiety.

It is also important to remember that an anxiety disorder can affect anyone. As I have said, it does not discriminate on the basis of gender, race, sexual orientation, ethnicity and/or age. Being aware of the signs and acting on them if you are concerned, no matter whether the person is male or female, young or old, could make a real difference to the outcome of a colleague's illness.

Self-help in the workplace

In the workplace, people can subconsciously develop unhealthy coping mechanisms in the hope of alleviating some of the symptoms surrounding their anxiety, such as overuse of caffeine, eating high sugar-foods and/or abusing prescription medication.

It is important to be mindful that these can often exacerbate the symptoms, so making the person feel more anxious rather than less.

There are some helpful strategies that can be used to help cope with anxiety at work. Anxiety can be infectious and can easily spiral out of control, so try to distance yourself from those who intensify the anxiety as much as impossible, as well as following some of the ideas below:

- **Make yourself a list** – If you are feeling overwhelmed, take the simple step of writing a list for yourself. This can help to make work tasks more manageable. It should also help you take back the feeling of control that anxiety can take away from you.
- **Try gentle stretching** – When you feel anxious, you may become aware of stress or tension in your muscles. By doing simple stretching it can relieve the stress in your muscles, leading to a reduction in anxiety levels (see Chapter 5 for *Applied Relaxation* techniques).
- **Drink more water** – While staying hydrated may not get rid of the anxiety fully, it can help reduce its intensity. Water has natural calming properties and can also help you feel centred and more able to concentrate – but don't over-do it: drinking too much water can wash out vital minerals.
- **Communicate with others** – Do not be afraid to communicate with others about what is causing your anxiety in the workplace. Sometimes just saying things out loud can help reduce the intense feelings that have been building up inside. For example, 'I am worried I will not complete this project in time.' Verbalising your concerns might be all that is needed.
- **Check in with your breathing** – Our breathing is linked with our 'fight or flight' response. Getting anxious can trigger this response, making our breathing shallow and

rapid to increase oxygen and making our bodies ready for action. Relaxed breathing (also known as the four-seven-eight breathing technique) involves breathing in for four seconds, holding the breath for seven seconds and exhaling for eight seconds; this helps by slowing down our breathing and rebalancing the amount of oxygen and carbon dioxide. It can also prevent stress and anxiety building up in the first place.

Charliee says of how important self-care is in holding down a job when suffering from mental health issues:

> Although I feel that I manage my anxiety quite well now, I still struggle with it every day. I work in healthcare and I am so confident with my job but some small tasks can be really exhausting and take a lot of courage to complete. This could be something as small as going to get petrol. If I wake up in a particularly anxious state then sometimes, I can be late for work as I may need to meditate or practise mindfulness. I've realised now how important self-care is!

How colleagues and employers can help

It is one thing to be concerned about someone at work but quite another to know what to do about it. Remember that everyone at work has the right to privacy and regardless of your relationship with them, sharing your concerns with others may breach this confidentiality. If your company has an HR department, this may well be the best place to take your concerns.

If you are close to them and consider yourselves friends as well as colleagues, then you may feel able to broach the subject with them directly. If that is the case, it is best not to accuse them of having a mental illness. Instead tell them why you are concerned and that you are there for them if they would like to talk or get further help. Encourage them to speak with a professional.

Whether or not someone in your team shows any sign of an anxiety disorder or indeed any other mental illness, if you are an employer you should feel a responsibility to make your workplace as open and supportive as possible – and that means doing the right thing as well as saying the right thing. Employers, line managers and HR teams should, if possible, send out a strong signal that their staff's mental health and well-being are valued and that people can feel confident that raising concerns about related issues will be supported and not discriminated against.

There are many ways that employers can demonstrate this. Simply by encouraging an environment where people are listened to will help to build trust. Allowing employees to speak up, to voice ideas, and/or to play a part in the direction of the company will reassure them that what they say matters. If and when in future they need the support of their employer, they will feel more confident that they are likely to get it. Being a considerate employer, creating opportunities and learning and encouraging regular one-to-one meetings and mentoring, will also help build trust and give employees somewhere to turn and raise concerns if they need to.

If an employer or manager finds out or suspects that an employee has an anxiety disorder, the first vital step is to give them the chance to talk honestly and openly and this should continue should they take time off sick.

They should ask what their employee needs, such as an extra break or time off for counselling or medical appointments, and make reasonable adjustments to help, such as flexible working hours. It is also important to remember that everyone's experience of mental health issues is different, and the support provided to employees should – as much as possible – be tailored to that individual's needs.

Elaine shares her experience in the workplace:

> What helped me at work was letting them know about what I
> was going through and needing a space where I could go if I
> was feeling anxious. It is vital that you have support at work. I
> also had a phased return to work.

It is not an employer's job to be a therapist to someone in their team. Instead they should provide the individual concerned with access to information which they can use to get the support they need. This may include details of a confidential telephone service or of one-to-one counselling sessions with a qualified therapist.

One relatively new concept that is gathering ground is training employees to become mental health first aiders. Candidates undertake mental health first aid training courses that teach them how to identify signs of mental ill health and to guide people towards getting support. The first aiders are not trained to be therapists but they are empowered with the skills to listen and respond, sometimes in a crisis and ideally before a crisis happens. By providing this training for their teams, employers are helping to break the stigma around mental illness and giving their staff the confidence to talk about these issues, thereby helping those in need get support earlier. In the long term it helps build the foundations of a positive attitude towards all aspects of health and well-being.

Pete says of how more awareness and acceptance of mental health issues in the workplace would have helped him:

> It would always have been useful to have training on mental
> health issues to help me recognise what was going on and the
> opportunity to discuss this with someone like a mental health
> first aider would have helped a lot. For me, I really struggled
> with stigma and felt I couldn't talk about anxiety because I'd
> be seen as weak. I remember trying to raise some of my fears
> and being told that I just shouldn't think that way and that my
> anxiety was unfounded. This just made the stigma worse and

caused me to believe that I was weak and didn't belong in my job or the company I worked for.

Promoting well-being at work

It is important to remember that those who suffer from mental illness are, by law, entitled to protection at work. In other words, employers cannot discriminate against people with a mental illness based on their anxiety disorder or any other mental health problem.

In addition to providing an open and supportive environment at work, employees and employers – and businesses themselves – will also reap the rewards of a workplace that actively promotes and encourages well-being. From providing strong managerial support to introducing well-being activities such as yoga and / or meditation, a responsible and caring employer can have a truly positive impact on its team's mental health and happiness.

Jenny shares her thoughts on her workplace:

There are lots of things to look at, our well-being portal has lots of information but in a sales role or customer facing role, there often isn't the time to stop and take a look – despite being told to! Luckily I've never personally felt the need to look into it but having seen at first hand the attitude of certain line managers/ bosses at work, I do still think that there is some type of stigma attached to any time taken off for anxiety/depression meaning many people don't talk about it, therefore perpetuating the feelings of shame and not being able to cope.

As well as looking at the messages that their attitude gives out, employers should also consider how the work culture of the office may have an impact on those struggling with an anxiety disorder. Are colleagues encouraged to leave their desks or is there an unspoken expectation of not taking a break at all? Do employees have their own 'safe' space in the office or is there a hot-desking policy (which a study suggests may be detrimental to mental health [65])?

Creating a working environment that promotes a good work-life balance is paramount for overall good mental and physical health. Recognising when someone feels overworked, under-valued, lonely and/or disrespected reflects an employer who cares about their workforce. Promoting discussions about well-being and good mental health is also important. It shows that these are not taboo subjects and means employees will feel more able to raise their own issues or concerns more quickly.

Caitlin shares her thoughts on how companies can improve the mental well-being of employees:

> Having regular check-ins with staff to ask how they are doing and if there is anything they need adjusted and also having posters with self-help guides/websites.

Supporting those caring for someone suffering from an anxiety disorder

It is not just those who are suffering from a mental illness that need a supportive employer. People who are caring for or affected by someone else who is struggling also need understanding at work. Supporting a loved one with anxiety can be emotionally and mentally demanding and it can also take up a lot of time. Employers who can recognise this and who can make the adjustments that an employee may need will be rewarded in thanks and loyalty by their workforce.

Carers and loved ones should be treated with similar care and respect as an employee who actually has the illness themselves. They should be afforded privacy and confidentiality and be asked what adjustments would help them balance the demands of their work and home life. Pointing them towards professional help and support should they need it can also be valuable.

Lisa shares her experience:

> My husband developed PTSD after a traumatic experience I tried my best to still go to work as he had to take time off, but I too struggled. He wanted me to come to therapy with him and be at home with him, which obviously took a toll on my work. My boss was very supportive though and let me cut my hours down so I could also support my husband's recovery.

To conclude

We spend so long at work, it is little surprise that our working environment can have a big impact on our mental health. As a result of the hours people spend there and the connections they make, workplaces and the people in them have an absolutely crucial part to play in recognising an anxiety disorder and other conditions. The way that employers and fellow employees react to a colleague with a mental illness can also play a part in determining how supported or abandoned their struggling workmate feels. There is growing recognition that companies with an enlightened and positive attitude towards mental health will reap the rewards in terms of the happiness and productivity of their employees and the more firms can build on this, through schemes such as mental health first aid training, the more change they can bring about in terms of society as a whole's attitude towards those living with a mental illness.

Chapter 10

Anxiety and the online world

Welcome to society
by Samantha Crilly

Hello and welcome to society, we hope that you
enjoy your stay.
We will make it as relaxing as possible as long as you do
things our way.
First of all and most importantly, make sure you fix up
your exterior –
If you slack at any point, we will soon make
you feel inferior.
Secondly, your life will be controlled by pieces of paper –
We will count it up and decide how important
you are later.
Thirdly, we want you to make your time here look as
perfect as possible;
Even if you're having a bad day this is not optional.
Fourthly, make sure you post every day on social media –
Once is fine at first, but we'll soon get needier.
In fact we can guarantee we'll be getting greedier
and greedier.

Oh, and in terms of your meals,
We tend to advertise things to make you ill –
It keeps our drug companies going if you will.
Trust us, the more pills you pop, the better you'll feel …
Lastly, just so you know, our planet is on its way out
But it has to keep up with our needs so that's not
something we talk about.
So good luck and we hope everything is clear?
Oh, and don't smile too much – people will think
you're weird.

Caring effectively for someone suffering from an anxiety disorder takes hard work, determination, perseverance, patience and compassion from everyone involved. It is essential, where possible, to provide coherent and consistent support to counteract the destructive force of the illness.

Any cracks in that support strategy could allow the mental illness to permeate its way through, so it is paramount that you, the carer, do everything in your power to try to make sure that does not happen. However, one of the things that could infiltrate your support network and potentially undo all your hard-won progress is… the internet and social media.

The perennial question of whether the internet is a force for good or for ill continues to be debated and this discussion can get particularly heated when it comes to issues around mental health. Perhaps because of the relative infancy of the online world, evidence about the influence of social media use on our mental health is often contradictory. For example, while one 2018 study from the University of Pennsylvania found a link between social media and lower mood,[66] another study from Oxford University in 2019 concluded that social media had little effect on the happiness levels of teenagers.[67] The truth, I suspect, is that the influence of the online world on our mental health depends on a number of factors, from how long each individual spends on particular sites to the strength of their own self-esteem and many other considerations besides.

The internet can be a valuable source of help and encouragement for sufferers and carers alike, linking them to people enduring similar situations throughout the world and creating a mutually supportive, positive online community. However, the internet's ability to unite like-minded people can be both a blessing and a curse. While few of us could function without it, it can, at times, be unregulated and should be used with the same degree of caution that you would use – and advise your loved ones to use – in the real world.

Melissa Helliwell, vice principal at Oak Academy in Bournemouth, shares her thoughts:

> *Parents have the foremost duty of care for their children but are often baffled by the world their children live in and what they could possibly be 'depressed about'. Generally, this is a lack of education on the effects and impacts of the world, which in many cases is viewed almost wholly through a screen by young people, and then lack of the knowledge as to how to deal with the aftermath of those impacts. Social media is not a total enemy; indeed, there are many excellent platforms that seek to support and encourage healthy lifestyle provisions. However, for every positive there are also negatives that seek to control and manipulate impressionable minds. Our young people need exposure to safe online practices; to understand and know where they can turn to for support and what constitutes a negative influence.*

People have their own opinions about whether the positive impact of the media (raising awareness, highlighting support and, in terms of responsible bloggers and influencers, being a source of empathy and understanding) outweighs the negatives.

It may be helpful to understand just what a potential minefield this is by explaining the most extreme viewpoints. In the red corner we have the people who claim that mental illnesses are intensely private and emotionally driven, so it would be irresponsible to claim that factors such as our celebrity-worshipping culture, airbrushing, fashion and irresponsible 'influencers' could possibly be at their root; in the blue corner, we have those who argue that it is impossible to ignore other people's portrayals of their 'perfect' life. This involves increasingly unrealistic and artificially enhanced beauty paradigms, fuelled more and more by social media and other media platforms. The immense pressure to conform to these is enough to drive anyone to a mental illness.

Paige describes how the portrayal of the 'perfect' life on social media makes her feel:

> I am trying to get better and avoid listening to what the media says and make my own choices, but sometimes it is unavoidable. I feel this especially with how I should look instead of my own personal taste. I feel I should have a great body, exercise all the time, eat the perfect diet and travel the world whilst also having a good job and a brilliant relationship. In reality, these things aren't easy to have and/or balance, but they are constantly pushed in our faces and I feel this adds a lot of pressure to my life.

Like so many things in life, the online world can exert both a positive and a negative effect and I hope the rest of this chapter will help you understand how to maximise those upsides while understanding and avoiding many of the pitfalls.

Evelyn, who suffers from anxiety and borderline personality disorder, shares her thoughts on the pros and cons of the online world:

> Online communities both help and hinder because they can make you feel like you are not alone but then interaction on social media can also cause anxiety through a lack of understanding of your condition.

The good

Over a decade or so ago, those living with debilitating mental illness might have felt as though they were the only one battling in this way and have struggled to know what they could and should do to try to move forward. Nowadays, simply typing a few words into Google will introduce them to a whole community of help, support, understanding and empathy – immediately, right when they need it, without having to make an appointment, go on a waiting list or even venture outside their front door. As quickly as they can type the website address into their browser, the internet will take them to the blogs of people who understand their anxiety disorder and show them stories of those who have gone on to live and love in a way they can only dream of when they are stuck in a self-destructive cycle of illness.

Through blogs, social media and positive chatrooms, anyone can share their experience. They can provide the insight of real people in real situations and give people the 'virtual hug' they need when the going gets tough.

Eve tells us of her positive experience:

> Social media sites have been a fabulous place to see others share their stories and especially in helping out with my body dysmorphia and anxiety in social situations. This has meant I've made a lot of friends through the internet who I talk to a lot and we all understand how each other feels with our similar issues so, for me, it has been a great thing!

That kind of support is absolutely invaluable and many with mental illness will credit the solace they find through the internet as a key part of their journey to rehabilitation. Some people find it much easier to reach out and ask for help online than they might do face to face. The anonymity afforded by the internet can remove the stigma and shame that stops some people seeking support in the offline world.

Pete describes his positive views about online groups:

> I've found certain social media groups really helpful because you can articulate your fears in a very open way and interact with people who can often offer reassurance due to having similar experiences.

It can also be a lifeline for the carer and family members. They too can often feel isolated, and the internet can introduce carers to a community that cares and understands in a way that even their closest friends can often find hard to do. The advice available online can help them know what to do and what to say, and above all give them a really useful insight into what their loved one is going through. Where would many of us be without being able to search online and find that we are not alone in whatever is troubling us or those we care about?

Being able to communicate online can also break down some of the factors that can perpetuate the cycle of anxiety – namely, fear and isolation. The internet and social media also allow both carers and the person they are caring for to stay connected with friends. For those struggling with a mental illness this can be a very important reminder of the life that exists outside the illness they may find themselves imprisoned in. Staying in touch with friends on social media provides that portal to the outside world and, if they are connected with people they perhaps knew in happier times, it can remind them that their life was once very different – and that it can be again.

The bad

Sadly, there is a negative and very dark side to the internet and social media. For every positive, inspiring, supportive post, there may be another that is unhelpful, undermining and potentially dangerous. There are many different environmental factors that may contribute to poor mental health and now social media is close to the top of that list. Used by individuals of all ages and backgrounds, accessible from their handbag or pocket 24 hours a day, it has begun to play a larger part in how an illness such as an anxiety disorder can develop.

While it can be comforting to find people with like-minded experiences online, social media can sometimes prove to be something of a sham sanctuary for those in distress. Popular blogging and vlogging provide a very easily accessible stage for both the well-intentioned but unqualified influencer and those who intentionally wish to promote negative and potentially dangerous behaviours in the wider public, often targeting the most vulnerable. For those with anxiety or another mental illness, sites that promote messages of self-harm or glorify suicide can be very harmful and dangerous.

Caroline shares the experience of her young daughter, who has now recovered:

Our happy, confident 13-year-old daughter's mental health deteriorated and she plummeted into a very dark place. We couldn't quite get to the bottom of it. We knew she'd had some friendship issues previously and was feeling low because of some low-level bullying that had gone on for a few months beforehand but our lovely girl gradually became withdrawn from our family unit. She was writing down some very worrying things and her behaviour changed while we were left on the outside desperate to help but struggling to reach her. She'd also recently opened up a social media account and it turned out that a friend had tagged her on a depression site which meant that this site was now following her and bombarding her with new posts and updates throughout the day when her phone was turned on. The posts were quite hypnotic and you couldn't help but look at more and more of these updates and messages. They were also suggesting links for self-harming and suicide sites.

Social networking sites should also be handled with caution. While these sites themselves may not have any intention of promoting self-harm or suicide, they can unwittingly present an easy and instantaneous way for sufferers to share potentially damaging information.

This was highlighted by the very sad death of 14-year-old Mollie Russell who took her own life in 2017. One of her social media accounts was found to contain distressing material about depression and suicide. In the wake of her death, social media companies were called on to do much more to remove harmful material and, as a result, some have banned graphic images that may promote things like self-harm. While it is right for these companies to take responsibility, it is nevertheless impossible to remove or police all the content that may prove harmful. That is why it is essential that we all have a greater understanding of what dangers may lurk around the next 'online' corner and talk with our young people and loved ones about what to do when they encounter it (just as we would in the offline world). In the complex (and still much misunderstood) world of social media, we should also bear in mind that not everyone who posts a seemingly 'graphic' photo is seeking to cause harm to others. For some it may be a way of reaching out for help and as a result these social media sites can provide a vital way to reach others.

Dave Davies, manager of Frank Bruno, who has himself suffered from anxiety and who has other family members and clients who have suffered from anxiety and depression, says:

What concerns me is that social media can be the worst culprit for some sufferers. On a bad day they may post a 'please listen to me' message in the hope that some of their 'online friends' will say nice things to them, giving them the 'high' that they need for those five seconds. These feelings are of course short lived!

When it comes to the dangers that lurk online, it is important to discuss bullying. Around one in eight young people say they have been bullied on social media.[68] The particularly worrying thing about this type of bullying is that it can feel as if there is no escape from it.

Jan, an anxiety sufferer, shares her thoughts:

> It has become a place for some people to use and abuse others and hide behind the anonymity it provides. I try not to spend too much time on there and, when I do, I try to be careful and wary of what I say, just as I would in 'real life'.

Without wishing to minimise the pain of bullying in real life, at least in the days before social media, people could go home from school or work and have a break from their tormentors. With social media, bullies can now victimise the vulnerable 24 hours a day, seven days a week. Cyberbullying can leave people feeling there is nowhere they can hide as every time they access social media, they have to face unkind comments and criticism and threatening or aggressive messages. Cyberbullies often aim to sabotage friendships and encourage groups of people to exclude or abuse someone for usually very trivial reasons. At their worst cyberbullies actively encourage people to hurt themselves or even take their own lives and sadly tragedies have occurred.

While social media sites state that bullying and abusive behaviours which include harassment, impersonation and identity theft are and will be banned, sadly this kind of behaviour still continues to proliferate on most of the popular social media platforms. It can be very hard for someone who is being bullied to see a way out of this torment, but there are things that they and their loved ones can do.

Simply by talking about cyberbullying takes some of the power out of it. If you suspect that someone you care about is being bullied online, try to broach it with them or suggest they talk to someone else. Encourage them to use the 'block' function available on most social media sites to prevent further bullying from taking place. Most sites now have a system to report abusive or inappropriate messages and many will take action against users who repeatedly abuse rules. Use these systems to report bullying messages and remind the person to try not to respond to such messages and instead to delete or ignore them.

I have covered the more 'deliberate' threats to mental health from the online world, but there is also a much more insidious danger, inherent in social media in particular, that applies to all age groups: the effect of social comparison. Accessible to such a huge audience, for those who struggle with low self-esteem and anxiety, constantly scrolling through 'perfect' photos from friends, celebrities and models can greatly exacerbate the negative cycle that they find themselves in. The presentation of a perfect life with photographs of 'gorgeous' people enjoying great times can be intoxicating to many. For those already struggling with low self-esteem and self-worth, it can be all too easy to start believing that if only they had a life like that, they too would be happy and enjoy the same influence as the 'stars' of many of the social media platforms. Impressionable youngsters are of course particularly susceptible, but even someone like myself can, on occasions, feel the negative emotions associated with such posts, including loneliness, isolation, envy and even worthlessness. For some, these feelings will be fleeting. For others, they will constantly linger in the background. For the more vulnerable, they can have a real impact on their psychological state.

Niamh, who is 14 and suffers from general anxiety, shares her concerns over posting on social media:

> I don't have the confidence to post on social media; the more I look at the photos I take the uglier they seem. I am worried they aren't going to get as many likes as my friends or people will talk behind my back about the photo I have posted.

What we need to remember is that this online presentation of perfection, whether in how people look, where they holiday or who they surround themselves with, is deceptive. Despite how 'perfect' someone's life may appear, everyone has their upsets and battles – they just do not choose to show that side. Their photographs are likely to have been touched-up and filters applied, and the bad days they inevitably will have had will have effectively been erased from their personal history. These people may not have deliberately dangerous intentions, but for those at risk of mental illnesses, their false presentation of a perfect life combined with the negative self-perception of those with crushingly low self-esteem may be a recipe for untold damage.

Caroline, whose teenage daughter suffered from anxiety and depression, shares her experience:

Our family was often under scrutiny and our daughter was constantly comparing our family life to others – our table was never set as beautifully as someone else's; other families did much more exciting things at weekends than us; our meals were never quite as spectacular as others. Then came the photos from social events – some she was invited to, others she wasn't – which led to hurt and upset. Before long she was comparing her body to others which led to all sorts of insecurities and even mufti days at school became a nightmare. The night before was always fraught with upset and meltdowns. She had nothing to wear; she felt she looked fat in everything she owned. Others would post photos of what they were planning to wear which just caused her even more anxiety.

This can be particularly true when it comes to FOMO, an acronym for 'fear of missing out'. It sounds like a modern-day made-up illness, even something of a joke, but actually FOMO is very real and can have devastating effects on someone's life, particularly if they have a predisposition to negativity, anxiety, depression or are in the midst of other stressful events in their own life. FOMO is the feeling that others are experiencing greater joy or more exciting experiences than you are. While it existed before social media, seeing a carefully curated collection of family, friends' or colleagues' most positive, exciting and interesting experiences reflected in their daily or hourly posts (with all the boring, upsetting or negative bits deliberately left out) can supercharge all those insecurities.

Lottie shares her thoughts with us:

> It's really hard to not get jealous and to compare yourselves to others when scrolling around on social media. Everyone always says the celebrities are the damaging ones but I think your peers and friends can be the ones that make you feel the worst about yourself. You haven't got much in common with a celeb so don't feel bad when you see them at an event. However, when you see people you know having fun, at parties, with friends and you're just sat at home, it can make you feel really lonely and bad about yourself. Everyone uses social media to show off and so will show off anything they can, like their friends, their body or how much money they have. When this is all you immerse yourself in, you begin to obsess over everything and feel rubbish. I put a timer on my social media so I can't spend hours on it every day scrolling through stuff that I know will make me feel bad. Shutting off social media is refreshing and a well-needed break. Seeing people living their 'best lives' makes you want their life, not yours.

We have all felt this to a greater or lesser extent – for example, when seeing pictures of friends at a party which you knew nothing about or when someone shows off pictures of their amazing holiday that you could only dream of. However, for someone suffering from an anxiety disorder or prone to mental illness who may already feel trapped in a cycle of negativity, this extra assault on their self-esteem – when it is part of a wider picture of unhappiness and isolation and feeling unable to cope – can actually be harmful.

Caitlin explains how social media can have a negative effect on her:

> I also find there is a huge temptation to compare yourself to others online, even though a lot of the time you're not seeing the real person due to filters or photoshop. A lot of the online world is fake as well; you know what goes on in your friends' lives, yet you see them online and they paint it as rosy. People you don't know paint these 'perfect' lives and you're none the wiser to the fact it's maybe not the truth. So, you compare and beat yourself up because you've not got this 'perfect life'.

Social media and social anxiety

For those who face an almost paralysing fear about mixing with others in person, social media can be a powerful ally, although there can also be negative sides to its use. On the positive side, social media keeps the vital lines of communication open to the outside world. It can help people with anxiety to connect with others, while being shielded by the four walls of their home and the screen in front of them. It allows them to 'talk' to friends, loved ones and even strangers, with a confidence and fluency that they may feel unable to muster in real life. As they converse, they can often take time to craft their replies, to think about what they want to say, without the fluster and fear that can blight their social interactions in real life.

There are negatives though. Along with all the usual problems that can accompany social media use (covered in this chapter), there may be issues more specific to those with social anxiety. While the shield of a screen may be helpful, it may develop a kind of false positivity for people who struggle with social interactions. The personality they portray online could be different from what they are like in real life. That may not always be a negative, but it should be handled with care and caution. While much of life these days can be conducted online, direct interactions are still vital, and conversing online may not help them step out of their comfort zone and help them build the confidence and resilience that is needed to enjoy a full life.

Caitlin shares her thoughts on social media and her social anxiety:

> Social media can be good for socially anxious people as you have time to reply; you don't have the 'pressure' of face-to-face contact and you can choose whether to make that interaction. However, if you're facing trolls it can be terrible for anxiety and can make you believe that what they're saying is true and can make real-life social contact unbearable.

Social media and the Covid-19 pandemic

During the worst of the coronavirus outbreak many of us were very reliant on social media, grateful for the contact it gave us with the 'outside world'. But while there were undoubted upsides to being able to continue to socialise online, it also meant that all the negative effects of social media were magnified. Social media platforms can be judgemental places, rife with misinformation and rumour. They can also breed envy and insecurity, as well as fears about missing out or living a lesser life, somehow, than those we follow. None of this is helpful for those who suffer from anxiety, particularly at a time when our normal social lives are compromised, and our senses are heightened because of the worrying events unfolding around us.

What carers can do

Parents and carers can often feel powerless in the face of the onslaught from social media. While the pull of social media is indeed incredibly strong, there are nevertheless still things that carers and their families could do to counter its effects.

Jenny, whose teenage daughter suffers from anxiety, shares her stance:

> Paul (my husband) and I have mentioned to Niamh on more than one occasion that if you post anything, share any pictures or any part of your life on any social media platform, then you've got to be able to stand up face-to-face with everyone you know or who knows you via these platforms and say what you've said or show what you've shown – particularly when it comes to photos. Niamh is fully aware that posting anything anywhere stays in cyber space FOREVER. This was confirmed only (eye rolling from everyone) when a parent from school who is a barrister went into the school and talked to each year group about social media and the message was certainly age appropriate – the teenage girls were certainly worried that night whilst the parents were sighing in relief that what they had all being saying was finally being taken seriously!

It can at times feel like just another battle, but setting strong boundaries for online use can be vital. Age limits exist on social media sites for good reason (for most sites the age limit is 13) and you may want to think carefully about your own loved one's individual maturity, mental strength and toughness before you allow them to have accounts on these sites.

It is also vital to keep the channels of communication open with them and to counter the images and influence that they are exposed to with a reminder of the unreal side to social media. Helping your loved one to distinguish the good from the bad in the online world, and the life-changing from the life destroying, is another crucial thing you can do to help them. Even while watching TV, discuss whether what you are seeing is actually like real life. If you suspect your loved ones might be particularly susceptible to the unhealthy influence of social media, it might be helpful to start talking about that with them. Suggest that they replace the sites and accounts that bring them down with ones that inspire. Have a look with them to find people to follow that make them happy, not miserable or anxious. Encourage them to follow people who post inspirational messages and seek out role models that inspire through their good works or positive attitude.

Part of the potential negative ramifications of social media seem to relate to the amount of time spent on these channels. One study funded by the US National Institutes of Health, found that those who spent the most time on social media sites are 2.7 times more likely to feel anxious and depressed than those who spend the least time on the sites.[69] There are many caveats to this, not least that those already suffering from their mental health may turn to the online world more readily than those who are not.

Carly tells us of how she found a happy medium with her son's online gaming:

> My son was in pre-prep and I had not introduced any tech into his life as I thought it was healthier not too. He went off on a playdate where the boys were all playing Mario Kart and they were all saying to him 'Why are you so rubbish?' He was devastated and anxious about future playdates. I realised then that allowing him a little access to keep up with his peers was a better idea than no technology at all and him not being a part of the games they all played.
>
> He is 13 now and we still have a rule of no gaming during the week but he is confident on technology and plays online with friends regularly. We seem to have found a happy balance.

It is also noteworthy that one study by the Royal Society for Public Health[69] has concluded that the social media platforms that predominantly show images and photographs – often carefully edited, enhanced or filtered – are the most damaging to young people's mental health, while video-based platforms, where the content is more about sharing information, are the least harmful and may even be beneficial to the well-being of young people. The negative impact of image-based sites is particularly felt by young women, who may compare themselves against the unrealistic pictures that fill their social media feeds and be left feeling anxious, inadequate and with the feeling that their own lives do not measure up.

It may also be relevant that time spent on online channels is time that is not being used to exercise, enjoy the company of 'real' friends or do other activities that have been proven to boost mental health. Thus it is crucial for parents and carers to encourage their loved ones to participate in the pleasures and experiences the offline world has to offer, to get them out of the house, off their computers or phones, interacting with others and doing simple things, such as enjoying screen-free mealtimes together as a family. Reminding them of the joys and pleasures of the offline world may sound simplistic, but research consistently shows the positive effects this can have on our well-being.

Evelyn shares her thoughts on how carers can help:

> It might be good for carers to be available to talk through any upsetting or triggering content that sufferers come across online. Also, to monitor the amount of time being spent online and if this is becoming excessive, initiating some self-awareness that this is happening and suggesting alternatives, such as tabletop games rather than online ones etc. This can be useful (it has been to me when my social media use becomes excessive).

Away from social media you can talk together about the things that make you laugh. Ask your loved one about the good things that happened in their day, the acts of kindness they noted or the surprising things that made them smile. Consider keeping a positive diary, either as a family or individuals, to arm you all against the negative influences that surround you today more than ever.

To conclude

It is worth remembering that the internet is not an entirely bad influence. There are individuals and organisations both online and offline who want to help sufferers towards a healthy mindset and future and their positive influence should not be disregarded. You may find that these publications, sites and internet users contribute to your own network of support, providing ways and means of helping your loved one towards recovery which you are unable to do yourself.

The important thing is not to feel that you are powerless compared with the might of the media. Yes, the influence it exerts is strong, but as someone who cares deeply for a person battling an anxiety disorder, your strength and energy also hold huge sway. At times it may feel as if you are swimming against the tide but please do not give up. With your persistence and love, that tide will one day turn.

As with all elements of effective caring, in this instance knowledge again is power. Simply being aware of the existence of the dangers that lurk online, in particular, and being vigilant in checking for signs of what your loved one is accessing are better than having no knowledge of them at all. I hope that this chapter has given you some insight into the role of social networking sites and the internet and how they can play a part in both helping and hindering anxiety sufferers and their carers.

Above all, remember you are not powerless. Yes, the pull of the internet and social media is strong, but the love and caring of close, real-life relationships can never be replicated online.

What is recovery?

From my own personal and professional experience, I have learnt and believe that recovery from an anxiety disorder is not only possible, but also sustainable. Throughout this book, I hope I have helped you to understand and believe that recovery is achievable and have given you some of the tools to help you, your loved one and your family and friends, move forwards towards that goal.

However, what is not always clear to both the sufferer and their carers is when they have actually reached that place of 'recovery'. They are not only unsure of what recovery should look and feel like, but sometimes concerned because they have not got back to being the same person they were before they became ill. They may feel that they have not, and may not ever, be able to put the mental illness firmly behind them.

This is not necessarily true. Again, from my experience and that of my family, going through any mental illness can change a person. Therefore, the husband, wife, son, daughter, family member, partner or friend that emerges as they move forward into recovery may not necessarily be the person they were before the anxiety disorder began.

Recovery is not the finishing line you get to at the end of a race. It is a process to go through and an understanding to arrive at. It is an acceptance by the sufferer of who they are and how they want to live and it is rarely achievable without a lot of effort, support, perseverance, determination and hard work, through set-backs and obstacles, often over a number of months and possibly years.

It is also – and I cannot stress this enough – a completely in-dividual goal. It is a unique journey for everyone who has or has suffered from anxiety or any other mental illness and 'recovery' will look different for each and every one of those people. Some will know they have recovered when they never have another dark or distorted thought. Others will acknowledge those thoughts are still there but be able to control them through the coping mecha-nisms they have learnt, taking the power out of the destructive feelings so they no longer have the effect they once did.

For some it will be about themselves as a person and reaching a point of accepting who they are. Others will say that being able to enjoy life 'normally' with friends or family is their recovery milestone. For some sufferers, accepting that those destruc-tive thoughts may not fully go away but being able to live with them and control them is a good form of recovery. For others, feeling stronger than the anxiety disorder itself is a real marker. Some may eventually be able to reach a place where the anxiety disorder no longer plays any part in their life, perhaps where it feels like it happened to someone else.

Some of the contributors to this book are keen to help you, the reader, understand what recovery looks like and means to them. Their stories show some of the different guises of recovery, but there are many more. Recovery is, as I say, a unique place for each person suffering from an anxiety disorder, which can only be reached when that sufferer finds the right path for them.

Reaching your goals

Recovery to me doesn't necessarily mean that you're better, recovery to me is wanting it, fighting for it, pushing yourself to take little steps out of your comfort zone. Reaching your goals that the demons in your head stopped you from achieving. Learning to manage your symptoms and not letting your diagnosis win.

Rachel

Feeling calm and happy

Recovery to me is feeling calm and happy again. Not having this huge weight on my shoulders all the time.

Lottie

Freedom

Recovery is a constant journey which will have its ups and downs. For me, it is being able to control my anxiety and not let it control me or my life. It is also being able to find and use the right coping skills that will help me to control the anxiety and, therefore, allow me to have a bit more freedom in my life.

Paige

The inner power

I look back at my past knowing that I am not dictated by it anymore – I am in charge of how I choose to deal with it now. I am at cause for myself and not at the effect of something that happened to me. That probably is the biggest shift of all because when you realise you have the inner power to change the way you deal with things, then you can move forward and create a life you deserve.

Anabelle

I am enough

Recovery means looking beyond my limitations and living meaningfully in spite of them. It also means focusing on my strengths and maximising those rather than drowning in my weaknesses. It means that despite my condition, I am a valuable part of society and I have a contribution to make. It re-affirms the fact that I am enough.

Susanne

An enormous privilege

It means the world. Living without anxiety is an enormous privilege because living with it is something I found absolutely overwhelming and terrifying at times. I've made so much progress through exercise and although anxiety occasionally appears to upset me, it undoubtedly exists in the background.

Pete

Being happier

Being a happier, healthier more positive me in all aspects of my life. I look for the small good things which easily outweigh the heavy bad things as it's easy to dwell on the bad but that will only hold you back and drag your mood down.

Eve

To conclude

Never resign yourself to 'this is as good as it gets' because I have learnt, with time, it can always get better. Recovery from an anxiety disorder is possible. It is also personal. Recovery will look different to each and every sufferer and their loved ones. Recovery rarely means getting 'back' the person you had before, but your experience will have made you wiser, stronger and more empathetic to others. With recovery, you will look forward rather than back, embracing a future rather than harking back to the past.

Recovery is not easy, but it is achievable. Never resign yourself to anything.

Conclusion –
From me to you...

Over the last 19 years, I have fought and won my own battle with depression and have watched my beautiful daughter, Samantha, struggle, gain control and thankfully conquer her eating disorder and OCD. So, I can honestly say without hesitation that there is a light at the end of the dark tunnel for most people living with a mental illness and for those caring for them. These powerful and controlling illnesses were so entrenched in my daughter that I did not think it possible for her to make it out the other side... but she has, as have I. She is free from those crushing, all-consuming shackles and is now chasing her dreams. She has completed and graduated from a stage and media degree, has her own publishing contract and is now writing her own book of very powerful poetry (*Hope Through Poetry*) which, at the time of writing this, is due to be published in October 2020. Samantha is doing and experiencing things that neither she nor any of us ever dared to think possible. I can honestly say she is the happiest and healthiest I have seen her for many years and every day she continues to challenge herself, taking positive strides towards a future she now knows she has, due in large part to her own perseverance and determination to free herself from the chains of mental illness.

As for myself, I can honestly say that having faced and conquered mental illness and held my daughter's hand as she battled and overcame her own, I have emerged stronger and more confident. Both experiences have set me on a new career path which has enriched my life and still does on a daily basis. Using my new-found knowledge and insight into mental illness, I have been able not only to help and support other families and their loved ones through to recovery, but also to touch many more people's lives through my books, giving them the strength and courage to face and overcome their challenges, just as my husband, I and our daughters have. As a family, we take great strength from knowing that we have been able to turn something so negative in our lives into a force for good, giving others – whether they are the sufferer themselves or their loved ones – the HOPE that mental illness does not have to be a life sentence, and that recovery is possible and sustainable.

I know how it feels to be both a sufferer of depression and a carer of someone who is suffering multiple mental illnesses, so when I say 'never give up, never settle for "this is as good as it gets", and always believe that things can and will get better', I speak from experience. I know that caring for someone with a mental illness can be frustrating and exhausting and can often seem like a thankless task, but please be assured that there is always a way forward.

As I have mentioned over the pages of this book, each and every sufferer is unique and so is their recovery. There is no one-size-fits-all, so finding a course of treatment that is suited to them and their loved ones is crucial. If one treatment does not work, do not be afraid to try another and then another… . It may take some time before you find the right path to recovery but, please, do not give up. You will find it, remembering always that long-term recovery is possible, provided the sufferer wants it. Explore every avenue you can, ask the professionals as many questions as you need to and do not settle until you are happy with the answers and choices you and your loved ones have made. Keep in mind that it is about the right recovery path, not only for the sufferer but also for the family and loved ones as a whole. Mistakes will be made, which is only natural (I made enough of them too), but with every mistake a valuable lesson can be learnt.

Do not be afraid to stand up to the anxiety disorder or any other mental illness, by staying positive and working together to tackle it. Be prepared for the long haul as any recovery takes time, acceptance and understanding. Patience will need to be exercised at every turn, by everyone involved, but never lose sight of the fact that the person you love is still in there, trapped by the mental illness and waiting for your help to set them free. Your focus should remain entirely on what you *can* do for them – not what you *cannot* do.

There will also be times when you will need some down-time yourself, so make sure you take time out to catch up with your own friends or do something else that you enjoy. Spending quality time outside the restrictions of mental illness will help you to see things with renewed strength and focus, ready to tackle the next challenge that your loved one will face.

What of the end of the journey, when your loved one has made their recovery? Where does that leave you? It is very common and completely natural to feel mixed emotions at this stage. Your life, which has previously been dominated by your loved one's illness, may feel a little empty and sometimes as their carer you may lose your own identity and direction. I know I did. At this stage, I would highly recommend thinking about some form of support for yourself, such as life-coaching sessions. They gave me a new lease of life and enabled me to look forward to a better, brighter future, not just for Samantha but for the family as a whole.

I sincerely hope that, with each chapter, this book has helped you to gain a clearer understanding of this most devastating and sometimes totally misunderstood mental illness and given you the hope that anxiety disorders can be conquered. Never give up – families, relationships and lives can be rebuilt. My family is living proof of that.

I will leave you with my guiding principle:

The cure is in the recovery. There is no elevator; you have to take the stairs.

Yours with hope…

Lynn Crilly x

Kevin leaves you with:

> I have been around mental illness for years and as much as I have tried, I still don't understand it. What I do know now, is that if it isn't treated and the person doesn't receive help, it's not going away and could manifest into something much worse! Thankfully my lovely Sam is back with us now, from wherever she was.

Charlotte leaves you with:

> Although, at times, it can be hard to come to terms with why mental illness chose your family and loved one to hurt, when I look back now I realise that I wouldn't change anything. Otherwise, we wouldn't be where we are today. I do feel in the long run it has brought us all closer together, especially my relationship with my sister.

Samantha finishes with her words of hope:

> I know and believe that everyone has the strength to beat their demons. It won't be easy. It will probably be one of the hardest challenges you will ever face but one thing I can promise from the bottom of my heart is that, when you come out the other side, you will feel exhilarated with life. You will see beautiful things around you that you never noticed before and most of all feel an abundance of freedom and power in yourself. Trust me on this one – you will never ever regret recovery.

Resources

Charities

SANE

www.sane.org.uk

0300 304 7000 (4.30 pm – 10.30 pm daily)

SANE is a UK-wide charity working to improve the quality of life for people affected by mental illness. SANE has three main objectives linked to its aims and outcomes:

1. To raise awareness and combat stigma about mental illness, educating and campaigning to improve mental health services

2. To provide care and emotional support for people with mental health problems, their families and carers as well as information for other organisations and the public

3. To initiate research into the causes and treatments of serious mental illness such as schizophrenia and depression and the psychological and social impact of mental illness.

SANE offers emotional support and information to anyone affected by mental health problems through their helpline and email services and their online Support Forum where people share their feelings and experiences.

Registered Charity Number: 296572

Anxiety UK

www.anxietyuk.org.uk

Helpline: 03444 775 774 Text Service: 07537 416 905

Anxiety UK was established to promote the relief and rehabilitation of those living with agoraphobia and associated anxiety disorders, phobias and conditions, in particular but not exclusively, by raising awareness in such topics.

Registered Charity Number: 1113403

Samaritans

www.samaritans.org

Tel: 116 123 (UK) / 116 123 (ROI)

Samaritans offer a safe place for you to talk any time you like, in your own way – about whatever's getting to you. They are available round the clock, 24 hours a day, 365 days a year. If you need a response immediately, it's best to call Samaritans on the phone. This number is FREE to call.

Samaritans is a charity registered in England and Wales (219432) and in Scotland (SC040604).

The Grace Dear Trust

www.thegracedeartrust.co.uk

Facebook: @gracedeartrust Twitter: @GraceDearTrust1

Instagram: @gracedeartrust

The Grace Dear Trust is a Surrey-based Mental Health charity spreading and raising awareness around the county.

The Trust was set up in memory of Grace, who was a loving member of the Dear family and an amazing friend to many. She died in early 2017 after suffering from mental health problems for a number of years, in part falling victim to the inability to communicate her problems early enough or effectively enough to save her life.

'It's okay not to be okay.'

Registered Charity Number: 1175955

The Frank Bruno Foundation

www.thefrankbrunofoundation.co.uk

0800 368 8196

'We are aiming to bring together the benefits of non-contact boxing with a solution focused well-being programme. The aim is to bring healthy-body and healthy-mind approaches together to provide a holistic and enjoyable approach to supporting people with mental health problems. The aim is to help people to develop a healthier body and a healthier mind, building on their existing physical and emotional strengths and achievements. Our aspiration is that people will use the skills they learn on the programme to develop a happier, more fulfilling and successful future.'

Registered Charity Number: 1171012

Zero Suicide Alliance

www.zerosuicidealliance.com

The Zero Suicide Alliance is a collaboration of National Health Service trusts, businesses and individuals who are all committed to suicide prevention in the UK and beyond. The alliance is ultimately concerned with improving support for people contemplating suicide by raising awareness of and promoting FREE suicide prevention training which is accessible to all. The aims of this training are to: enable people to identify when someone is presenting with suicidal thoughts/behaviour, to be able to speak out in a supportive manner, and to empower them to signpost the individual to the correct services or support.

MindEd

themindedtrust.org

The MindEd Trust is a Registered Charity which is focused on the prevention of mental illness in young people and early intervention strategies for those experiencing trauma.

The Trust was established following the tragic death of Edward Mallen, an outstanding young man who took his life on the railway following the inexplicable, rapid and catastrophic onset of severe depression in February 2015.

'We mind what happened to Edward Mallen and we will do all we can to avert similar tragedies through the prevention and alleviation of mental ill-health amongst young people.'

Via mindEducation programmes, the Trust is mindEd to improve mental health for young people. Key objectives include:

- To promote and assist in the creation of embedded, whole school mental illness prevention and early intervention programmes throughout the education system.
- To destroy the stigma and guilt associated with mental ill-health so that people experiencing trauma come forward early and openly to seek help. On moral, social and economic grounds, prevention is far better than cure, enhancing resilience and preventing people falling into crisis.
- To actively press for urgent policy and funding reform throughout the education and health system, ensuring that parity of esteem is matched by parity of funding and parity of care.

Registered Charity Number: 1163922

NSPCC

www.nspcc.org.uk

NSPCC stands for the National Society for the Prevention of Cruelty to Children. It means that each of us has a responsibility to keep childhood free from abuse, and we must do everything possible to protect children and prevent it from happening.

- Help for adults concerned about a child – 0808 800 5000
- Help for children and young people – call Childline on 0800 1111

- For donation and fundraising queries – 020 7825 2505
- Registered Charity Number: 216401

National Autistic Society

www.autism.org.uk

Founded in 1962, the National Autistic Society are the UK's leading charity for autistic people and their families. Their goal is to help transform lives, change attitudes and create a society that works for autistic people.

Registered Charity Number: England and Wales (269425) and in Scotland (SC039427)

Mental Health Foundation

www.mentalhealth.org.uk

Since 1949 the Foundation has been the UK's leading charity for everyone's mental health, with prevention at the heart of what it does.

Registered Charity Number: England 801130; Scotland 039714.

Professionals

Sally Baker – Senior therapist

www.workingonthebody.com

email: sally@workingonthebody.com

Tel: +44(0)7986812851

Twitter : @sally_therapist

Instagram: sally_therapist

Gill Bescoby BSc (hons), Lic Ac, MBAcC – Acupuncturist

www.maihealing.co.uk

email: gill@maihealing.co.uk

Tel: +44(0)1243 514606 / +44(0)7515709405

Charlie Brooks – Actor, drama teacher and founder of online drama school, I Am Pro:
www.iampro.com
Instagram: @Iampro
Facebook: @Iampro
Twitter: iamprouk

Judith Cocking – Resilience and performance coach
email: judithc@unwindyourminduk.co.uk
Tel: +44(0)7947353653
Facebook: @unwindyourmind

Dionne Curtis – Hypnotherapist, NLP practitioner and TFT practitioner DipIPch
www.whatiftherapy.co.uk
email: dionne@whatiftherapy.co.uk
Tel: +44(0)7533149242

Alison Fuller – Hypnotherapist and reflexologist specialising in women's health
www.thehormonaltherapist.co.uk
email: info@thehormonaltherapist.co.uk
Tel: +44(0)7811123494

Kate Guest – Registered general nurse, mindset coach, trainer, speaker
Also trained as a: Hypnotherapist, NLP Master Practitioner, EMDR Practitioner, Auricular Acupressure and Acupuncture Practitioner, Psy-TaP Practitioner, Reiki Practitioner, SleepTalk® Children's Resilience Practitioner, Further Education Teacher
www.kate-guest.co.uk
email: info@kate-guest.co.uk
Tel: +44(0)7790303806 / +44(0)1626 833306

Jay Hurley – Personal trainer at Body Fusion Fitness
www.bodyfusion.fitness
email: jayhurley@hotmail.co.uk
Tel: +44(0)7774320855

Deanne Jade – Psychologist and founder of National Centre for Eating Disorders
www.eating-disorders.org.uk
email: admin@ncfed.com
Tel: +44(0)845 838 2040

Catherine Kell – Mindful self-compassion and mindfulness teacher, Compassion cultivation mentor and founder of the Self-Compassion Community
www.selfcompassioncommunity.com
email: catherine@selfcompassioncommunity.com
Instagram: @selfcompassioncommunity

Gabriella Kinnear-Nock, DipCNM, mBANT, rCNHC
Registered nutritional therapist
www.gabriellasnutrition.com
email: contact@gabriellasnutrition.com

Corinne Laing – Wellness advocate of DoTerra Essential Oils
www.doterra.com
email: corinnelaing@sky.com

Kevin Laye, DPsy – Psychotherapist and founder of Psy-TaP, published author and international trainer and speaker
For training www.psy-tap.com
Director/Partner of www.zenpower.co.uk;
www.kevinlaye.co.uk
email: cameltrain@aol.com
Tel: +44(0)7803161021
Skype: Kevin.Laye1

Neil Long – Voice and confidence coach
www.becomefree.co.uk

Michele Paradise – Harley Street practitioner of NLP, Havening techniques and clinical hypnotherapist, published author, international trainer and speaker and personal development coach with Deepak Chopra
www.changeyourmindforgood.com
Tel: +44(0)7958607599

Debbie Pennington – Yoga and massage specialist
email: debcobb@hotmail.co.uk
Facebook: @holisticmeadow

Leanne Poyner – Personal performance and life coach
email: leannepoyner@yahoo.com
Tel: +44(0)7868650021

Tan Quddus – Personal trainer
Instagram: @tanqud

Dr Lucy Viney – Clinical psychologist and co-founder of the Fitzrovia Psychology Clinic
www.thefitzroviaclinic.com
email: lucy@thefitzroviaclinic.com
Tel: +44(0)20 8012 8344
Instagram: @fitzroviapsychologyclinic

Nicholas Warburton – Psy-TaP practitioner
www.improvemymindset.com

Laura Whitcher – Massage therapist at Wellness Aware
email: lwhitcher@hotmail.com
Tel: +44(0)7532202884

Useful websites

A guide for online self-help
www.getselfhelp.co.uk

Contributors

(Happy to be contacted)

Frank Bruno MBE
Charity www.thefrankbrunofoundation.co.uk
www.frankbruno.co.uk
Twitter: Frankbrunoboxer
Facebook: Frank Bruno MBE

Dave Davies – Sports agent
www.tobn.co.uk I www.soccerbid.co.uk

Susanne Muwazi
Susanne writes her own blog about living with social anxiety
disorder.
myjourneymysong.com

Me and My Mental Health Matters
A personal blog looking into living with mixed depressive and
anxiety disorder, and emotionally unstable personality disorder.
meandmymentalhealthmatters.wordpress.com
Twitter @Meandmymhmatter
Facebook facebook.com/meandmymentalhealthmatters
Instagram @meandmymhmatters

References

1. Anxiety or depression affects nearly one in five UK adults. *The Guardian*. 19 June 2013 www.theguardian.com/society/2013/jun/19/anxiety-depression-office-national-statistics. [accessed 9 April 2019]

2. Fundamental Facts About Mental Health 2016. *Mental Health Foundation: London. Mental Health Foundation*. 2016. www.mentalhealth.org.uk/sites/default/files/fundamental-facts-about-mental-health-2016.pdf [accessed 29 April 2020]

3. NHS.Generalised Anxiety Disorder in adults. www.nhs.uk/conditions/generalised-anxiety-disorder [accessed 28 April 2020]

4. Martin-Merino E, Ruigomez A, Wallander M, Johansson S, GarciaRodriguez L. (2009). Prevalence, incidence, morbidity and treatment patterns in a cohort of patients diagnosed with anxiety in UK primary care. *Family Practice*, 2009; 27(1): 9-16.

5. Mental Heath Foundation. *Living with Anxiety: understanding the role and impact of anxiety in our lives* 2014 www.mentalhealth.org.uk/publications/living-with-anxiety/

6. NHS. Generalised Anxiety Disorder in adults. www.nhs.uk/conditions/generalised-anxiety-disorder [accessed 28 April 2020]

7. State of Caring 2015. *Carers UK*. www.carersuk.org/for-professionals/policy/policy-library/state-of-caring-2015 [accessed 6 April 2020]

8. NHS. Generalised Anxiety Disorder in adults. www.nhs.uk/conditions/generalised-anxiety-disorder/ [accessed 28 April 2020]

9. NHS. Generalised Anxiety Disorder in adults. www.nhs.uk/conditions/generalised-anxiety-disorder/ [accessed 28 April 2020]

10. Hamilton M, Coates S. Coronavirus and anxiety, Great Britain: 3 April to 10 May 2020. Office for National Statistics. 15 June 2020. www.ons.gov.uk/peoplepopulationandcommunity/wellbeing/articles/coronavirusandanxietygreatbritain/3april2020to10may2020 [accessed 18 August 2020]

11. NHS. Panic Disorder. www.nhs.uk/conditions/panic-disorder/ [accessed 28 April 2020]

12. Ankrom S. DSM-5 Criteria for Diagnosing Panic Disorder. *VeryWellMind*. www.verywellmind.com/diagnosing-panic-disorder-2583930 [accessed 28 April 2020]

13. NHS. Panic Disorder. www.nhs.uk/conditions/panic-disorder/ [accessed 8 April 2020]

14. Claustrophobia. Wikipedia. https://en.wikipedia.org/wiki/Claustrophobia [accessed 28 April 2020]

15. Angelakis S, Nixon RDV. The Comorbidity of PTSD and MDD: Implications for Clinical Practice and Future Research. Cambridge.org. www.cambridge.org/core/services/aop-cambridge-core/content/view/S0813483914000266 [accessed 28 April 2020]

16. NICE. Post-traumatic stress disorder. *National Institute for Health and Care Excellence*. (section 1.7.1). https://www.nice.org.uk/guidance/ng116/chapter/Recommendations [accessed 28 April 2020]

17. Walker LS, Beck J, Anderson J. Functional abdominal separation anxiety: helping the child return to school. *Pediatr Ann*. 2009 May;38(5):267-71. PMID: 19476299; PMCID: PMC3205969.

18. Dermatillomania (Skin Picking). *Psychology Today*. www.psychologytoday.com/gb/conditions/dermatillomania-skin-picking [accessed 28 April 2020]

19. NHS. Selective Mutism. www.nhs.uk/conditions/selective-mutism/ [accessed 28 April 2020]

20. NHS England. IAPT at 10: Achievements and challenges. www.england.nhs.uk/blog/iapt-at-10-achievements-and-challenges/ [accessed 26 May 2020]

21. Living with Anxiety Report, Mental Health Foundation 2014. Mental Health Foundation. www.mentalhealth.org.uk/publications/living-with-anxiety [accessed 28/04/2020]

22. Mind. 40 per cent of all GP appointments about mental health.

5 June 2018.www.mind.org.uk/news-campaigns/news/40-per-cent-of-all-gp-appointments-about-mental-health/ [accessed 18 August 2020]

23. Perlin H. Long waits for mental health treatment lead to divorce, job loss and money problems, RCPsych finds. *Royal College of Psychiatrists.* www.rcpsych.ac.uk/news-and-features/latest-news/detail/2018/10/08/long-waits-for-mental-health-treatment-lead-to-divorce-job-loss-and-money-problems-rcpsych-finds. [accessed 28 April 2020]

24. NHS. Pregabalin. www.nhs.uk/medicines/pregabalin/ [accessed 28/04/2020]

25. Young SN. How to increase serotonin in the human brain without drugs. *J Psychiatry Neurosci* 2007; 32(6): 394-399.

26. Penedo FJ, Dahn JR. Exercise and well-being: a review of mental and physical health benefits associated with physical activity. *Current Opinion in Psychiatry* 2005; 18(2): 189–193.

27. NHS. Water, drinks and your health. www.nhs.uk/live-well/eat-well/water-drinks-nutrition/ 14 June 2018. [accessed 18 August 2020]

28. WHO. CANNABIDIOL (CBD) Critical Review Report. World Health Organization. www.who.int/medicines/access/controlled-substances/CannabidiolCriticalReview.pdf [accessed 28 April 2020]

29. Lu WA, Chen G-Y, Kuo C-D. Foot Reflexology can increase vagal modulation, decrease Sympathetic Modulation, and lower blood pressure in healthy subjects and patients with coronary artery disease. *Alternative Therapies in Health and Medicine* 2011; 17(4): 8-14.

30. Errington-Evans N. Randomised controlled trial on the use of acupuncture in adults with chronic, non-responding anxiety symptoms. *Acupunct Med* 2015; 33(22): 98-102.

31. Mayo Clinic Health System. Can massage relieve symptoms of depression, anxiety and stress? 25 June 2014. www.mayoclinichealthsystem.org/hometown-health/speaking-of-health/can-massage-relieve-symptoms-of-depression-anxiety-and-stress [accessed 18 August 2020]

32. NHS. One You. Our Apps. www.nhs.uk/oneyou/apps/ [accessed 28 April 2020]

33. Bostock S, Crosswell AD, Prather AA, Steptoe A. Mindfulness

on-the-go: Effects of a mindfulness meditation app on work stress and well-being. *Journal of Occupational Health Psychology* 2019; 24(1): 127-138.

34. Bostock S, Crosswell AD, Prather AA, Steptoe A. Mindfulness on-the-go: Effects of a mindfulness meditation app on work stress and well-being. *Journal of Occupational Health Psychology*, 2019; 24(1), 127–138. https://psycnet.apa.org/doiLanding?doi=1 0.1037%2Focp0000118

35. Having a dog can help your heart — literally. Harvard Health Publishing. www.health.harvard.edu/staying-healthy/having-a-dog-can-help-your-heart--literally [accessed 28 April 2020]

36. Zhou Y, Cao Z, Yang M, et al. Comorbid generalized anxiety disorder and its association with quality of life in patients with major depressive disorder. *Sci Rep* 2017; 7: 40511. doi. org/10.1038/srep40511

37. Kaye WH, Bulik CM, Thornton L, et al. Comorbidity of anxiety disorders with anorexia and bulimia nervosa. *Am J Psychiatry* 2004; 161(12): 2215-2221.

38. Harned MS, Valenstein HR. Treatment of borderline personality disorder and co-occurring anxiety disorders. *F1000Prime Rep* 2013; 5: 15. doi:10.12703/P5-15 39. Salters-Pedneault K. A Guide to When BPD and Depression Occur Together. VeryWellMind. www.verywellmind.com/bpd-and-depression-425421 [accessed 29 April 2020]

39. Ott CA. Treatment of anxiety disorders in patients with comorbid bipolar disorder. *Ment Health Clin.* 2018;8(6):256–263. doi:10.9740/mhc.2018.11.256

40. Lohano K, El-mallakh RS. The Anxious Bipolar Patient. *Psychiatric Times* 6 September 2011. www.psychiatrictimes.com/bipolar-disorder/anxious-bipolar-patient [accessed 29 April 2020]

41. Achim AM, Sutliff S, Roy MA. Treating Comorbid Anxiety Disorders in Patients With Schizophrenia: A New Pathway. *Psychiatric Times* 30 January 2015. www.psychiatrictimes.com/special-reports/treating-comorbid-anxiety-disorders-patients-schizophrenia-new-pathway [accessed 29 April 2020]

42. Legg TJ. Alcohol and anxiety. *Healthline* 26 September 2019. www.healthline.com/health/alcohol-and-anxiety (accessed 10 September 2020)

43. Driessen M, Meier S, Hill A, Wetterling T, Lange W, Junghanns K. (2001) The course of anxiety, depression and drinking behaviours after completed detoxification in alcoholics with and without comorbid anxiety and depressive disorders. *Alcohol and Alcoholism* 2001; 36(3): 249-255. alcalc.oxfordjournals.org/content/36/3/249

44. Naylor C, Parsonage M, McDaid D, et al. *Long-term conditions and mental health the cost of co-morbidities.* The Kings Fund. February 2012. www.kingsfund.org.uk/sites/default/files/field/field_publication_file/long-term-conditions-mental-health-cost-comorbidities-naylor-feb12.pdf [accessed 4 May 2020]

45. NHS. One in eight of five to 19 year olds had a mental disorder in 2017 – major new survey finds. Mental Health of Children and Young People in England *NHS Digital* 22 November 2018. https://digital.nhs.uk/news-and-events/latest-news/one-in-eight-of-five-to-19-year-olds-had-a-mental-disorder-in-2017-major-new-survey-finds. [accessed 18 August 2020]

46. Lukats P. One in three teachers fears harm for pupils waiting for mental health treatment. *Stem4.* https://stem4.org.uk/one-in-three-teachers-fears-harm-for-pupils-waiting-for-mental-health-treatment/. [accessed 18 August 2020]

47. Mental House Foundation. Millions still feeling hopeless as lockdown eases: new briefing from the Mental Health Foundation. 9 July 2020. www.mentalhealth.org.uk/news/millions-still-feeling-hopeless-lockdown-eases-new-briefing-mental-health-foundation [accessed 18 August 2020]

48. Climate anxiety: Survey for BBC Newsround shows children losing sleep over climate change and the environment. BBC. 3 March 2020. www.bbc.co.uk/newsround/51451737 [accessed 29 April 2020]

49. Mental health statistics: poverty. *Mental Health Foundation.* www.mentalhealth.org.uk/statistics/mental-health-statistics-poverty. [accessed 29 April 2020]

50. Children and Young People with Learning Disabilities: Understanding their mental health. *Young Minds.* http://vox.mtcserver3.com/wp-content/uploads/2015/01/Children-Young-People-with-Learning-Disabilities.pdf. [accessed 29 April 2020].

51. Anxiety and Autism. Autistica. www.autistica.org.uk/what-is-

autism/signs-and-symptoms/anxiety-and-autism [accessed 29 April 2020]

52. One in eight of five to 19 year olds had a mental disorder in 2017 major new survey finds. *NHS Digital.* https://digital.nhs.uk/news-and-events/latest-news/one-in-eight-of-five-to-19-year-olds-had-a-mental-disorder-in-2017-major-new-survey-finds. [accessed 29 April 2020]

53. NHS. Drug addicition: getting help. www.nhs.uk/live-well/healthy-body/drug-addiction-getting-help/ [accessed 18 August 2020]

54. NHS. Acne. 12 July 2019. www.nhs.uk/conditions/acne/ [accessed 18 August 2020]

55. Golchai J, Khani SH, Heidarzadeh A, Eshkevari SS, Alizade N, Eftekhari H. Comparison of anxiety and depression in patients with acne vulgaris and healthy individuals. *Indian J Dermatol* 2010; 55(4): 352–354. doi:10.4103/0019-5154.74539

56. Draper T. On average three children in every class have a mental health issue: and yet funding is being cut. *TES* 8 February 2016. www.tes.com/news/average-three-children-every-class-have-mental-health-issue-and-yet-funding-being-cut [accessed 29 April 2020]

57. Weale S. Levels of distress and illness among students in UK 'alarmingly high'. *The Guardian* 5 March 2019. www.theguardian.com/education/2019/mar/05/levels-of-distress-and-illness-among-students-in-uk-alarmingly-high [accessed 29/04/2020]

58. 12 statistics to get you thinking about mental health in young people. *MQ Transforming Mental Health through Research* 10 November 2017. www.mqmentalhealth.org/posts/12-statistics. [accessed 18 August 2020]

59. Princes Responsible Business Network. Seizing the momentum. Mental Health at Work Report 2018. *Business in the Community.* www.bitc.org.uk/wp-content/uploads/2019/10/bitc-wellbeing-report-mentalhealthatworkreport2018execsummary-oct2018.pdf [accessed 18 August 2020]

60. Mental ill-health in the workplace is costing UK employers billions. *ACAS.* http://www.acas.org.uk/index.aspx?articleid=3915 [accessed 29 April 2020]

61. NHS. Bullying at work *NHS.* www.nhs.uk/conditions/stress-

anxiety-depression/bullying-at-work/ - [accessed 29 April 2020]

62. Suicide by occupation, England: 2011 to 2015 ONS 2017 *Office for National Statistics*. www.ons.gov.uk/peoplepopulationandcommunity/birthsdeathsandmarriages/deaths/articles/suicidebyoccupation/england2011to2015. [accessed 29 April 2020]

63. Nuffield Health. Working from home taking its toll on the mental health and relationships of the nation. 19 June 2020. www.nuffieldhealth.com/article/working-from-home-taking-its-toll-on-the-mental-health-relationships-of-the-nation. [accessed 18 August 2020]

64. Webber A. Hot desking affects wellbeing for eight in 10 office workers. *Personnel Today*. https://www.personneltoday.com/hr/hot-desking-affects-wellbeing-for-eight-in-10-office-workers/. [accessed 29 April 2020]

65. Berger MW. Social media use increases depression and loneliness. *Penn Today* 9 November 2018. https://penntoday.upenn.edu/news/social-media-use-increases-depression-and-loneliness. [accessed 29 April 2020]

66. Harding E. Social media does NOT harm teenagers, Oxford study says amid claims online activity only has a 'trivial' effect on their happiness. *Mail Online* 7 May 2019. www.dailymail.co.uk/news/article-6999807/Social-media-does-not-harm-teenagers-Oxford-study-says.html [accessed 18 August 2020]

67. Children and Parents: Media Use and Attitudes Report. *OFCOM* 29 November 2017. www.ofcom.org.uk/__data/assets/pdf_file/0020/108182/children-parents-media-use-attitudes-2017.pdf [accessed 18 August 2020]

68. Social Media Use Associated With Depression Among US. Young Adults. *UPMC Life Changing Medicine* 22 March 2016. www.upmc.com/media/news/lin-primack-sm-depression. [accessed 18 August 2020]

69. #StatusOfMind. In May 2017, RSPH and the Young Health Movement published a report examining the positive and negative effects of social media on young people's health. *Royal Society for Public Health*. www.rsph.org.uk/our-work/campaigns/status-of-mind.html. [accessed 29 April 2020]

Index

Index

Index

Index

Index

Index